Introduction to QUEUEING THEORY

Robert B. Cooper
Georgia Institute of Technology

THE MACMILLAN COMPANY, NEW YORK
COLLIER-MACMILLAN LIMITED, LONDON

For Sandie

THE MACMILLAN COMPANY
866 THIRD AVENUE, NEW YORK, NEW YORK 10022
COLLIER-MACMILLAN CANADA, LTD., TORONTO, ONTARIO

Library of Congress catalog card number: 78-163614

First Printing

Preface

This is a textbook in queueing theory for senior and graduate students in operations research and industrial engineering. The mathematical prerequisites are a working knowledge of calculus and differential equations at the level usually taught in engineering undergraduate schools, and a good knowledge of elementary applied probability. In particular, the student is assumed to be at ease with the notions of sample space, distribution function, moment, random variable, conditional probability, and total probability. Some of these topics are reviewed early in the text, but this review will not be sufficient for one who is meeting these concepts for the first time.

The presentation is informal, with the emphasis on the probabilistic reasoning underlying the various approaches. Mathematical difficulties and fine points, which are inherent in any application of the theory of stochastic processes, are noted but not dwelled upon. Heuristic methods are used where it seems profitable to do so, but care is taken in these cases to observe where rigor is lacking.

The text material of each chapter is complemented by a set of exercises. These exercises are only occasionally simple applications of the formulas derived in the chapter. More often the exercises are outlines of derivations of important results not covered in the chapter, or are different derivations of old results by important or interesting methods. Many of the exercises require insight, as opposed to long calculations, for their solutions. In other cases, the exercises require the student to fill in mathematical and algebraic arguments that would tend to distract from the main ideas of the discussion in the chapter if they were included there.

The book is not intended to be characterized as either "theoretical" or "applied." The emphasis of the book is on understanding the interplay of mathematical and heuristic reasoning that underlies queueing theory and its applications, with the following two objectives:

1. To give the student sufficient understanding of the theory so that he will be able to apply it in the practice of operations research, and
2. To give the student the background required to read the literature and embark on research.

The choice of subject matter from the huge literature of queueing theory has been based on these two objectives, and is also, of course, a reflection of my own experience, taste, and knowledge.

The book is the outgrowth of a set of notes I prepared for a course entitled "Probability Applied to Traffic Engineering," which I taught at Bell Telephone Laboratories, Holmdel, New Jersey. Presently, I am using the book for a two-course graduate sequence, totaling about 70 lecture-hours, in the School of Industrial and Systems Engineering at Georgia Institute of Technology.

The book reflects its origins as a text for telephone traffic engineers and researchers. Indeed, teletraffic researchers have made large contributions to the development of queueing theory, as exemplified by A. K. Erlang's historic work in the early 1900s. Throughout the book, examples drawn from telephony are used, thereby illustrating the theory with a coherent class of authentic examples. Of course, no technical knowledge of telephony is presumed.

Although this book is intended as a textbook, with an emphasis on explanations and interpretations that are directed toward the student rather than the researcher, some of the material should be of interest to those who are in no need of an introductory text. The book includes material that is not widely known outside of the field of teletraffic theory. Some of this material has been published in journals devoted mainly to communications research and technology, and hence may have been overlooked by operations researchers in general, while other material included here has not been previously published. A list of references is also given, but these are restricted to works cited directly in the text, with no attempt at furnishing a complete bibliography.

While recognizing that this is a textbook rather than a historical survey, I have tried to be accurate in the attribution of results, especially in those cases in which the results were previously unpublished.

Many colleagues helped in the preparation of this book by commenting on parts of the manuscript and giving me the benefit of their ideas and suggestions. In particular, I wish to acknowledge the aid of Grace M. Carter, Roger D. Coleman, Sandra J. Cooper, Norman Farber, Allan L. Gutjahr, Daniel P. Heyman, Derek J. Hudson, Joseph G. Kappel, Anatol Kuczura, Scotty R. Neal, Joel D. Raphael, Roger I. Wilkinson, and Eric Wolman. The numerical example of Section 4–6 was provided by Martin Eisenberg. Alfred Descloux made helpful suggestions and generously allowed me access to his unpublished work. I am especially indebted to Paul J. Burke, who also furnished me access to unpublished work, and who generously contributed his time and ideas throughout the period of writing. Finally, I want to thank Roseann P. Bell and Dollie Metts for typing the manuscript.

R.B.C.

$\begin{bmatrix} Contents \end{bmatrix}$

3 *Birth-and-Death Queueing Models*

4 *Multidimensional Birth-and-Death Queueing Models*

5 *Imbedded Markov Chain Queueing Models*

6 *Waiting Times*

Scope and Nature of Queueing Theory

1–1. This text is concerned with the mathematical analysis of systems subject to demands whose occurrences and lengths can, in general, be specified only probabilistically.

For example, consider a telephone system, whose function is to provide communication paths between pairs of telephone sets (customers) on demand. The provision of a permanent communications path between each pair of telephone sets would be astronomically expensive, to say the least, and perhaps impossible. In response to this problem, the facilities needed to establish and maintain a talking path between a pair of telephone sets are provided in a common pool, to be used by a call when required and returned to the pool when no longer needed. This introduces the possibility that the system will be unable to set up a call on demand because of a lack of available equipment at that time. Thus the question immediately arises, How much equipment must be provided so that the proportion of calls experiencing delays will be below a specified acceptable level?

Questions similar to that just posed arise in the design of many systems quite different in detail from a telephone system. How many taxi cabs should be on the streets of New York City? How many beds should a hospital provide? How many teletypewriter stations can a time-shared computer service?

The answers to these questions will be based in part on such diverse considerations as politics, economics, and technical knowledge. But they share a common characteristic: in each case the times at which requests for service will occur and the lengths of times that these requests will occupy facilities cannot be predicted except in a statistical sense.

The purpose of this text is to develop and expose a mathematical theory that has application to the problems of design and analysis of such systems. Although these systems are usually very complex, it is often possible to abstract from the system description a mathematical model whose analysis yields useful information.

This mathematical theory is a branch of applied probability theory and is known variously under the names traffic theory, queueing theory, congestion theory, the theory of mass service, and the theory of stochastic service systems. The term traffic theory is often applied to theories of telephone and communications traffic, and similarly to theories of vehicular traffic flow. These two areas share some common ground, and the material we shall develop will be useful in both fields. The term queueing theory is often used to describe the more specialized mathematical theory of waiting lines (queues). But some of the most interesting and most useful models are based on systems in which queues are not allowed to form, so that the term queueing theory does not seem completely appropriate. The subject of this text is perhaps better described by the broader terms congestion theory or stochastic service system theory. However, the name queueing theory has become most widely used to describe the kind of material presented in this text and therefore I chose to entitle the book *Introduction to Queueing Theory.*

Historically, the subject of queueing theory has been developed largely in the context of telephone traffic engineering. Some of our examples will be drawn from this area, but it should be kept in mind that the theory has many areas of applicability in engineering and operations research. Also, it is worth noting that the mathematics underlying queueing theory is quite similar to that underlying such seemingly unrelated subjects as inventories, dams, and insurance.

Consider the following model. Customers request the use of a particular type of equipment (server). If a server is available, the arriving customer will seize and hold it for some length of time, after which the server will be made immediately available to other incoming or waiting customers. If the incoming customer finds no available server, he then takes some specified action such as waiting or going away. Hence the model is defined in terms of three characteristics: the input process, the service mechanism, and the queue discipline.

The *input process* describes the sequence of requests for service. Often, for example, the input process is specified in terms of the distribution of the lengths of time between consecutive customer arrival instants. The *service mechanism* is the category that includes such characteristics as the number of servers and the lengths of time that the customers hold the servers. For example, customers might be processed by a single server, each customer holding the server for the same length of time. The *queue discipline* specifies the disposition of blocked customers (customers who find all servers busy). For example, it might be assumed that blocked customers leave the system immediately or that blocked customers wait for service in a queue and are served from the queue in their arrival order.

We now use a model of this type to illustrate some important points about queueing theory: (a) The subject matter is of great practical value. (b) Heuristic and intuitive reasoning is often useful. (c) Mathematical subtleties abound.

Consider two cities interconnected by a group of s telephone trunks (servers). Suppose that arrivals finding all trunks busy do not wait but immediately depart from the system. (Technically, no "queueing" occurs.) What proportion of incoming calls (customers) will be unable to find an idle trunk (and thus are lost)?

We wish to derive a formula that will predict the proportion of calls lost as a function of the demand; that is, we wish to derive a formula that allows estimation of the number of trunks required to meet a prespecified service criterion from an estimate of the telephone traffic load generated between the two cities. The great practical value of any model that leads to such a formula is obvious. The fact that such models have been successfully employed has spurred continuing investigations by industrial and academic researchers throughout the world.

We shall now give a heuristic derivation of the required formula, using a concept of great importance in science and engineering, that of *conservation of flow*. It is important for the reader to realize that since the following derivation is heuristic, he should not expect to understand it completely; our "derivation" is really a plausibility argument that, as will be demonstrated later, is correct in certain circumstances. With this disclaimer, let us now proceed with the argument.

When the number of customers in the system is j, the system is said to be in state $E_j(j = 0, 1, \ldots, s)$. Let P_j be the proportion of time that j

trunks are busy; P_j is the proportion of time the system spends in state E_j. Denote by λ the call arrival rate; λ is the average number of requests for service per unit time. Consider first the case $j < s$. Since calls arrive with overall rate λ, and since the proportion of time the system spends in state E_j is P_j, the rate at which the transition $E_j \rightarrow E_{j+1}$ occurs (the average number of such transitions per unit time) is therefore λP_j. Now consider the case when $j = s$. Since the state E_{s+1} represents a physically impossible state (there are only s trunks), the transition $E_s \rightarrow E_{s+1}$ cannot occur, so the rate of transition $E_s \rightarrow E_{s+1}$ is zero. Thus the rate at which the upward transition $E_j \rightarrow E_{j+1}$ occurs is λP_j when $j = 0$, $1, \ldots, s - 1$ and is zero when $j = s$.

Let us now consider the downward transition

$$E_{j+1} \rightarrow E_j \qquad (j = 0, 1, \ldots, s - 1).$$

Suppose that the mean holding time (the average length of time a call holds a trunk) is τ. Then, if a single trunk is busy, the average number of calls terminating during an elapsed time τ is 1; the termination rate for a single call is therefore $1/\tau$. Similarly, if two calls are in progress simultaneously and the average duration of a call is τ, the average number of calls terminating during an elapsed time τ is 2; the termination rate for two simultaneous calls is therefore $2/\tau$. By this reasoning, then, the termination rate for $j + 1$ simultaneous calls is $(j + 1)/\tau$. Since the system is in state E_{j+1} a proportion of time P_{j+1}, we conclude that the downward transition $E_{j+1} \rightarrow E_j$ occurs at rate $(j + 1)\tau^{-1}P_{j+1}$ transitions per unit time $(j = 0, 1, \ldots, s - 1)$.

We now apply the principle of conservation of flow. If the system is to be in *statistical equilibrium*, that is, if the relative proportion of time that the system spends in each state is to be a stable quantity, then the upward transition $E_j \rightarrow E_{j+1}$ must occur at the same rate as the downward transition $E_{j+1} \rightarrow E_j$. Thus we have the so-called statistical equilibrium balance equations

$$\lambda P_j = (j + 1)\tau^{-1}P_{j+1} \qquad (j = 0, 1, \ldots, s - 1). \qquad (1.1)$$

These equations can be solved recurrently; the result, which expresses each P_j in terms of the value P_0, is

$$P_j = \frac{(\lambda\tau)^j}{j!} P_0 \qquad (j = 0, 1, \ldots, s). \qquad (1.2)$$

Since the numbers $\{P_j\}$ are proportions, they must sum to unity:

$$P_0 + P_1 + \cdots + P_s = 1. \tag{1.3}$$

Using the normalization equation (1.3) together with equation (1.2), we can determine P_0:

$$P_0 = \left(\sum_{k=0}^{s} \frac{(\lambda\tau)^k}{k!} \right)^{-1}. \tag{1.4}$$

Thus we obtain for the proportion P_j of time that j trunks are busy the formula

$$P_j = \frac{(\lambda\tau)^j/j!}{\sum\limits_{k=0}^{s} (\lambda\tau)^k/k!} \qquad (j = 0, 1, \ldots, s). \tag{1.5}$$

An important observation to be made from formula (1.5) is that the proportions $\{P_j\}$ depend on the arrival rate λ and mean holding time τ only through the product $\lambda\tau$. This product is a measure of the demand made on the system; it is often called the *offered load* and given the symbol a, $a = \lambda\tau$. The numerical values of a are expressed in units called *erlangs* (*erl*), after the Danish mathematician A. K. Erlang, who first published the formula (1.5) in 1917 (see Brockmeyer et al. [1948]).

When $j = s$ in formula (1.5), the right-hand side becomes the well-known *Erlang loss formula*, denoted in the United States by $B(s, a)$ and in Europe by $E_{1,s}(a)$:

$$B(s, a) = \frac{a^s/s!}{\sum\limits_{k=0}^{s} a^k/k!}. \tag{1.6}$$

We shall derive these results more carefully later in the text. The point to be made here is that some potentially useful mathematical results have been derived using only heuristic reasoning. The question we must now answer is what, if any, are the conditions under which these results are valid?

More precisely, what assumptions about the input process and service mechanism are required for the validity of formulas (1.5) and (1.6)? What assumptions are required for the validity of this derivation? (These two questions may have different answers.) Can the assertion that the downward transition rate is proportional to the reciprocal of the mean holding time be justified? What is the relationship between the proportion P_j of time that j calls are in progress and the proportion Π_j, say, of arriving calls that find j other calls in progress? How widely applicable is the conservation-of-flow analysis? How does one handle processes for which this type of analysis is inapplicable?

Questions of this nature sometimes require highly sophisticated mathematical arguments. In this text we shall take a middle ground with regard to the use of advanced mathematics. We shall attempt to impart an understanding of the theory without recourse to the use of abstract and measure theoretic tools; the material is presented in a mathematically informal manner with emphasis on the underlying physical ideas. Mathematical difficulties and fine points will be noted but not dwelled upon. The material should be accessible to a student who *understands* applied probability theory and those areas of mathematics traditionally included in undergraduate programs in engineering and the physical sciences.

A word about the range of applicability of these models is in order here. The example discussed above is based on a telephone traffic application, but it should be clear that the identification of the customers as "calls" and the servers as "trunks" in no way limits the generality of the model.

As mentioned previously, telephone applications have provided the context for the development of much of queueing theory (and this example illustrates why). We shall occasionally refer to telephone applications, thereby illustrating the general principles of the theory with a coherent class of authentic examples. Of course, no technical knowledge of telephony is required.

In summary, this is a textbook in queueing theory, a subject of practical importance and theoretical interest. Although the book is directed toward the student, some of the relatively unknown concepts and results from telephone traffic theory should prove of interest in their own right, apart from their values in illustrating the theory. The material is presented with an emphasis on the underlying physical processes and the interplay between physical and mathematical reasoning. Heuristic and intuitive approaches are used where helpful. Mathematical subtleties are observed and are explored where it is profitable to do so without recourse to methods of abstract analysis. It is hoped that the reader will find this material both interesting and useful.

Exercises

1. In what ways are telephone traffic theory and vehicular traffic theory similar, and in what ways are they different?

2. List some applications of the Erlang loss model.

3. Discuss ways in which queueing models might be used in the following:
   a. Highway design.
   b. City planning.
   c. Hospital management.
   d. Airport design.
   e. Reliability engineering.
   f. Demography.
   g. Epidemiology.
   h. Computer design.

4. Extend the heuristic conservation-of-flow argument to include the case in which all customers who find all servers busy wait until served.
   a. Show that

$$P_j = \begin{cases} \dfrac{a^j}{j!}\, P_0 & (j = 0, 1, \ldots, s) \\[2mm] \dfrac{a^j}{s!\, s^{j-s}}\, P_0 & (j = s, s+1, \ldots), \end{cases} \tag{4.1}$$

where

$$P_0 = \left(\sum_{k=0}^{s-1} \frac{a^k}{k!} + \frac{a^s}{(s-1)!\,(s-a)} \right)^{-1}. \tag{4.2}$$

   b. What restriction must be placed on the magnitude a of the offered load in order that (4.2) be correct? Give a physical interpretation of this restriction.
   c. Show that the proportion of customers who must wait for service (the proportion of customers not served immediately upon arrival) is given by

$$C(s, a) = \frac{a^s/[(s-1)!\,(s-a)]}{\displaystyle\sum_{k=0}^{s-1} (a^k/k!) + a^s/[(s-1)!\,(s-a)]}. \tag{4.3}$$

   This is the well-known *Erlang delay formula*, which we shall discuss in detail in Chapter 3.
   d. What assumption, if any, have you made about the order in which waiting customers are selected from the queue when a server becomes idle? Is such an assumption necessary? Why?
   e. Show that, if all servers are busy, the probability p_j that j customers are waiting for service is given by

$$p_j = (1 - \rho)\rho^j \quad (j = 0, 1, \ldots) \tag{4.4}$$

where $\rho = a/s$. [The probabilities defined by (4.4) comprise the *geometric distribution*.]

f. Suppose it is known that at least $k > 0$ customers are waiting in the queue. Show that the probability that the number of waiting customers is exactly $j + k$ is p_j, given by equation (4.4). Note that this probability is independent of the value of the index k.

Review of Topics from Probability Theory 2

This chapter reviews and summarizes some aspects of probability theory that have direct application to elementary queueing theory. The material given here is intended not only as a reference and refresher in probability theory, but also as an introduction to queueing theory. It is assumed that the reader is already familiar with the basic concepts of probability theory as covered, for example, in Feller [1968] and Part 1 of Fisz [1963]. Specifically, we assume of the reader working knowledge of the basic notions of event, probability, statistical dependence and independence, distribution and density function, conditional probability, and moment. These concepts will be used freely where required. Random variables, birth-and-death processes, generating functions, and the properties of some important distributions will be discussed in some detail. Examples will be drawn largely from queueing theory.

2–1. Random Variables

The concept of random variable should be familiar to anyone who has studied elementary applied probability. However, a brief review in the context of queueing theory might be useful.

From an applied point of view, the theory of probability is concerned with the description of frequencies of occurrence of events. The mathematical definition of event involves the notions of set and measure theory, but for most practical purposes, intuitive notions of event are sufficient. Examples of the kinds of events of interest in queueing theory are {an arbitrary customer finds all servers busy}, {an arbitrary customer must wait more than 3 seconds for service}, and {the number of waiting customers at an arbitrary instant is j}.

In each of these examples, the event can be expressed in numerical terms in the following ways. Define N to be the number of customers in an s-server system found by an arbitrary arriving customer. Then the event {an arbitrary customer finds all s servers busy} can be written $\{N \geq s\}$ and the probability of occurrence of this event can be represented by $P\{N \geq s\}$.

Similarly, let W be the waiting time of an arbitrary customer, and let Q be the number of waiting customers (queue length) at an arbitrary instant. Then the second two events are $\{W > 3\}$ and $\{Q = j\}$, with probabilities $P\{W > 3\}$ and $P\{Q = j\}$, respectively.

The quantities N, W, and Q defined above are random variables. Each of them has the property that it represents an event in terms of a numerical value about which a probability statement can be made.

A *random variable* is a function defined on a given event space, and about whose values a probability statement can be made.

The question of precisely which functions can qualify as random variables is, like that of the notion of event, a mathematical one. For our purposes, it will be sufficient to consider the use of random-variable notation as simply a device for describing events, without explicit concern for the underlying probability space.

A random variable is defined by assigning a numerical value to each event. For example, in a coin-tossing experiment, the event {head} can be assigned the value 1, and the event {tail} the value 0. Call the describing random variable X. Then at each toss a head will occur with probability $P\{X = 1\}$ and a tail with probability $P\{X = 0\}$. This use of the random-variable notation may seem artificial since the association of the event {head} with the value $X = 1$ is arbitrary, and the value $X = 2.6$ might just as well have been chosen. But it will be seen that judicious choices of the random-variable definitions often lead to simplifications.

Suppose, for example, that we wish to study the random variable S_n, which we define to be the number of heads occurring in n tosses. Let the random variable X_j describe the jth toss; let $X_j = 1$ if the jth toss results in a head, and $X_j = 0$ for a tail. Then the random variable S_n can be interpreted as the sum $S_n = X_1 + \cdots + X_n$. The interpretation of S_n as a sum of random variables allows its study in terms of the simpler $\{X_j\}$, without further regard to the physical meaning of S_n. We shall return to this example later.

In most of the queueing theory problems we shall encounter, however, the assignment of random-variable values to events is quite natural from the context of the problem. Only a malcontent would choose to assign the value $Q = 4.2$ to the event {6 customers are waiting}.

2–2. Birth-and-Death Processes

The theory of birth-and-death processes, developed largely by Feller, comprises part of the subject matter commonly called stochastic processes. For an introductory treatment, more general than the present one, see Chapter XVII of Feller [1968], Chapter 8 of Fisz [1963], or the books by Bailey [1964], Cox and Miller [1965], or Karlin [1966].

Consider a system that for each fixed t $(0 \leq t < \infty)$ can be described by a random variable $N(t)$ with realizations $0, 1, 2, \ldots$. Examples are (a) a telephone switchboard, where $N(t)$ is the number of calls occurring in an interval of length t; (b) a queue, where $N(t)$ is the number of customers waiting or in service at time t; (c) an epidemic, where the number of deaths that have occurred in $(0, t)$ is $N(t)$; and (d) a city whose population is $N(t)$ at time t.

We wish to study processes that can be described by such a random variable $N(t)$. We shall make some assumptions about the behavior of the process that are simple enough to obviate intractable analysis but that nevertheless lead to useful models.

We say that a system is in state E_j at time t if $N(t) = j$. Then a process obeying the following postulates is called a *birth-and-death process*:

If at any time t the system is in state E_j, the conditional probability that during $(t, t + h)$ the transition $E_j \rightarrow E_{j+1}$ $(j = 0, 1, \ldots)$ occurs equals $\lambda_j h + o(h)$ as $h \rightarrow 0$, and the conditional probability of the transition $E_j \rightarrow E_{j-1}$ $(j = 1, 2, \ldots)$ equals $\mu_j h + o(h)$ as $h \rightarrow 0$. The probability that during $(t, t + h)$ the index j changes by more than one unit is $o(h)$ as $h \rightarrow 0$. (A quantity $f(h)$ is said to equal $o(h)$ as $h \rightarrow 0$ if $\lim_{h \rightarrow 0} [f(h)/h] = 0$.)

We now set $P_j(t) = P\{N(t) = j\}$. It follows from the postulates and the law of total probability that (see Exercise 1)

$$P_j(t + h) = \lambda_{j-1}hP_{j-1}(t) + \mu_{j+1}hP_{j+1}(t)$$
$$+ [1 - (\lambda_j + \mu_j)h]P_j(t) + o(h)$$
$$[h \to 0; j = 0, 1, \ldots; \lambda_{-1} = \mu_0 = P_{-1}(t) = 0]. \quad (2.1)$$

Rearranging equation (2.1) and dividing through by h, we have

$$\frac{P_j(t + h) - P_j(t)}{h} = \lambda_{j-1}P_{j-1}(t) + \mu_{j+1}P_{j+1}(t)$$

$$- (\lambda_j + \mu_j)P_j(t) + \frac{o(h)}{h}$$

$$[h \to 0; j = 0, 1, \ldots; \lambda_{-1} = \mu_0 = P_{-1}(t) = 0]. \quad (2.2)$$

We now let $h \to 0$ in equation (2.2). The result is the following set of differential-difference equations for the birth-and-death process:

$$\frac{d}{dt} P_j(t) = \lambda_{j-1}P_{j-1}(t) + \mu_{j+1}P_{j+1}(t) - (\lambda_j + \mu_j)P_j(t)$$

$$[j = 0, 1, \ldots; \lambda_{-1} = \mu_0 = P_{-1}(t) = 0]. \quad (2.3)$$

If at time $t = 0$ the system is in state E_i, the initial conditions that complement equation (2.3) are

$$P_j(0) = \begin{cases} 1 & \text{if } j = i \\ 0 & \text{if } j \neq i. \end{cases} \quad (2.4)$$

The coefficients $\{\lambda_j\}$ and $\{\mu_j\}$ are called the *birth* and *death rates*, respectively. When $\mu_j = 0$ for all j, the process is called a *pure birth process*; and when $\lambda_j = 0$ for all j, the process is called a *pure death process*.

In the case of either a pure birth process or a pure death process, it is easy to see that the differential-difference equations (2.3) can always be solved, at least in principle, by recurrence (successive substitution).

For example, consider the important special case of the pure birth process with constant birth rate $\lambda_j = \lambda$. (This model is often used to describe the arrival process of customers at a queue.) If we assume that the system is initially in state E_0, then for this case equations (2.3) and (2.4) become

$$\frac{d}{dt} P_j(t) = \lambda P_{j-1}(t) - \lambda P_j(t) \qquad [j = 0, 1, \ldots ; P_{-1}(t) = 0] \qquad (2.5)$$

and

$$P_j(0) = \begin{cases} 1 & \text{if } j = 0 \\ 0 & \text{if } j \neq 0. \end{cases} \qquad (2.6)$$

An easy solution by recurrence (or induction) gives

$$P_j(t) = \frac{(\lambda t)^j}{j!} e^{-\lambda t} \qquad (j = 0, 1, \ldots). \qquad (2.7)$$

Note that the probabilities given by (2.7) satisfy the normalization condition

$$\sum_{j=0}^{\infty} P_j(t) = 1 \qquad (t \geq 0). \qquad (2.8)$$

(The normalization condition (2.8) is not satisfied for every choice of the birth coefficients. For a more extensive treatment, see Chapter XVII of Feller [1968].)

According to equation (2.7), $N(t)$ has the *Poisson* distribution with mean λt; that is, $N(t)$ describes a *Poisson process*. Since the assumption $\lambda_j = \lambda$ is often a realistic one in the construction of queueing models, the simple formula (2.7) is important in queueing theory. The Poisson distribution possesses important theoretical properties and plays a central role in queueing theory.

Another important example is the special case of the pure death process with death rate μ_j proportional to the index of the state E_j; that is, $\mu_j = j\mu$. (A real system that might fit this model is a population in which only deaths occur and where the death rate is proportional to the population size.) If we assume that the system is in state E_n at $t = 0$, then equations (2.3) and (2.4) become

$$\frac{d}{dt} P_n(t) = -n\mu P_n(t) \qquad [P_n(0) = 1] \qquad (2.9)$$

$$\frac{d}{dt} P_j(t) = (j + 1)\mu P_{j+1}(t) - j\mu P_j(t)$$

$$[P_j(0) = 0; j = n - 1, n - 2, \ldots, 2, 1, 0]. \qquad (2.10)$$

Solving these equations by recurrence, it is easy to verify that the general form of the solution $P_j(t)$ is

$$P_j(t) = \binom{n}{j} (e^{-\mu t})^j (1 - e^{-\mu t})^{n-j} \qquad (j = 0, 1, \ldots, n). \qquad (2.11)$$

We remark that the probabilities defined by (2.11) comprise a binomial distribution, and therefore sum to unity.

We have observed that in the case of the pure birth process ($\mu_j = 0$), the differential-difference equations (2.3) can always be solved recurrently, at least in principle. Therefore, even though the number of equations is, in general, infinite, there is no question about the existence of a solution since the solution can be exhibited. On the other hand, it is not necessarily true that the solution $\{P_j(t)\}$ comprises a proper probability distribution. In any particular case, a good strategy may be to find the solution first, and then determine if the solution comprises a proper probability distribution, rather than vice versa.

In the case of the pure death process ($\lambda_j = 0$), the differential-difference equations (2.3) offer less theoretical difficulty, since not only can they be solved recurrently, but also they are finite in number.

In contrast, in the general case, equations (2.3) of the birth-and-death process do not yield to solution by recurrence, as one can easily verify. Also, in general, these equations are infinite in number. Therefore, both practical and theoretical difficulties present themselves.

The questions of existence and uniqueness of solutions are difficult and will not be discussed here. Suffice it to say that in almost every case of practical interest, equations (2.3) and (2.4) have a unique solution that satisfies

$$\sum_{j=0}^{\infty} P_j(t) = 1 \qquad [0 \leqq P_j(t) \leqq 1; 0 \leqq t < \infty]. \qquad (2.12)$$

The question is discussed in some detail in Chapter XVII of Feller [1968], who also gives several pertinent references.

As an example of the use of the birth-and-death process in a queueing theory context, we consider a queueing system with one server and no waiting positions. Specifically, we assume that the probability of a request in $(t, t + h)$ is $\lambda h + o(h)$ as $h \to 0$, and assume that if the server is busy at t, the probability that the customer in service will end in $(t, t + h)$ is $\mu h + o(h)$ as $h \to 0$. Assume further that every customer who finds the server occupied leaves the system immediately and thus has no effect upon it.

In terms of the postulates for the birth-and-death process, this queueing model corresponds to a two-state birth-and-death process. E_0 corresponds to the state {server idle} and E_1 corresponds to the state {server busy}. Since, by assumption, an arrival that occurs when the server is busy has no effect on the system, an arrival will cause a state transition if and only if it occurs when the server is idle. Therefore, the effective arrival rates are $\lambda_0 = \lambda$ and $\lambda_j = 0$ for $j \neq 0$. Similarly, no customers can complete service when no customers are in the system, so that $\mu_j = 0$ when $j \neq 1$, and, by assumption, $\mu_1 = \mu$. The birth-and-death equations (2.3) for these particular choices of the birth-and-death coefficients are

$$\frac{d}{dt} P_0(t) = \mu P_1(t) - \lambda P_0(t) \tag{2.13}$$

and

$$\frac{d}{dt} P_1(t) = \lambda P_0(t) - \mu P_1(t). \tag{2.14}$$

Standard techniques exist for the solution of sets of simultaneous linear differential equations, but we shall solve this simple set by using its special properties.

First note that when equations (2.13) and (2.14) are added, we obtain

$$\frac{d}{dt} [P_0(t) + P_1(t)] = 0$$

so that the sum of the probabilities is constant for all $t \geq 0$,

$$P_0(t) + P_1(t) = c. \tag{2.15}$$

We require that the system initially be describable by a probability distribution, so that

$$P_0(0) + P_1(0) = 1. \tag{2.16}$$

Then equations (2.15) and (2.16) require $c = 1$, and hence

$$P_0(t) + P_1(t) = 1 \qquad (t \geq 0). \tag{2.17}$$

Substitution of equation (2.17) into (2.13) yields

$$\frac{d}{dt} P_0(t) + (\lambda + \mu)P_0(t) = \mu,$$

which has homogeneous solution $P_0(0)e^{-(\lambda+\mu)t}$ and particular solution $[\mu/(\lambda + \mu)](1 - e^{-(\lambda+\mu)t})$. Therefore, the general solution (the sum of the homogeneous and particular solutions) is

$$P_0(t) = \frac{\mu}{\lambda + \mu} + \left(P_0(0) - \frac{\mu}{\lambda + \mu}\right) e^{-(\lambda+\mu)t}. \qquad (2.18)$$

By symmetry, equations (2.17) and (2.14) yield

$$P_1(t) = \frac{\lambda}{\lambda + \mu} + \left(P_1(0) - \frac{\lambda}{\lambda + \mu}\right) e^{-(\lambda+\mu)t}. \qquad (2.19)$$

2–3. Statistical Equilibrium

Suppose that we are interested in the behavior of the system just described for large values of t, that is, after it has been in operation for a long period of time. The state probabilities as functions of time are given by equations (2.18) and (2.19). Letting $t \to \infty$ in (2.18) and (2.19) we obtain

$$P_0 = \lim_{t \to \infty} P_0(t) = \frac{\mu}{\lambda + \mu} \qquad (3.1)$$

and

$$P_1 = \lim_{t \to \infty} P_1(t) = \frac{\lambda}{\lambda + \mu}. \qquad (3.2)$$

Observe that

$$P_0 + P_1 = 1 \qquad (3.3)$$

so that the limiting distribution is proper. Note that the limiting values of the probabilities are independent of the initial values $P_0(0)$ and $P_1(0)$. In other words, after a sufficiently long period of time the state probabilities are independent of the initial conditions, and the system is said to be in *statistical equilibrium*.

An important characteristic of the statistical equilibrium distribution is that it is *stationary*; that is, it maintains itself. For example, if our system were assumed to be in statistical equilibrium at some time t, say $t = 0$, so that $P_0(0) = \mu/(\lambda + \mu)$ and $P_1(0) = \lambda/(\lambda + \mu)$, then equations (2.18) and (2.19) make it clear that these initial values will persist for all $t \geq 0$. In other words, when a system is in statistical equilibrium the state probabilities remain constant in time.

Suppose that we are primarily interested in the statistical equilibrium properties of a system. Since in this example the limiting probabilities $\lim_{t \to \infty} P_j(t) = P_j$ have been shown directly to exist, it follows from equations (2.13) and (2.14) that $\lim_{t \to \infty} (d/dt)P_j(t) = 0$. This suggests that the limiting probabilities might follow directly from equations (2.13) and (2.14) when the time derivatives are set equal to zero. That is, letting $t \to \infty$ in (2.13) and (2.14) we obtain

$$0 = \mu P_1 - \lambda P_0 \tag{3.4}$$

and

$$0 = \lambda P_0 - \mu P_1. \tag{3.5}$$

Equations (3.4) and (3.5) are identical; they yield

$$P_1 = \frac{\lambda}{\mu} P_0. \tag{3.6}$$

Since the initial conditions (2.16), which led to the normalization equation (2.17), no longer appear, we must specify that

$$P_0 + P_1 = 1. \tag{3.7}$$

We then obtain from equations (3.6) and (3.7) that $P_0 = \mu/(\lambda + \mu)$ and $P_1 = \lambda/(\lambda + \mu)$, in agreement with the previous results (3.1) and (3.2). Thus we have obtained the statistical equilibrium solution by solving the linear difference equations (3.4) and (3.5) instead of the more difficult linear differential-difference equations (2.13) and (2.14).

We have shown that, in this simple example at least, the statistical equilibrium distribution can be obtained in two different ways:

1. Solve the differential-difference equations (2.3), with appropriate initial conditions, to obtain $P_j(t)$, and then calculate the limits $\lim_{t \to \infty} P_j(t) = P_j$.
2. Take limits as $t \to \infty$ throughout the basic differential-difference equations (2.3), set $\lim_{t \to \infty} (d/dt)P_j(t) = 0$ and $\lim_{t \to \infty} P_j(t) = P_j$, solve the resulting set of difference equations, and normalize so that $\sum_{j=0}^{\infty} P_j = 1$.

Method 2 is clearly the easier way to obtain the equilibrium distribution, since the problem is reduced to solving a set of difference equations instead of a set of differential-difference equations.

Let us now move from this simple motivating example to the general birth-and-death process. One might hope that method 2 applies to the general birth-and-death equations (2.3). It does. We state the following theorem without proof (see any text on stochastic processes):

The statistical equilibrium distribution

$$P_j = \lim_{t \to \infty} P_j(t) \qquad (j = 0, 1, \ldots) \tag{3.8}$$

for the general birth-and-death equations (2.3) exists and can be found by method 2. If all $\mu_j > 0$ and the series

$$S = 1 + \frac{\lambda_0}{\mu_1} + \frac{\lambda_0 \lambda_1}{\mu_1 \mu_2} + \cdots + \frac{\lambda_0 \lambda_1 \cdots \lambda_{j-1}}{\mu_1 \mu_2 \cdots \mu_j} + \cdots \tag{3.9}$$

converges, then

$$P_0 = S^{-1} \tag{3.10}$$

and

$$P_j = \frac{\lambda_0 \lambda_1 \cdots \lambda_{j-1}}{\mu_1 \mu_2 \cdots \mu_j} S^{-1} \qquad (j = 1, 2, \ldots). \tag{3.11}$$

If the series (3.9) diverges, then

$$P_j = 0 \qquad (j = 0, 1, \ldots). \tag{3.12}$$

It is instructive to assume the truth of equation (3.8), and derive the results (3.9)–(3.12):

It follows from equations (2.3) that, if equation (3.8) holds, then the time derivatives on the left-hand side of (2.3) are zero. Therefore, taking limits throughout equations (2.3) as $t \to \infty$, we have, after rearranging, the fundamental set of linear difference equations for the statistical equilibrium probabilities:

$$(\lambda_j + \mu_j)P_j = \lambda_{j-1}P_{j-1} + \mu_{j+1}P_{j+1}$$
$$(\lambda_{-1} = \mu_0 = 0; j = 0, 1, \ldots). \tag{3.13}$$

The set of linear difference equations (3.13) can be written in the form

$$\lambda_j P_j - \mu_{j+1}P_{j+1} = \lambda_{j-1}P_{j-1} - \mu_j P_j$$
$$(\lambda_{-1} = \mu_0 = 0; j = 0, 1, \ldots). \tag{3.14}$$

Equation (3.14) exhibits the important property that the left-hand side is of the same form as the right-hand side; that is, if we define

$$f(j) = \lambda_j P_j - \mu_{j+1} P_{j+1} \qquad (j = 0, 1, \ldots),$$

then equation (3.14) can be written

$$f(j) = f(j - 1) \qquad [f(-1) = 0; j = 0, 1, \ldots].$$

This implies that $f(j) = $ constant, and, since $f(-1) = 0$, it follows that

$$f(j) = 0 \qquad (j = 0, 1, \ldots).$$

Thus equation (3.13) implies (and, clearly, is implied by)

$$\lambda_j P_j = \mu_{j+1} P_{j+1} \qquad (j = 0, 1, \ldots). \tag{3.15}$$

Equations (3.15) allow the statistical equilibrium state probabilities to be calculated by recurrence (if $\mu_{j+1} > 0$):

$$P_{j+1} = \frac{\lambda_j}{\mu_{j+1}} P_j \qquad (j = 0, 1, \ldots) \tag{3.16}$$

or equivalently,

$$P_j = \frac{\lambda_0 \lambda_1 \cdots \lambda_{j-1}}{\mu_1 \mu_2 \cdots \mu_j} P_0 \qquad (j = 1, 2, \ldots). \tag{3.17}$$

As previously observed, the unknown probability P_0 is determined by the normalization condition

$$\sum_{j=0}^{\infty} P_j = 1. \tag{3.18}$$

The sum on the left-hand side of (3.18) may fail to converge when (3.17) is substituted into it unless $P_0 = 0$. This implies that $P_j = 0$ for all finite j (so that, roughly speaking, in this case the state of the system grows without bound). These results are equivalent to equations (3.9)–(3.12).

If $\mu_j = 0$ for some $j = k$, then, as equation (3.15) shows, $P_j = 0$ for $j = 0, 1, \ldots, k - 1$. An extreme example is provided by the pure birth process, where $\mu_j = 0$ for all values of the index j. Thus $P_j = 0$ $(j = 0, 1, \ldots)$ for the pure birth process; that is, no proper equilibrium distribution exists. In the particular case of the Poisson process, for example, where $\lambda_j = \lambda$ ($j = 0, 1, \ldots$), the time-dependent probabilities $\{P_j(t)\}$ are given by equation (2.7), from which we see that these probabilities are all positive and sum to unity for all finite $t > 0$, but that each probability approaches zero as $t \to \infty$.

Equation (3.13) admits of a simple and important intuitive interpretation: to write down the statistical equilibrium state equations, simply equate the rate at which the system leaves state E_j to the rate at which the system enters state E_j. Similarly, equation (3.15) can be interpreted as stating that the rate at which the system leaves state E_j for a higher state equals the rate at which the system leaves state E_{j+1} for a lower state.

Equations (3.13) and (3.15) are statements of conservation of flow. Recall that in Chapter 1 we gave a heuristic derivation of an important queueing formula using this concept. Specifically, we appealed to this concept to derive the statistical equilibrium balance equation (1.1) of Chapter 1:

$$\lambda P_j = (j + 1)\tau^{-1}P_{j+1} \qquad (j = 0, 1, \ldots, s - 1).$$

Observe that this equation is the special case of the statistical equilibrium state equation (3.15) with $\lambda_j = \lambda$ and $\mu_{j+1} = (j + 1)\tau^{-1}$ for $j = 0, 1, \ldots,$ $s - 1$ and $\lambda_j = 0$ for $j \geq s$, and that the heuristic conservation of flow argument of Chapter 1 is identical with the intuitive interpretation of equation (3.15).

Thus far our discussion has been limited to birth-and-death processes for which the ordering of states $E_0, E_1, E_2, \ldots$ arises quite naturally. As we shall see, however, this is not always the case. Quite often problems arise in which the natural definition of states requires two variables, for example, E_{ij} ($i = 0, 1, 2, \ldots$; $j = 0, 1, 2, \ldots$). Of course, these two-dimensional states can always be relabeled so that the problem reduces to the one-dimensional case, but then the analysis becomes less intuitive. The multidimensional state equation problem will be discussed in detail in Chapter 4. For the present, we simply remark that the "rate out equals rate in" approach, as exemplified by equation (3.13), is usually the most direct method of analysis. Therefore, a convenient operational definition of statistical equilibrium is the following:

A system with discrete states is in statistical equilibrium if the rate of occurrence of transitions out of any state equals the rate of occurrence of transitions into that state. The statistical equilibrium probabilities are defined by these equalities and the condition that the probabilities sum to unity.

We have shown that for the one-dimensional case, the "rate out equals rate in" formulation (3.13) is equivalent to the mathematically simpler "rate up equals rate down" formulation (3.15). We shall show in Chapter 4 that this approach has a sometimes useful analogue in the multidimensional case.

The reader might have noticed that throughout our discussion of the birth-and-death process no mention has been made of the meaning of the probabilities whose calculation we have so carefully detailed. The birth-and-death process occurs in continuous time, and is described by a sequence of discrete probabilities. The deeper question of the interpretation of these probabilities (as opposed to their calculation) requires an understanding of the underlying mathematical structure, whose treatment is beyond the scope of this text. The question will be investigated in more detail in Chapter 3, although we will continue to avoid abstract mathematical arguments. We will content ourselves for the present by simply stating how the probabilities are to be interpreted.

Although we have been using a model to describe a single system, strictly speaking the definition of probability applies to collections rather than individuals. Thus, consider an infinite set of identical systems. By definition, $P_j(t)$ is the proportion of these systems in state E_j at time t, and the statistical equilibrium probability P_j is the limit $P_j = \lim_{t \to \infty} P_j(t)$.

The probability P_j can also be interpreted as follows: Suppose that a single system is observed over a long period of time $(0, x)$. Then in the limit as $x \to \infty$, P_j is the proportion of the time interval $(0, x)$ that the system spends in state E_j.

The latter interpretation is usually the more useful one in queueing theory. The equivalence of these two interpretations is a consequence of a deep theorem (called an *ergodic theorem*) of stochastic processes. A good discussion is given in Khintchine [1969].

To summarize, a system is said to be in statistical equilibrium if its state probabilities are constant in time, that is, if the state distribution is stationary. This does not mean that the system does not fluctuate from state to state, but rather that no net trends result from the statistical fluctuations. From a practical point of view, it is assumed that a system is in statistical equilibrium after it has been in operation long enough for the effects of the initial conditions to have worn off. The statistical equilibrium state equations are obtained from the birth-and-death equations by setting the time derivatives of the state probabilities equal to zero, which reflects the idea that during statistical equilibrium the state distribution is constant in time. Equivalently, the statistical equilibrium state probabilities are defined by the equation rate out equals rate in. The statistical equilibrium probability P_j is interpreted as the proportion of time that the system will spend in state E_j ($j = 0, 1, 2, \ldots$), taken over any long period of time throughout which statistical equilibrium prevails.

It should be apparent that a deep understanding of the theory of birth-and-death processes requires extensive mathematical preparation. The interested reader should consult texts on stochastic processes and Markov processes. (Roughly speaking, a *Markov process* is a process whose future probabilistic evolution after any time t depends only on the state of the system at time t, and is independent of the history of the system prior to time t. It should be easy for the reader to verify that a birth-and-death process is a Markov process.) Hopefully, it is also apparent that the birth-and-death process has sufficient intuitive appeal so that useful insights can be gained from the preceding cursory summary. We shall return to the birth-and-death process in Chapter 3, where we shall develop queueing models by judiciously choosing the birth-and-death coefficients.

2–4. Probability Generating Functions

Many of the random variables of interest in queueing theory assume only the integral values $j = 0, 1, 2, \ldots$. Let K be a nonnegative integer-valued random variable with probability distribution $\{p_j\}$, where $p_j = P\{K = j\}$ ($j = 0, 1, 2, \ldots$). Consider now the power series $g(z)$,

$$g(z) = p_0 + p_1 z + p_2 z^2 + \cdots, \tag{4.1}$$

where the probability p_j is the coefficient of z^j in the expansion (4.1). Since $\{p_j\}$ is a probability distribution, therefore $g(1) = 1$. In fact, $g(z)$ is convergent for $|z| \leq 1$ [so that the function (4.1) is holomorphic at least on the unit disk—see any standard text in complex variable or analytic function theory]. Clearly, the right-hand side of (4.1) characterizes K, since it displays the whole distribution $\{p_j\}$. And, since the power series representation of a function is unique, the distribution $\{p_j\}$ is completely and uniquely specified by the function $g(z)$. The function $g(z)$ is called the *probability generating function* for the random variable K. The variable z has no inherent significance although, as we shall see, it is sometimes useful to give it a physical interpretation.

The notion of a generating function applies not only to probability distributions $\{p_j\}$, but to any sequence of real numbers. However, the generating function is a particularly powerful tool in the analysis of probability problems, and we shall restrict ourselves to probability generating functions. The generating function transforms a discrete sequence of numbers (the probabilities) into a function of a dummy variable, much the same way the Laplace transform changes a function of a particular variable into another function of a different variable. As with all transform methods, the use of generating functions not only preserves the information while changing its form, but also presents the information in a form that often simplifies manipulations and provides insight.

As examples of probability generating functions, we consider those for the Bernoulli and Poisson distributions. A random variable X has the *Bernoulli* distribution if it has two possible realizations, say 0 and 1, occurring with probabilities $P\{X = 0\} = q$ and $P\{X = 1\} = p$, where $p + q = 1$. As discussed in Section 2–1, this scheme can be used to describe a coin toss, with $X = 1$ when a head appears and $X = 0$ when a tail appears. Referring to (4.1), we see that the Bernoulli variable X has probability generating function $b(z)$

$$b(z) = q + pz. \tag{4.2}$$

(If this seems somewhat less than profound, be content with the promise that this simple notion will prove extremely useful.)

In Section 2–2 we considered the random variable $N(t)$, defined as the number of customers arriving in an interval of length t, and we showed that with appropriate assumptions this random variable is described by the Poisson distribution

$$P\{N(t) = j\} = \frac{(\lambda t)^j}{j!} e^{-\lambda t} \qquad (j = 0, 1, \ldots).$$

If we denote the probability generating function of $N(t)$ by $p(z)$, then

$$p(z) = \sum_{j=0}^{\infty} \frac{(\lambda t)^j}{j!} e^{-\lambda t} z^j = e^{-\lambda t} \sum_{j=0}^{\infty} \frac{(\lambda t z)^j}{j!}$$

and this reduces to

$$p(z) = e^{-\lambda t(1 - z)}. \tag{4.3}$$

Having defined the notion of probability generating function and given two important examples, we now discuss the special properties of probability generating functions that make the concept useful. Since the probability generating function $g(z)$ of a random variable X contains the distribution $\{p_j\}$ implicitly, it therefore contains the information specifying the moments of the distribution $\{p_j\}$. Consider the mean $E(K)$,

$$E(K) = \sum_{j=1}^{\infty} jp_j. \tag{4.4}$$

It is easy to see that (4.4) can be obtained formally by evaluating the derivative $(d/dz)g(z) = \sum_{j=1}^{\infty} jp_j z^{j-1}$ at $z = 1$:

$$E(K) = g'(1). \tag{4.5}$$

From (4.2) and (4.5) we see that the Bernoulli random variable X has mean

$$E(X) = p \tag{4.6}$$

and from (4.3) and (4.5) we see that the Poisson random variable $N(t)$ has mean

$$E[N(t)] = \lambda t. \tag{4.7}$$

Similarly, it is easy (and we leave it as an exercise) to show that the variance $V(K)$ can be obtained from the probability generating function as

$$V(K) = g''(1) + g'(1) - [g'(1)]^2. \tag{4.8}$$

Formula (4.8) gives for the Bernoulli variable

$$V(X) = pq \tag{4.9}$$

and for the Poisson variable

$$V[N(t)] = \lambda t. \tag{4.10}$$

Sometimes, as we shall see, it is easier to obtain the probability generating function than it is to obtain the whole distribution directly. In such cases, formulas (4.5) and (4.8) often provide the easiest way of obtaining the mean and variance. The higher moments can also be calculated in a similar manner from the probability generating function, but the complexity of the formulas increases rapidly. If primary interest is in the moments of a distribution rather than the individual probabilities, it is often convenient to work directly with the moment generating function or the related characteristic function, which generate moments similar to the way (4.1) generates probabilities. These topics are covered in most texts on mathematical statistics, such as Fisz [1963].

Another important use of probability generating functions is in the analysis of problems concerning sums of independent random variables. Suppose $K = K_1 + K_2$, where K_1 and K_2 are independent, nonnegative, integer-valued random variables. Then $P\{K = k\}$ $(k = 0, 1, 2, \ldots)$ is given by the convolution

$$P\{K = k\} = \sum_{j=0}^{k} P\{K_1 = j\}P\{K_2 = k - j\}. \tag{4.11}$$

Let K_1 and K_2 have generating functions $g_1(z)$ and $g_2(z)$, respectively:

$$g_1(z) = \sum_{j=0}^{\infty} P\{K_1 = j\}z^j$$

and

$$g_2(z) = \sum_{j=0}^{\infty} P\{K_2 = j\}z^j. \tag{4.12}$$

Then term-by-term multiplication shows that the product $g_1(z)g_2(z)$ is given by

$$g_1(z)g_2(z) = \sum_{k=0}^{\infty} \left[\sum_{j=0}^{k} P\{K_1 = j\}P\{K_2 = k - j\} \right] z^k. \tag{4.13}$$

If K has generating function $g(z) = \sum_{k=0}^{\infty} P\{K = k\}z^k$, then (4.11) and (4.13) show that

$$g(z) = g_1(z)g_2(z). \tag{4.14}$$

Thus we have the important result: The generating function of a sum of mutually independent random variables is equal to the product of their respective generating functions.

Consider again the coin-tossing experiment described in Section 2–1. A coin is tossed n times, with $X_j = 1$ if a head appears and $X_j = 0$ if a tail appears on the jth toss. We wish to determine the probability that k heads appear in n tosses. Let

$$S_n = X_1 + \cdots + X_n \tag{4.15}$$

so that the value of the random variable S_n is the number of heads appearing in n tosses. S_n is the sum of n mutually independent, identically distributed Bernoulli variables $\{X_j\}$, each with generating function $b(z)$ given by (4.2). Therefore, S_n has generating function $[b(z)]^n$ so that

$$(q + pz)^n = \sum_{k=0}^{\infty} P\{S_n = k\}z^k. \qquad (4.16)$$

Expanding the left-hand side of (4.16) by the binomial theorem, we obtain

$$(q + pz)^n = \sum_{k=0}^{n} \binom{n}{k} (pz)^k q^{n-k}. \qquad (4.17)$$

Equating coefficients of z^k in (4.16) and (4.17) yields

$$P\{S_n = k\} = \begin{cases} \binom{n}{k} p^k q^{n-k} & (k = 0, 1, \ldots, n) \\ 0 & (k > n) \end{cases} \qquad (4.18)$$

which is, of course, the binomial distribution.

The result (4.18) could have been obtained by direct probabilistic reasoning. [Any particular sequence of k heads and $n - k$ tails has probability $p^k q^{n-k}$, and there are $\binom{n}{k}$ such sequences.] In this example, the direct probabilistic reasoning concerning the possible outcomes of n tosses is replaced by the simpler probabilistic reasoning concerning the possible outcomes of one toss and the observation (4.15) that leads to the use of probability generating functions. In a sense, probabilistic or intuitive reasoning has been traded for more formal mathematical manipulation. In the present case both approaches are simple, but this is not always true. Roughly speaking, the difficulties encountered in the generating function approach, when applicable, are not extremely sensitive to the underlying probabilistic structure. Thus the use of generating functions tends to simplify hard problems and complicate easy ones.

Another example is provided by the Poisson distribution. Let $N = N_1 + N_2$, where N_i is a Poisson random variable with mean λ_i; $P\{N_i = j\} = (\lambda_i^j/j!)e^{-\lambda_i}$. Then N has probability generating function

$$p(z) = e^{-\lambda_1(1-z)}e^{-\lambda_2(1-z)} = e^{-(\lambda_1+\lambda_2)(1-z)}. \qquad (4.19)$$

Equation (4.19) shows (with no effort) that the sum of two independent Poisson variables with means λ_1 and λ_2 is itself a Poisson variable with mean $\lambda = \lambda_1 + \lambda_2$.

Perhaps the most important use of probability generating functions in queueing theory is in the solution of probability state equations. Consider, for example, the birth-and-death equations (2.3) with $\lambda_j = \lambda$, $\mu_j = j\mu$ $(j = 0, 1, 2, \ldots)$, and initial condition $P_0(0) = 1$. The equations are

$$\frac{d}{dt} P_j(t) = \lambda P_{j-1}(t) + (j + 1)\mu P_{j+1}(t) - (\lambda + j\mu)P_j(t)$$

$$[P_{-1}(t) = 0; j = 0, 1, \ldots]. \quad (4.20)$$

Equations (4.20) describe the following important queueing model. Customers request service from an infinite-server group. The probability that exactly one customer arrives in $(t, t + h)$ is $\lambda h + o(h)$ as $h \to 0$. If there are j customers in service at time t, the probability that exactly one customer will complete service in $(t, t + h)$ is $j\mu h + o(h)$ as $h \to 0$. And the probability that more than one change (arrivals and/or service completions) occurs in $(t, t + h)$ is $o(h)$ as $h \to 0$. (As we shall see, these assumptions are true if the customers arrive according to a Poisson process with rate λ, and the service times are mutually independent, identically distributed exponential random variables, each with mean μ^{-1}.) $P_j(t)$ is the probability that j customers are in service at time t.

Although this model is an important one in queueing theory, we shall defer discussion of it to later chapters. Our present concern is simply the application of the theory of probability generating functions to the solution of the probability state equations (4.20).

We emphasize that (4.20) is an infinite set of simultaneous linear differential-difference equations, an apparently hopeless case. Undaunted, we define the probability generating function $P(z, t)$,

$$P(z, t) = \sum_{j=0}^{\infty} P_j(t)z^j. \quad (4.21)$$

Now multiply each equation in $(d/dt)P_j(t)$ of the set (4.20) by z^j and add all the equations. The result is

$$\sum_{j=0}^{\infty} \frac{d}{dt} P_j(t)z^j = \lambda \sum_{j=1}^{\infty} P_{j-1}(t)z^j + \mu \sum_{j=0}^{\infty} (j + 1)P_{j+1}(t)z^j$$

$$- \lambda \sum_{j=0}^{\infty} P_j(t)z^j - \mu \sum_{j=1}^{\infty} jP_j(t)z^j, \quad (4.22)$$

which, in view of (4.21), can be written

$$\frac{\partial}{\partial t} P(z, t) = \lambda z P(z, t) + \mu \frac{\partial}{\partial z} P(z, t) - \lambda P(z, t) - \mu z \frac{\partial}{\partial z} P(z, t).$$

$$(4.23)$$

When rearranged into standard form, equation (4.23) reads

$$\frac{\partial}{\partial t} P(z, t) - (1 - z)\mu \frac{\partial}{\partial z} P(z, t) = -\lambda(1 - z)P(z, t). \qquad (4.24)$$

Thus we have transformed the infinite set of simultaneous linear differential-difference equations (4.20) for $P_j(t)$ into the single linear first-order partial differential equation (4.24) for the generating function $P(z, t)$. It remains to solve (4.24) for $P(z, t)$ and invert.

Equation (4.24) can be solved in general by well-known techniques. (See any standard text, such as Garabedian [1964].) The solution that satisfies $P(z, 0) = 1$, corresponding to the initial condition $P_0(0) = 1$, is

$$P(z, t) = \exp\left[-\frac{\lambda}{\mu}(1 - e^{-\mu t})(1 - z)\right], \qquad (4.25)$$

as is readily verified by substitution into (4.24). The state probabilities $P_j(t)$ are easily found by recognizing (4.25) as the probability generating function for the Poisson distribution with mean $(\lambda/\mu)(1 - e^{-\mu t})$:

$$P_j(t) = \frac{[(\lambda/\mu)(1 - e^{-\mu t})]^j}{j!} \exp\left[-\frac{\lambda}{\mu}(1 - e^{-\mu t})\right] \qquad (j = 0, 1, \ldots).$$

$$(4.26)$$

Several observations are in order. As in Section 2–2, we have solved the birth-and-death equations (2.3) completely for a particular choice of birth and death rates and a particular initial condition. The normalization requirement (2.12) is satisfied since, for any t, $P_j(t)$ is a Poisson probability. Equivalently, $P(1, t) = 1$ as (4.25) shows. The statistical equilibrium distribution can be obtained directly by taking limits in (4.26):

$$P_j = \lim_{t \to \infty} P_j(t) = \frac{(\lambda/\mu)^j}{j!} e^{-(\lambda/\mu)} \qquad (j = 0, 1, \ldots). \qquad (4.27)$$

The limiting distribution is the Poisson distribution with mean λ/μ.

The limiting distribution (4.27) can also be obtained by taking limits in the probability generating function (4.25). In general, it is true that a sequence of probability distributions converges to a limiting distribution if and only if the corresponding generating functions converge. (See Chapter XI.6 of Feller [1968].)

Finally, note that (4.27) can be obtained directly from the statistical equilibrium state equations and the normalization condition, that is, from (3.17) and (3.18) with $\lambda_j = \lambda$, $\mu_j = j\mu$ $(j = 0, 1, 2, \ldots)$.

It was mentioned previously that the variable z has no inherent significance, but that it is sometimes useful to give it a physical interpretation. In this way, it is sometimes possible to obtain the generating function directly from probabilistic considerations. Consider, for example, the generating function (4.21). The right-hand side of (4.21) can be given the following interpretation:

Suppose that each arriving customer is (independently) given an identifying mark with probability $1 - z$. Then $P_j(t)z^j$ is the probability that at time t there are j customers in the system, none of which is marked. Therefore, $P(z, t) = \sum_{j=0}^{\infty} P_j(t)z^j$ is the probability that no marked customers are in the system at time t.

Thus the generating function might be found by evaluating this probability directly rather than by deriving and solving the partial differential equation (4.24). This scheme is van Dantzig's *method of collective marks* (see Runnenburg [1965]). We shall use it in Chapter 3 to solve a more general problem of which the present problem is a special case. See also Exercise 16.

2–5. Some Important Probability Distributions

We consider several distributions that are important in queueing theory.

Bernoulli Distribution

A random variable X has the Bernoulli distribution if it has two possible outcomes, say $X = 1$ and $X = 0$ (often called success and failure, respectively) occurring with probabilities $P\{X = 1\} = p$ and $P\{X = 0\} = q$, where $p + q = 1$. As mentioned previously, this scheme is often used to describe a coin toss, with $X = 1$ when a head occurs. The Bernoulli variable has probability generating function $q + pz$, mean p, and variance pq.

Binomial Distribution

The binomial distribution describes the number of successes in n Bernoulli trials without regard to order, where at each trial the probability of success is p. If S_n is the number of successes in n Bernoulli trials, then S_n can be represented as the sum $S_n = X_1 + \cdots + X_n$, where X_j is the Bernoulli variable with value $X_j = 1$ if the jth trial results in success and $X_j = 0$ for failure. Since the $\{X_j\}$ are mutually independent, identically distributed random variables, each with probability generating function $q + pz$, then S_n has generating function $(q + pz)^n$. Expansion of the generating function shows that S_n has distribution $P\{S_n = k\} = b(k; n, p)$:

$$b(k; n, p) = \binom{n}{k} p^k (1 - p)^{n-k}. \tag{5.1}$$

As mentioned previously, equation (5.1) can be derived directly by probabilistic reasoning: Since the trials are mutually independent, each trial having probability p of success, any sequence of k successes and $n - k$ failures has probability $p^k (1 - p)^{n-k}$. There are $\binom{n}{k} = n!/[k!(n - k)!]$ ways to choose the k locations of the successes in a sequence of k successes and $n - k$ failures. Thus there are altogether $\binom{n}{k}$ different sequences of k successes and $n - k$ failures, and equation (5.1) follows.

The binomial distribution is often used to describe the number of busy telephone lines in a line group. This use of formula (5.1) is based on the implicit assumptions that each line has equal probability p of being busy, and that the lines become busy and idle independently of each other. These implicit assumptions are often not true, in which case formula (5.1) provides only a rough approximation.

The random variable S_n with distribution (5.1) has mean np and variance npq, which follows directly from the interpretation of S_n as a sum of n identical, mutually independent Bernoulli variables.

Multinomial Distribution

Suppose that we have a sequence of n independent trials, but at each trial the number of possible outcomes is $r \geq 2$. That is, at the jth trial, there are r possible outcomes with respective probabilities $p_1, \ldots, p_r$ (subject, of course, to $p_1 + \cdots + p_r = 1$). Let N_i be the number of times the ith outcome occurs in n trials. The joint probability that in n trials the ith outcome occurs k_i times, where $k_1 + \cdots + k_r = n$, is

$$P\{N_1 = k_1, \ldots, N_r = k_r\} = \frac{n!}{k_1! \cdots k_r!} p_1^{k_1} \cdots p_r^{k_r}. \tag{5.2}$$

Equation (5.2) defines a multivariate distribution, for which probability generating functions can be defined in a manner analogous to that presented for univariate distributions. We shall not go into this subject further, but simply call attention to (5.2), which we shall have occasion to use later. Note that (5.2) reduces to the binomial distribution when $r = 2$.

Geometric Distribution

In a sequence of Bernoulli trials, the probability that the first success occurs after exactly k failures is $(1 - p)^k p$, where p is the probability of success at any particular trial. Let N be the number of failures preceding the first success. (N is often called the waiting time to the first success.) Then N has the geometric distribution

$$P\{N = k\} = (1 - p)^k p \qquad (k = 0, 1, \ldots). \qquad (5.3)$$

Notice that N has an infinite number of possible realizations, as opposed to the Bernoulli, binomial, and multinomial distributions, which are defined on finite sample spaces. For any $0 < p < 1$ we have $\sum_{k=0}^{\infty} (1 - p)^k p = 1$, so that the distribution (5.3) is proper and there is no need to assign a positive probability to the realization $N = \infty$.

The random variable N has probability generating function

$$p \sum_{k=0}^{\infty} q^k z^k = \frac{p}{1 - qz},$$

mean q/p, and variance q/p^2, where $q = 1 - p$.

From (5.3) the probability that the waiting time to the first success is at least k is

$$P\{N \geq k\} = \sum_{j=k}^{\infty} q^j p = \frac{pq^k}{1 - q} = q^k, \qquad (5.4)$$

which is just what we should expect; q^k is the probability that each of the first k trials results in failure.

Formula (5.3) gives the probability that exactly k failures precede the first success in a series of independent trials, where each trial has the same probability p of success. Since the probability of success at each trial is independent of the number of preceding trials, it should be clear that the conditional probability that N will equal $j + k$, given that N is at least

j $(j = 0, 1, 2, \ldots)$, is exactly the same as the unconditional probability (5.3) that N equals k. The definition of conditional probability yields

$$P\{N = j + k \mid N \geq j\} = \frac{P\{N = j + k, N \geq j\}}{P\{N \geq j\}}$$

$$= \frac{P\{N = j + k\}}{P\{N \geq j\}} = \frac{q^{j+k}p}{q^j} = q^k p \qquad (5.5)$$

or, equivalently,

$$P\{N \geq j + k \mid N \geq j\} = q^k. \qquad (5.6)$$

Comparison of (5.6) and (5.4) shows that, if N has a geometric distribution, then

$$P\{N \geq j + k \mid N \geq j\} = P\{N \geq k\}. \qquad (5.7)$$

This property of independence of past history, called the lack of memory or *Markov property*, plays an important role in queueing theory.

The geometric distribution may be used to describe the duration of service of a customer. For the service time might be viewed as the waiting time for the first success in a sequence of Bernoulli trials, one trial performed per unit of time. (Failure means service continues; success means service is completed.) This crude model will prove to be surprisingly relevant.

Negative Binomial (Pascal) Distribution

The number N of failures preceding the first success in a sequence of Bernoulli trials has the geometric distribution (5.3). Let S_n be the number of failures preceding the nth success. ($S_n + n$ is the number of trials up to and including the nth success.) Then $S_n = N_1 + \cdots + N_n$, where N_j $(j = 1, 2, \ldots, n)$ is the number of failures occurring between the $(j - 1)$th and jth successes. The $\{N_j\}$ are mutually independent, identically distributed random variables, each with the geometric distribution (5.3) and probability generating function $p/(1 - qz)$. Hence, S_n has probability generating function $[p/(1 - qz)]^n$. The distribution of S_n, the total number of failures preceding the nth success in a sequence of Bernoulli trials, is called the negative binomial or Pascal distribution. Expansion of the probability generating function shows that the negative binomial distribution is given by

$$P\{S_n = k\} = \binom{n + k - 1}{k} q^k p^n \qquad (k = 0, 1, \ldots). \qquad (5.8)$$

When $n = 1$, formula (5.8) reduces to (5.3).

Formula (5.8) is perhaps more easily derived through direct probabilistic reasoning. The nth success will be preceded by exactly k failures if there are exactly k failures and $n - 1$ successes in any order among the first $n + k - 1$ trials, and the $(n + k)$th trial results in success. Any such sequence has probability $q^k p^{n-1} p$. There are $\binom{n + k - 1}{k}$ ways of choosing the k failures out of the first $n + k - 1$ trials, and formula (5.8) follows.

Since S_n can be interpreted as a sum of n mutually independent, identically distributed geometric random variables, S_n has mean nq/p and variance nq/p^2.

Uniform Distribution

Let T be a continuous random variable that takes values in $(0, t)$, with distribution function $P\{T \leq x\} = F(x)$,

$$F(x) = \begin{cases} 0 & (x < 0) \\ \dfrac{x}{t} & (0 \leq x \leq t) \\ 1 & (x > t) \end{cases} \qquad (5.9)$$

and corresponding density function $f(x) = (d/dx)F(x)$

$$f(x) = \begin{cases} \dfrac{1}{t} & (0 < x < t) \\ 0 & (x < 0, x > t). \end{cases} \qquad (5.10)$$

T has mean value

$$E(T) = \int_0^t x f(x)\, dx = \frac{t}{2}$$

and variance

$$V(T) = \int_0^t \left(x - \frac{t}{2}\right)^2 f(x)\, dx = \frac{t^2}{12}.$$

[In general, the uniform distribution is defined over an arbitrary interval (t_1, t_2), but for simplicity we have taken $t_1 = 0$. The standard definition, however, uses the interval $(0, 1)$. Of course, all these definitions are equivalent, corresponding only to changes in scale and location.]

According to formula (5.9), T takes on values between zero and t, and the probability that T lies in any subinterval of $(0, t)$ is proportional by $1/t$ to the length of the subinterval. The random variable T is said to be uniformly distributed on $(0, t)$. Since there is no tendency to prefer one point over any other when sampling is performed according to (5.9), a point chosen from a uniform distribution is often said to be chosen *at random*.

The probability is x/t that a point chosen at random in $(0, t)$ will lie in a subinterval of length x, and the probability is $1 - (x/t)$ that a randomly chosen point will lie outside the designated subinterval. Thus, if n points are independently chosen at random from $(0, t)$, the probability is $(x/t)^k[1 - (x/t)]^{n-k}$ that k specific points will fall in the designated subinterval of length x and $n - k$ specific points outside it. Since there are $\binom{n}{k}$ ways of specifying k points out of n, then k out of n points chosen at random from $(0, t)$ will fall in any prespecified subinterval of length x with probability

$$\binom{n}{k} \left(\frac{x}{t}\right)^k \left(1 - \frac{x}{t}\right)^{n-k}.$$

Reference to (5.1) shows that this is the binomial probability with $p = x/t$.

Similarly, suppose that $(0, t)$ is divided into r subintervals of respective lengths x_i, such that $x_1 + \cdots + x_r = t$. Choose n points at random from $(0, t)$, and let N_i be the number of points that fall within the ith subinterval (of length x_i). Then the joint distribution of the numbers of points falling in each subinterval is given by the multinomial probabilities (5.2), with $p_i = x_i/t$.

In the special case $x_1 = x_2 = \cdots = x_r = t/r$, each subinterval has the same probability of containing k points ($k = 0, 1, 2, \ldots, n$) as each other subinterval. Although the numbers of points falling in each subinterval of equal length are in general unequal, there is no tendency for any particular subinterval to be favored over any other. Thus the uniform distribution has the properties one would desire from any distribution so named.

Let us consider the question of points uniformly distributed over an interval $(0, t)$ in more depth. We have shown that when the interval $(0, t)$ is divided into subintervals, the probability that a randomly chosen point will lie in a given subinterval is proportional to the subinterval's length; the probability that k of n randomly chosen points will all lie in a subinterval of length x is $b(k; n, x/t)$ given by (5.1). Let us now turn our attention from the discrete distribution describing the number of points in a subinterval to the continuous distribution describing the distances between successive points. We shall find the distribution of the distance between any two consecutive points of n points uniformly distributed over $(0, t)$.

Suppose that n points $T_1, \ldots, T_n$ are chosen at random from $(0, t)$. Let $T_{(k)}$ be the kth smallest, $T_{(1)} \leqq T_{(2)} \leqq \cdots \leqq T_{(n)}$. ($T_{(k)}$ is called the kth *order statistic*.) What is the distribution of the distance $T_{(k+1)} - T_{(k)}$ between two arbitrary successive points?

We have argued previously that points distributed uniformly over an interval are spread evenly throughout the interval in the sense that the probability that a particular point will lie in any given subinterval is proportional to the subinterval's length, regardless of the relative location of the subinterval within the interval $(0, t)$. This suggests that the distribution of the distance between any two successive points should be the same for every pair of consecutive points, even when one of the pair is an end point. Thus, if we take $T_{(0)} = 0$ and $T_{(n+1)} = t$, then the probability $P\{T_{(k+1)} - T_{(k)} > x\}$ should be independent of the index k. Hence it is necessary to evaluate $P\{T_{(k+1)} - T_{(k)} > x\}$ for only one value of k. The evaluation for $k = 0$ is particularly easy: $T_{(1)}$ will exceed x if and only if all n points fall in (x, t). The probability of this occurrence for any one point is $1 - (x/t)$, and since the points are selected independently of each other, the required probability is $P\{T_{(1)} > x\} = [1 - (x/t)]^n$. Therefore, the probability that any two consecutive points are separated by more than x when n points are selected at random in $(0, t)$ is

$$P\{T_{(k+1)} - T_{(k)} > x\} = \left(1 - \frac{x}{t}\right)^n$$

$$(T_{(0)} = 0, \; T_{(n+1)} = t; \; k = 0, 1, \ldots, n). \qquad (5.11)$$

The result (5.11) has been obtained through intuitive reasoning. Its validity rests on the truth of the symmetry argument that $T_{(k+1)} - T_{(k)}$ is independent of k, even for the end points $T_{(0)} = 0$ and $T_{(n+1)} = t$.

We shall now verify (5.11) by a more mathematical argument, which is of interest in itself. Choose n points at random in $(0, t)$. We wish to calculate the probability that of these n points, exactly one point lies in the differential element $(\xi, \xi + d\xi)$, exactly $k - 1$ points lie in $(0, \xi)$, and

exactly $n - 1 - (k - 1)$ points lie in $(\xi + x, t)$. The simple diagram,
Figure 2–1,

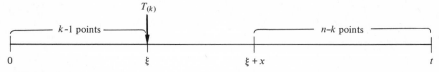

$T_{(k)}$

k-1 points

n-k points

0   ξ $\xi + x$ t

Figure 2–1.

shows that this particular arrangement implies $T_{(k+1)} - T_{(k)} > x$.

The probability that any particular point lies in $(\xi, \xi + d\xi)$ is
$f(\xi)\, d\xi = (1/t)\, d\xi$. The probability that any particular point lies in
$(0, \xi)$ is ξ/t, so that the probability that any particular $k - 1$ (independently chosen) points all lie in $(0, \xi)$ is therefore $(\xi/t)^{k-1}$. Similarly, for
any particular choice of $n - k$ points, the probability that all lie in
$(\xi + x, t)$ is $\{[t - (\xi + x)]/t\}^{n-k}$. Therefore the probability that, out
of n points, a particular point lies in $(\xi, \xi + d\xi)$, $k - 1$ particular points
lie in $(0, \xi)$, and $n - k$ particular points lie in $(\xi + x, t)$ is given by the
product

$$\left(\frac{\xi}{t}\right)^{k-1} \left(\frac{t - (\xi + x)}{t}\right)^{n-k} \frac{1}{t}\, d\xi.$$

This expression represents the required probability for a particular choice
of the points falling in each interval. Since there are n points, there are n
different choices for the point that falls in $(\xi, \xi + d\xi)$. And for each
such choice, there are $\binom{n - 1}{k - 1}$ different choices for the $k - 1$ points
falling in $(0, \xi)$. Once these k points are specified, then the remaining
$n - k$ points falling in $(\xi + x, t)$ are automatically specified. Thus the
probability that, out of n points, any one lies in $(\xi, \xi + d\xi)$, any $k - 1$
lie in $(0, \xi)$, and any $n - k$ lie in $(\xi + x, t)$ is given by

$$n \binom{n - 1}{k - 1} \left(\frac{\xi}{t}\right)^{k-1} \left(\frac{t - (\xi + x)}{t}\right)^{n-k} \frac{1}{t}\, d\xi.$$

Finally, the value ξ can be anywhere from zero to $t - x$, so that

$$P\{T_{(k+1)} - T_{(k)} > x\} = n \binom{n - 1}{k - 1} \int_0^{t-x} \left(\frac{\xi}{t}\right)^{k-1} \left(\frac{t - (\xi + x)}{t}\right)^{n-k} \frac{1}{t}\, d\xi$$

$$(k = 1, 2, \ldots, n; \; T_{(n+1)} = t). \qquad (5.12)$$

We have already shown that $P\{T_{(1)} > x\} = [1 - (x/t)]^n$. Evaluation of (5.12) for $k = 1$ easily shows that $P\{T_{(2)} - T_{(1)} > x\} = [1 - (x/t)]^n$. It would now be surprising if our intuitive derivation of formula (5.11) were incorrect. Further straightforward (although complicated) calculations would show that the result (5.11) is indeed correct.

Negative Exponential Distribution

Let T be a continuous random variable with distribution function $P\{T \leq x\} = F(x)$, where

$$F(x) = \begin{cases} 1 - e^{-\mu x} & (x \geq 0) \\ 0 & (x < 0) \end{cases} \tag{5.13}$$

and with corresponding density function $f(x) = (d/dx)F(x)$. Thus

$$f(x) = \mu e^{-\mu x} \qquad (x \geq 0). \tag{5.14}$$

Then T has the negative exponential distribution with mean $E(T) = \mu^{-1}$ and variance $V(T) = \mu^{-2}$.

In the discussion of the geometric distribution, we showed [see equation (5.4)] that in a sequence of Bernoulli trials, each trial having probability of success p, the first k trials will all result in failures with probability $(1 - p)^k$. That is, $(1 - p)^k$ is the probability that the waiting time (number of trials) to the first success is at least k.

The mean number of successes in k independent Bernoulli trials is kp. Hence, if k trials are conducted in a time interval of length x, the mean number of successes per unit time, say μ, is

$$\mu = \frac{kp}{x}. \tag{5.15}$$

Now let $p \to 0$ (and therefore $k \to \infty$) in such a way that μ remains constant. That is, we envision an experiment with an infinite number of trials performed in a finite length of time x, each trial taking vanishingly small time and each trial with vanishingly small probability of success, but with the mean number of successes being equal to the constant $\mu x > 0$. We have

$$\lim_{\substack{p \to 0 \\ k \to \infty \\ pk = \mu x}} (1 - p)^k = \lim_{k \to \infty} \left(1 - \frac{\mu x}{k}\right)^k = e^{-\mu x}. \tag{5.16}$$

Equation (5.16) shows that the geometric distribution approaches the negative exponential in the limit as the trials are taken infinitely close together, each with vanishingly small probability of success, but with the average number of successes per unit time remaining constant. Thus, if T is the random variable representing the (continuous) time to the first success, rather than the (discrete) number of trials preceding the first success, then $P\{T > x\} = e^{-\mu x}$, where μ^{-1} is the mean time to the first success.

We mentioned previously that the number of trials preceding the first success in a sequence of Bernoulli trials provides a crude but suggestive model for the description of service times. This assertion is further supported by the fact that in the limit the geometric distribution approaches the negative exponential distribution, and observation has shown the negative exponential distribution to provide a good statistical description of some service time distributions. For example, it has long been known that telephone call durations are well described by the negative exponential distribution. As we shall see, it is indeed fortunate that this is so; the special properties of the exponential distribution greatly simplify what might otherwise be intractable mathematics. Because of these simplifying mathematical properties, and because data support its use in some important applications such as telephony, it is common in the construction of queueing models to assume exponential service times. We shall now investigate some of these important mathematical properties.

A continuous nonnegative random variable T is said to have the *Markov property* if, for every $t > 0$ and every $x > 0$,

$$P\{T > t + x \mid T > t\} = P\{T > x\}. \tag{5.17}$$

A random variable with the Markov property (5.17) is often said, for obvious reasons, to have no memory.

Recall from equation (5.6) that a random variable with a geometric distribution has this characteristic property of lack of memory. As pointed out in the discussion of (5.6), the existence of the Markov property is self-evident in that case. It is easy to show that the Markov property of the (discrete) geometric distribution carries over to the (continuous) exponential distribution. Using the definition of conditional probability we have

$$P\{T > t + x \mid T > t\} = \frac{e^{-\mu(t+x)}}{e^{-\mu t}} = e^{-\mu x}. \tag{5.18}$$

Equation (5.18) implies, for example, that a call with duration distributed according to (5.13) has the same distribution of remaining holding time after it has been in progress for any length of time $t > 0$ as it had initially at $t = 0$.

Although at first glance one might find the property (5.18) to have little intuitive appeal, it should immediately be stocked in one's inventory of intuition, since the simplifications to which it leads are enormous.

Consider, for example, a two-server system with one waiting position, and suppose that at some time t there are three customers in the system. If the waiting customer waits as long as required for a server to become idle, what is the probability that the waiting customer will be the last of the three to complete service?

We assume that service times are mutually independent random variables, each with the negative exponential distribution (5.13). The waiting customer will complete service last if and only if his service time exceeds the remaining service time of the customer still in service when the first customer leaves. But because of the Markov property, this remaining time is independent of the previously elapsed time. Therefore, the last two customers have the same distribution (exponential) of time left in the system; that is, there is no bias in favor of either of the customers, so that the required probability is $\frac{1}{2}$.

The problem was solved without knowledge of the instants at which the various customers seized the servers. Even the mean service time was not used in the calculation. It should be clear that without the assumption of negative exponential service times this problem would have been much more difficult.

Let a random variable T represent the duration of some process, and assume that T has the exponential distribution function given by (5.13). Suppose that at some time t the process is uncompleted. (For example, if T is the duration of a telephone call, then we suppose the call to be in progress at time t.) Then the Markov property (5.18) implies that the process will complete in $(t, t + h)$ with probability

$$1 - e^{-\mu h} = 1 - \left(1 - \mu h + \frac{(\mu h)^2}{2!} - + \cdots\right) = \mu h + o(h) \qquad (h \to 0).$$

Conversely, suppose that if a process whose duration is given by a continuous random variable T is still in progress at time t, then the probability of completion in $(t, t + h)$ is $\mu h + o(h)$ as $h \to 0$ for all $t \geq 0$. That is, assume that

$$P\{T > t + h \mid T > t\} = 1 - \mu h + o(h) \qquad (t \geq 0, h \to 0). \qquad (5.19)$$

Then, using the definition of conditional probability,

$$P\{T > t + h \mid T > t\} = \frac{P\{T > t + h\}}{P\{T > t\}},$$

rearranging, and letting $h \to 0$ in (5.19) we obtain the differential equation

$$\frac{d}{dt} P\{T > t\} = -\mu P\{T > t\}, \tag{5.20}$$

which has the unique solution

$$P\{T > t\} = e^{-\mu t} \tag{5.21}$$

satisfying $P\{T > 0\} = 1$.

Finally, note that the Markov property $P\{T > x + y \mid T > x\} = P\{T > y\}$ and the definition of conditional probability

$$P\{T > x + y \mid T > x\} = \frac{P\{T > x + y\}}{P\{T > x\}}$$

together give the functional equation

$$P\{T > x + y\} = P\{T > x\}P\{T > y\}.$$

It can be shown (see Chapter XVII.6 of Feller [1968]) that, if $u(x)$ is defined for $x > 0$ and bounded in each finite interval, then the only nontrivial solution of the functional equation

$$u(x + y) = u(x)u(y) \tag{5.22}$$

is $u(x) = e^{-\mu x}$ for some constant μ.

We conclude that the negative exponential distribution is the only continuous distribution with the important "lack of memory" Markov property (5.17).

Consider now n mutually independent random variables, $T_1, \ldots, T_n$, each distributed according to (5.13). The probability that all T_i $(i = 1, \ldots, n)$ exceed x is $(e^{-\mu x})^n = e^{-n\mu x}$. We have proved the important fact: The distribution of the smallest of n independently chosen values from a negative exponential distribution is again a negative exponential distribution, with mean $1/n$ times the mean of the original distribution.

Suppose that the samples are ordered: $T_{(1)} \leq \cdots \leq T_{(n)}$. (The parentheses enclosing the subscripts refer to the ordering of the random variables corresponding to increasing realized values.) For the sake of example, let us identify the random variables $T_1, \ldots, T_n$ with the durations of n independent simultaneously running time intervals, so that $T_{(j)}$ is the duration of the jth shortest interval. We have just shown that the distribution of the duration of the shortest of the n time intervals is exponential with mean $(n\mu)^{-1}$; that is, $P\{T_{(1)} > x\} = e^{-n\mu x}$. At the point of completion of the shortest interval, the distribution of remaining duration for each of the $n - 1$ uncompleted intervals is, by the Markov property, unchanged. Hence, $P\{T_{(2)} - T_{(1)} > y\} = e^{-(n-1)\mu y}$. The general rule should now be obvious.

Suppose that we are given a number of time intervals whose durations $T_1, \ldots, T_n$ are identically distributed mutually independent exponential random variables with common mean μ^{-1}, and all durations are longer than x. We seek the probability that exactly j of these intervals are longer than $x + t$. Because of the Markov property, the value of x is irrelevant. Therefore, let us take time x as the origin; $x = 0$.

Now let $N(t)$ be the number of these intervals still uncompleted at time t, and let $P\{N(t) = j\} = P_j(t)$. Since the ith (unordered) interval has duration T_i with the exponential distribution function (5.13), the probability that any particular one of these intervals is still uncompleted after an elapsed time t is

$$P\{T_i > t\} = e^{-\mu t} \qquad (i = 1, 2, \ldots, n).$$

Since the $\{T_i\}$ are also mutually independent, it follows that the distribution $\{P_j(t)\}$ is the binomial distribution

$$P_j(t) = \binom{n}{j} (e^{-\mu t})^j (1 - e^{-\mu t})^{n-j} \qquad (j = 0, 1, \ldots, n). \qquad (5.23)$$

This problem can also be viewed in the framework of the pure death process. If the system is in state E_j at time t, then the same reasoning that led to (5.23) shows that the conditional probability of transition $E_j \to E_j$ in $(t, t + h)$ is given by

$$P\{N(t + h) = j \mid N(t) = j\} = e^{-j\mu h} = 1 - j\mu h + o(h) \qquad (h \to 0).$$

Similarly, the conditional probability of transition $E_j \to E_{j-1}$ in $(t, t + h)$ is given by

$$P\{N(t + h) = j - 1 \mid N(t) = j\} = je^{-(j-1)\mu h}(1 - e^{-\mu h})$$
$$= j\mu h + o(h) \qquad (h \to 0).$$

Since we must have

$$\sum_{i=0}^{j} P\{N(t + h) = i \mid N(t) = j\} = 1$$

it follows that

$$P\{N(t + h) \leq j - 2 \mid N(t) = j\} = o(h) \qquad (h \to 0).$$

Thus we have shown that $N(t)$ obeys the postulates of the pure death process with death coefficients $\mu_j = j\mu$ $(j = 0, 1, \ldots, n)$ and initial condition $N(0) = n$. This is precisely the case we considered in Section 2–2 as an example of the pure death process. The corresponding equations are given by (2.9) and (2.10), and the solution by (2.11). The solution (2.11) is identical, of course, with that just obtained by more direct reasoning, the binomial distribution (5.23). [This should not be surprising, since we implicitly assumed (5.23) when we specified the transition probabilities.]

We have thus also shown that if $N(t)$ obeys the postulates of the pure death process with $\mu_j = j\mu$, then the aggregate death process is the same as if it were composed of j mutually independent processes whose durations are identically distributed negative exponential random variables each with mean μ^{-1}. (But it does not necessarily follow that the aggregate process is in fact such a superposition of independent exponential processes.)

We can calculate from (5.23) the distribution function of the length of time required for all n simultaneously running time intervals to complete. The time required for all of the intervals to complete is the time required for $N(t)$ to reach zero; that is, $\{T_{(n)} \leq t\} \leftrightarrow \{N(t) = 0\}$. Hence $P\{T_{(n)} \leq t\} = P_0(t) = (1 - e^{-\mu t})^n$. To calculate $E(T_{(n)})$ without performing any integration, let X_j be the elapsed time between the jth and the $(j - 1)$th completions,

$$X_j = T_{(j)} - T_{(j-1)} \qquad (j = 1, 2, \ldots, n; T_{(0)} = 0).$$

Then $T_{(n)} = X_1 + X_2 + \cdots + X_n$, and since X_j is exponentially distributed with mean $[(n - j + 1)\mu]^{-1}$, it follows that

$$E(T_{(n)}) = \frac{1}{n\mu} + \frac{1}{(n - 1)\mu} + \cdots + \frac{1}{\mu}.$$

$\Big[$Thus we have deduced that

$$n\mu \int_0^\infty t(1 - e^{-\mu t})^{n-1} e^{-\mu t} \, dt = \frac{1}{\mu}\left(1 + \frac{1}{2} + \cdots + \frac{1}{n}\right).\Big]$$

For example, consider a queueing system with n customers in service and no customers waiting at time zero, and assume that no new customers are allowed into the system. If the service times are independently exponentially distributed according to (5.13), then we let $N(t)$ be the number of servers busy at time t and $T_{(n)}$ be the length of time until all servers become idle.

In another common application, reliability theory, a device depends on n independent components, each assumed to have a length of life distributed according to (5.13). The device continues to operate as long as at least one of the n components is functioning. Then we can let $N(t)$ be the number of components still functioning at time t and $T_{(n)}$ be the time at which the device fails.

Poisson Distribution

Thus far we have discussed the exponential distribution mainly with respect to its use as a description of service times. But just as it may be useful as a description of durations of service, likewise it may be useful as a description of durations of elapsed time between customer arrival epochs. More generally, we consider points on a line (or customers arriving in time), and we make the assumption that the distances between successive points are independently, identically exponentially distributed. That is, we label these points $T_1, T_2, \ldots$, and assume that the random variable $X_j = T_j - T_{j-1}$ $(j = 1, 2, \ldots; T_0 = 0)$ has the exponential distribution

$$P\{X_j > t\} = e^{-\lambda t} \qquad (j = 1, 2, \ldots). \tag{5.24}$$

We ask the question, If the distances (lengths of time) $X_j = T_j - T_{j-1}$ between successive points are independently distributed according to (5.24), what is the distribution of the number of points occurring in a fixed interval of length t?

Let $N(t)$ be the number of points occurring in $(0, t)$, with $P\{N(t) = j\} = P_j(t)$. Let the lengths of time between successive points be independent and have the exponential distribution (5.24). Then the probability that at least one point will occur in $(t, t + h)$ is $1 - e^{-\lambda h} = \lambda h + o(h)$ as $h \to 0$. And the probability that exactly one point will occur in $(t, t + h)$ is

$$\int_0^h \lambda e^{-\lambda x} e^{-\lambda(h-x)} \, dx = \lambda h e^{-\lambda h} = \lambda h + o(h) \qquad (h \to 0).$$

Thus the probability of occurrence of two or more points in $(t, t + h)$ is $1 - e^{-\lambda h} - \lambda h e^{-\lambda h} = o(h)$ as $h \to 0$.

Hence, $N(t)$ satisfies the postulates of the pure birth process with $\lambda_j = \lambda \, (j = 0, 1, 2, \ldots)$. This case has already been discussed in Section 2–2. The problem formulation is given by equations (2.5) and (2.6), and the solution by (2.7):

$$P_j(t) = \frac{(\lambda t)^j}{j!} e^{-\lambda t} \qquad (j = 0, 1, \ldots). \tag{5.25}$$

The probabilities given by (5.25) comprise the ubiquitous Poisson distribution. $N(t)$ has probability generating function $p(z)$ given by (4.3),

$$p(z) = e^{-\lambda t(1-z)}, \tag{5.26}$$

with mean and variance given by (4.7) and (4.10):

$$E[N(t)] = V[N(t)] = \lambda t. \tag{5.27}$$

As has been shown [see equation (4.19)], the generating function (5.26) can be used to prove that if $S_n(t) = N_1(t) + \cdots + N_n(t)$, where the $\{N_i(t)\}$ are mutually independent and $N_i(t)$ has the Poisson distribution with mean $\lambda_i t$, then $S_n(t)$ has the Poisson distribution with mean $\lambda_1 t + \cdots + \lambda_n t$.

Because of the Markov property of the exponential distribution, it is not necessary that counting start at any special point $T_0 = 0$; formula (5.25) gives the distribution of the number of points occurring in any interval or set of disjoint subintervals of total length t.

Conversely, when the distribution of the number of points occurring in any interval of length t (regardless of the number of points occurring in any preceding interval) is given by the Poisson distribution (5.25), then the distances between successive points are mutually independent, identically distributed exponential variables, with common mean λ^{-1}. Setting $j = 0$ in (5.25) shows that the distance to the first point is exponentially distributed. Suppose that the first point is located at $T_1 = \tau$. Since

(5.25) is assumed to hold for any interval of length t, then the probability of j points in $(\tau, \tau + t)$ is again given by (5.25). Thus the distance between the first point and the second point is independent of and has the same distribution as the distance to the first point. Repeated use of this reasoning proves the assertion.

Thus equations (5.24) and (5.25) are equivalent: In a pure birth process with parameter λ (called a *Poisson process* with rate λ), the number of points occurring in a fixed interval of length t has the Poisson distribution (5.25), or equivalently, the lengths of the intervals separating successive points have independent, identical negative exponential distributions (5.24).

The Poisson process is often used as a description of the input process in queueing systems. That is, (5.24) is assumed to describe the customer interarrival time distribution, and (5.25) to describe the distribution of the number of customers arriving in a fixed interval of length t. An input process obeying (5.24) and (5.25) is called, naturally enough, *Poisson input*. Because of its mathematical properties, the assumption of Poisson input in the analysis of queueing systems often leads to the easiest mathematics. Specifically, we have, as a consequence of the Markov property, the following important facts:

With Poisson input at rate λ, the distribution of the length of time from an arbitrary instant until the next arrival epoch is the same as the distribution of the length of time between successive arrival epochs, that is, exponential with mean λ^{-1}. Similarly, looking backward from an arbitrary instant, the distribution of the length of time separating an arbitrary instant and the preceding arrival epoch is also exponentially distributed with mean λ^{-1} (assuming, of course, that the process is not measured from a finite origin).

We will use the Markov property to illustrate a point that may be confusing to the beginner. Suppose that an observer samples a queueing system with Poisson input at arbitrary instants, and asks for the mean length of time that will elapse until the next arrival epoch. According to the Markov property, the distribution of the length of time preceding the next arrival is the same as the interarrival time distribution. Therefore, the observer will wait a mean length of time λ^{-1} for the occurrence of the next arrival. But the observer's waiting time is, in general, less than the time between the two bracketing arrival epochs. (See Figure 2–2.) Hence the mean time separating the bracketing arrival epochs has mean value larger than λ^{-1}, in apparent contradiction to the assumption that λ^{-1} is the mean length of time between successive arrivals.

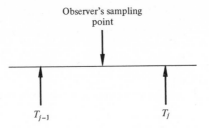

Figure 2–2.

Of course, there is no contradiction. The answer lies in the realization that the interval during which the observer samples does not have the same distribution as an arbitrary interarrival interval. A little reflection should convince the reader that an observer sampling at arbitrary instants is more likely to sample during a long interarrival interval than a short one. Thus the act of observing introduces a bias; the mean length of the sampling interval exceeds that of the arbitrary interarrival interval. This phenomenon, the biasedness of the sampling interval, is true in general, not just for Poisson input. We have mentioned it here because the use of the Markov property makes the existence of the phenomenon clear. We shall discuss the general problem in some detail in Chapter 5.

The geometric distribution describes the waiting time for the first success in a sequence of Bernoulli trials; the binomial distribution describes the number of successes in a fixed number of Bernoulli trials. Similarly, the exponential distribution describes a length of time preceding an event, while the Poisson distribution describes the number of such events occurring during a fixed time interval. We have shown [see equation (5.16)] that the geometric distribution function approaches the negative exponential in the limit as the trials are taken infinitely close together, each with vanishingly small probability of success, but with the average number of successes per unit time remaining constant. We should not be surprised then that a similar limiting process produces the Poisson distribution from the binomial:

$$\lim_{\substack{p\to 0 \\ n\to\infty \\ np=\lambda x}} \binom{n}{j} p^j (1-p)^{n-j} = \frac{(\lambda x)^j}{j!} e^{-\lambda x} \qquad (j = 0, 1, \ldots). \qquad (5.28)$$

Arrivals occurring according to a Poisson process are often said to occur *at random*. This is because the probability of arrival of a customer in a small interval of length h is proportional to the length h, and is independent of the amount of elapsed time from the arrival epoch of the last customer.

That is, when customers are arriving according to a Poisson process, a customer is as likely to arrive at one instant as any other, regardless of the instants at which the other customers arrive. This is similar to the property noted previously for points chosen independently from a uniform distribution on $(0, t)$. However, in that case, the length t of the interval containing the points is known. One might conjecture, therefore, that when it is known that a given number n of arrivals generated by a Poisson process have occurred in an interval $(0, t)$, these arrival epochs are (conditionally) uniformly distributed throughout the interval. This is indeed true.

More precisely, we shall now prove that if the number $N(t)$ of Poisson arrivals in $(0, t)$ is n, then the joint distribution of the arrival epochs $T_1, T_2, \ldots, T_n$ is the same as the joint distribution of the coordinates arranged in increasing order of n independent points, each of which is uniformly distributed over the interval $(0, t)$:

Let $0 \leq x_1 \leq x_2 \leq \cdots \leq x_n \leq t$. Then, using the definition of conditional probability,

$$P\{T_1 \leq x_1, T_2 \leq x_2, \ldots, T_n \leq x_n \mid N(t) = n\}$$

$$= \frac{P\{T_1 \leq x_1, T_2 \leq x_2, \ldots, T_n \leq x_n, N(t) = n\}}{P\{N(t) = n\}},$$

we have

$$P\{T_1 \leq x_1, T_2 \leq x_2, \ldots, T_n \leq x_n \mid N(t) = n\}$$

$$= \frac{\displaystyle\sum_{\{j_1, j_2, \ldots, j_n\}} \left\{\frac{(\lambda x_1)^{j_1}}{j_1!} e^{-\lambda x_1}\right\} \left\{\frac{[\lambda(x_2 - x_1)]^{j_2}}{j_2!} e^{-\lambda(x_2 - x_1)}\right\} \cdots \left\{\frac{[\lambda(x_n - x_{n-1})]^{j_n}}{j_n!} e^{-\lambda(x_n - x_{n-1})}\right\} \{e^{-\lambda(t - x_n)}\}}{\dfrac{(\lambda t)^n}{n!} e^{-\lambda t}}$$

$$= \sum_{\{j_1, j_2, \ldots, j_n\}} \frac{n!}{j_1! \, j_2! \cdots j_n!} \left(\frac{x_1}{t}\right)^{j_1} \left(\frac{x_2 - x_1}{t}\right)^{j_2} \cdots \left(\frac{x_n - x_{n-1}}{t}\right)^{j_n}$$

$$(5.29)$$

where the summation is extended over all those sets of nonnegative integers $\{j_1, j_2, \ldots, j_n\}$ for which $j_1 + j_2 + \cdots + j_n = n$ and $j_1 + j_2 + \cdots + j_k \geq k$ ($k = 1, 2, \ldots, n - 1$). Comparison with Exercise 4 shows that our assertion is proved.

We have already shown that if $N_1(t), \ldots, N_n(t)$ are mutually independent random variables, and $N_i(t)$ has the Poisson distribution with mean $\lambda_i t$ $(i = 1, 2, \ldots, n)$, then the sum $N_1(t) + \cdots + N_n(t)$ also has the Poisson distribution, with mean $\lambda_1 t + \cdots + \lambda_n t$. This implies that the superposition of n streams of Poisson arrivals is again a Poisson stream, with mean equal to the sum of the means of the component streams.

The question naturally arises, Can a Poisson process conversely be viewed as the superposition of any number of mutually independent component Poisson processes? Suppose, for example, that telephone calls arrive according to a Poisson process with parameter λ at a device that distributes the calls to n machines for processing. If each arrival is directed to machine j randomly with probability λ_j/λ, where $\lambda = \lambda_1 + \cdots + \lambda_n$, then the probability that a call will arrive at machine j in $(t, t + h)$ is $(\lambda_j/\lambda)[\lambda h + o(h)] = \lambda_j h + o(h)$ as $h \to 0$; and likewise the probability of two or more arrivals to machine j is $o(h)$ as $h \to 0$. Hence machine j sees arrivals occurring according to a Poisson process with parameter λ_j. And because of the Markov property, the arrival processes at the different machines are mutually independent.

We now illustrate the mutual independence by considering the case of two machines. We evaluate the conditional probability $P\{N_1(t) = j \mid N_2(t) = k\}$ that j calls have arrived at machine 1, given k arrivals at machine 2 in an interval of length t:

$$
\begin{aligned}
P\{N_1(t) = j \mid N_2(t) = k\} &= \frac{P\{N_1(t) = j, N_2(t) = k\}}{P\{N_2(t) = k\}} \\[2mm]
&= \frac{\dfrac{(\lambda t)^{j+k}}{(j+k)!} e^{-\lambda t} \dbinom{j+k}{j} \left(\dfrac{\lambda_1}{\lambda}\right)^j \left(\dfrac{\lambda_2}{\lambda}\right)^k}{[(\lambda_2 t)^k/k!]\, e^{-\lambda_2 t}} \\[2mm]
&= \frac{(\lambda_1 t)^j}{j!} e^{-\lambda_1 t}.
\end{aligned}
\tag{5.30}
$$

Thus the distribution of the number of calls offered to the first machine in an interval of length t is independent of the number offered to the second machine. We conclude: A Poisson process can be viewed as the superposition of any number of mutually independent component Poisson processes.

We have shown that the Poisson distribution possesses many elegant properties. The simplifications resulting from the exploitation of these properties permit the solution of many problems that might otherwise be intractable.

Erlangian (Gamma) Distribution

Again we consider points on a line (or customers arriving in time) and assume that the distances between successive points are independently, identically, exponentially distributed. That is, we label these points $T_1, T_2, \ldots$ and assume that the random variable $X_j = T_j - T_{j-1}$ $(j = 1, 2, \ldots; T_0 = 0)$ has the exponential distribution, $P\{X_j > t\} = e^{-\lambda t}$ $(j = 1, 2, \ldots)$ [and therefore the number of points occurring in $(0, t)$ has the Poisson distribution with mean λt]. We wish to find the distribution of the distance spanning n consecutive points, that is, the distribution of the sum of n mutually independent, identically distributed exponential random variables, $S_n = X_1 + \cdots + X_n$. S_n will be less than x if and only if the number of points occurring in $(0, x)$ is at least n. Therefore, $P\{S_n \leqq x\} = F(x)$ is

$$F(x) = 1 - \sum_{j=0}^{n-1} \frac{(\lambda x)^j}{j!} e^{-\lambda x} \qquad (\lambda > 0, x \geqq 0). \qquad (5.31)$$

The component random variables $\{X_j\}$ are sometimes considered to be *phases*, and consequently the distribution function defined by (5.31) is called the n-phase Erlangian distribution function.

The Erlangian density function $f(x) = (d/dx)F(x)$ can also be written down directly as was the distribution function (5.31). Interpret $f(x)\,dx$ as the probability that the nth point lies in the differential element about the point x. The probability that exactly $n - 1$ points lie in $(0, x)$ is $[(\lambda x)^{n-1}/(n-1)!]e^{-\lambda x}$; the (conditional) probability that a new point occurs at x is then $\lambda\,dx$. Hence the probability that $n - 1$ points lie in $(0, x)$ and that the nth point occurs in $(x, x + dx)$ is $f(x)\,dx = [(\lambda x)^{n-1}/(n-1)!]e^{-\lambda x}\lambda\,dx$; the density function is

$$f(x) = \frac{(\lambda x)^{n-1}}{(n-1)!} \lambda e^{-\lambda x} \qquad (\lambda > 0, x \geqq 0). \qquad (5.32)$$

Of course, (5.32) follows directly from (5.31) by differentiation.

From the interpretation of S_n as a sum of n mutually independent, identical, exponentially distributed phases, each with mean λ^{-1} (and variance λ^{-2}), we immediately obtain the mean $E(S_n) = n\lambda^{-1}$ and variance $V(S_n) = n\lambda^{-2}$. As might be expected, the Erlangian distribution is easier to handle than are distributions in general, but not so easy as the exponential.

The n-phase Erlangian distribution arises quite naturally in the consideration of input processes. Suppose, for example, that a device distributes incoming requests for service to two groups of servers on an alternating basis. Then the input to each group of servers is Erlangian with $n = 2$ phases. (But these input processes are not independent.)

Similarly, the Erlangian distribution (5.31) can be used to describe service times that are assumed to be composed of independent phases, each with the same exponential distribution. These phases may correspond to reality in the sense that each phase represents an identifiable component of the service, or they may be hypothesized in order to fit a theoretical distribution to data. In the former case, the number n of phases is equal to the number of components of the service time, whereas in the latter case, the number n of phases is determined from the data.

As noted previously, if S_n is composed of n independent, identically distributed exponential phases, each phase of mean length λ^{-1}, then S_n has mean $E(S_n) = n\lambda^{-1}$ and variance $V(S_n) = n\lambda^{-2}$. As the number of phases increases and the mean phase length decreases in such a way that $E(S_n)$ remains constant, $E(S_n) = c$, the variance $V(S_n)$ goes to zero:

$$\lim_{\substack{\lambda \to \infty \\ n \to \infty \\ n\lambda^{-1} = c}} V(S_n) = \lim_{\substack{\lambda \to \infty \\ n \to \infty \\ n\lambda^{-1} = c}} n\lambda^{-1}\lambda^{-1} = 0. \qquad (5.33)$$

Thus, in the limit, the random variable S_n becomes a constant, $S_\infty = c$. Hence, the Erlangian distribution provides a model for a range of input processes (or service times), characterized by complete randomness when $n = 1$ and no randomness when $n = \infty$.

Observe that the Erlangian distribution is the continuous analogue of the negative binomial distribution, just as the exponential is the continuous analogue of the geometric.

The n-phase Erlangian distribution, where n is a positive integer, is actually a special case of the gamma distribution, defined by the density function

$$f(x) = \frac{(\lambda x)^{p-1}}{\Gamma(p)} \lambda e^{-\lambda x} \qquad (p > 0, \lambda > 0, x \geqq 0). \qquad (5.34)$$

The gamma distribution can be viewed as the generalization of the p-phase Erlangian, where the number p of phases is no longer required to be an integer. As expected, we have $E(S_p) = p\lambda^{-1}$ and $V(S_p) = p\lambda^{-2}$. Thus the gamma distribution provides a potentially useful generalization of the Erlangian distribution. In particular, the gamma distribution extends the "sum" S_p to include the case of a fraction of a phase, since p

can be less than unity. Hence the gamma distribution provides a model for a range of input processes (or service times) characterized by an arbitrarily large variance when $p \to 0$ and $\lambda \to 0$ but $p\lambda^{-1} = c$, and zero variance when $p \to \infty$ and $\lambda \to \infty$, again holding $p\lambda^{-1} = c$. The term *hyperexponential* is sometimes used to describe the distribution (5.34), but this term is most descriptive if applied only when $0 < p < 1$. (The term *hyperexponential* has also been used by Morse [1958] to describe a distribution function that is a weighted sum of exponential distribution functions.)

2–6. Laplace–Stieltjes Transforms and Generating Functions

Laplace and Laplace–Stieltjes transforms should be familiar to every student of engineering and applied mathematics. We shall assume familiarity with their mathematical properties and merely mention for completeness some analogies between Laplace–Stieltjes transforms and probability generating functions. Most important, we shall point out a remarkable relationship between Laplace–Stieltjes transforms and probability generating functions that often appears in queueing theory.

As we have seen, the probability generating function $g(z)$ is a transform of a probability distribution $\{p_j\}$, for a discrete nonnegative random variable, into a continuous function of a dummy variable z: $g(z) = \sum_{j=0}^{\infty} p_j z^j$. Similarly, the Laplace–Stieltjes transform $L^*[F(t)]$ of a distribution function $F(t)$, for a (continuous or discrete) nonnegative random variable, maps the distribution function $F(t)$ into a different function $\phi(s)$ of a dummy variable s:

$$L^*[F(t)] = \phi(s) = \int_0^{\infty} e^{-st} \, dF(t) \qquad (\mathrm{Re}\ s \geqq 0). \qquad (6.1)$$

In fact, the probability generating function is actually a special case of the Laplace–Stieltjes transform: if a nonnegative integer-valued random variable has probability generating function $g(z)$ and Laplace–Stieltjes transform $\phi(s)$, then it follows easily from the definitions that $\phi(s) = g(e^{-s})$.

If $F(t)$ is differentiable, $F'(t) = f(t)$, then $\phi(s)$ is the ordinary Laplace transform $L[f(t)]$ of $f(t)$:

$$L^*[F(t)] = \int_0^{\infty} e^{-st} \, dF(t) = \int_0^{\infty} e^{-st} f(t) \, dt = L[f(t)]. \qquad (6.2)$$

The Laplace–Stieltjes transform $L^*[F(t)]$ and the corresponding ordinary Laplace transform $L[F(t)]$ are related as follows:

$$L^*[F(t)] = sL[F(t)]. \tag{6.3}$$

Like the probability generating function, the Laplace–Stieltjes transform (or the ordinary Laplace transform) uniquely determines the object distribution function $F(t)$.

Two important properties of the Laplace–Stieltjes transform, both of which have obvious analogies with the properties of probability generating functions, are

1. The moments of the distribution function $F(t)$ can be obtained directly from its Laplace–Stieltjes transform:

$$\int_0^\infty t^n \, dF(t) = (-1)^n \frac{d^n}{ds^n} \phi(s) \Big|_{s=0}. \tag{6.4}$$

2. If $F_1(t)$ and $F_2(t)$ have Laplace–Stieltjes transforms $\phi_1(s)$ and $\phi_2(s)$, then the Laplace–Stieltjes transform $\phi(s)$ of the convolution

$$F(t) = \int_0^t F_1(t - x) \, dF_2(x) = \int_0^t F_2(t - x) \, dF_1(x)$$

is the product

$$\phi(s) = \phi_1(s)\phi_2(s). \tag{6.5}$$

That is, if X_1 and X_2 are independent nonnegative random variables with distribution functions $F_1(t)$ and $F_2(t)$ and Laplace–Stieltjes transforms $\phi_1(s)$ and $\phi_2(s)$, then the distribution function of the sum $X_1 + X_2$ has Laplace–Stieltjes transform equal to the product of the component transforms.

We now proceed to an application of the Laplace–Stieltjes transform that arises frequently in queueing theory. Suppose that events occur according to a Poisson process with rate λ. Let P_j be the probability that j events occur during a time interval whose length is a random variable with distribution function $F(t)$. Then P_j is given by

$$P_j = \int_0^\infty \frac{(\lambda t)^j}{j!} e^{-\lambda t} \, dF(t) \qquad (j = 0, 1, \ldots).$$

If the distribution $\{P_j\}$ has generating function $g(z) = \sum_{j=0}^{\infty} P_j z^j$, then

$$g(z) = \sum_{j=0}^{\infty} \int_0^{\infty} \frac{(\lambda t)^j}{j!} e^{-\lambda t} \, dF(t) z^j$$

$$= \int_0^{\infty} e^{-\lambda t} \sum_{j=0}^{\infty} \frac{(\lambda t z)^j}{j!} \, dF(t) = \int_0^{\infty} e^{-\lambda(1-z)t} \, dF(t).$$

This last integral is the Laplace–Stieltjes transform with argument $\lambda(1 - z)$ of the distribution function $F(t)$:

$$g(z) = \phi(\lambda - \lambda z). \qquad (6.6)$$

Hence the generating function of the distribution of the number of occurrences generated by a Poisson process during a randomly generated interval is directly and simply related to the Laplace–Stieltjes transform of the distribution function of the interval length.

2–7. Remarks

We have reviewed some topics from probability theory that are particularly important in queueing theory. There are many books in which these and related topics are covered. We mention a few for reference.

The first of Feller's two volumes [1968] is an excellent treatment of applied probability theory. In particular, it contains valuable material on discrete probability distributions, generating functions, and stochastic processes. Feller's second volume [1971], which is considerably more advanced than the first, treats the negative exponential and uniform distributions, Laplace–Stieltjes transforms, and many other relevant topics. These two books comprise a most thorough and lucid treatment of probability theory and its applications.

Fisz [1963] gives a thorough introduction to basic probability theory and its applications, including material on important probability distributions and stochastic processes.

Bailey [1964] gives an elementary treatment of generating functions and the theory of stochastic processes from an applied point of view.

Cox and Miller [1965] and Karlin [1966] treat much the same material as Bailey, in more detail and on a more advanced level, but still with an emphasis on application of the theory.

Syski [1960] treats the whole field of congestion theory. His discussion of probability theory is perhaps more abstract than needed for our purposes, although the topics we have discussed are all covered, with particular attention paid to telephone applications. Syski's book is the definitive work in the field of congestion theory. Unfortunately, its encyclopedic range and detailed treatment of a highly specialized subject have caused it to run afoul of the laws of economics; it is currently out of print.

Exercises

1. Fill in the details of the argument leading from the postulates for the birth-and-death process to the system of differential-difference equations (2.3).
2. Suppose n dice are rolled. Let K be the value of the roll (the total number of spots showing). Find the probability generating function of K.
3. *Yule–Furry process.* A population consists of individuals each of which has the following property. An individual present at time t will split in two (become two new individuals) in $(t, t + h)$ with probability $\lambda h + o(h)$ and will remain unchanged throughout $(t, t + h)$ with probability $(1 - \lambda h) + o(h)$ as $h \to 0$. Let $N(t)$ be the number of individuals in the population at time t, with $N(0) = 1$.
   a. With $P\{N(t) = j\} = P_j(t)$, write the differential-difference equations that determine $P_j(t)$.
   b. Show that $N(t)$ has probability generating function

   $$P(z, t) = \frac{ze^{-\lambda t}}{1 - z + ze^{-\lambda t}}$$

   satisfying the initial condition $N(0) = 1$.
   c. Find $E(N(t))$.
   d. Find $P_j(t)$.
   e. Find $P(z, t)$, $E(N(t))$, and $P_j(t)$ satisfying the initial condition $N(0) = n \geq 1$.

   Answer: $P_j(t) = \binom{j - 1}{j - n} e^{-n\lambda t}(1 - e^{-\lambda t})^{j-n}$.

4. Show that if $X_1, X_2, \ldots, X_n$ are independently uniformly distributed on $(0, t)$, then the joint distribution function of the order statistics $X_{(1)} \leq X_{(2)} \leq \cdots \leq X_{(n)}$ is given by

$$P\{X_{(1)} \leq x_1, X_{(2)} \leq x_2, \ldots, X_{(n)} \leq x_n\}$$

$$= \sum_{\{j_1, j_2, \ldots, j_n\}} \frac{n!}{j_1! \, j_2! \cdots j_n!} \left(\frac{x_1}{t}\right)^{j_1} \left(\frac{x_2 - x_1}{t}\right)^{j_2} \cdots \left(\frac{x_n - x_{n-1}}{t}\right)^{j_n},$$

where $0 \leq x_1 \leq x_2 \leq \cdots \leq x_n \leq t$, and the summation is extended over all those sets of nonnegative integers $\{j_1, j_2, \ldots, j_n\}$ for which

$$j_1 + j_2 + \cdots + j_n = n$$

and

$$j_1 + j_2 + \cdots + j_k \geq k \qquad (k = 1, 2, \ldots, n - 1).$$

5. Feller [1971]. Consider a circle of unit length and a point t on its circumference. Let two points be chosen independently and at random on the circumference, partitioning the circle into two arcs, one of which contains the point t. Show that the mean length of the arc that covers the point t is $\frac{2}{3}$. [*Hint:* Consider the line segment obtained by cutting the circle at the point t.]

6. Let $X_1, \ldots, X_n$ $(n \geq 2)$ be mutually independent, identically distributed exponential random variables. Define the range $R = \max_i X_i - \min_i X_i$. Show, with no calculation, that the distribution function $P\{R \leq x\}$ of the range is given by $P\{R \leq x\} = (1 - e^{-\mu x})^{n-1}$.

7. Let $X_1, \ldots, X_n$ be a sequence of mutually independent random variables, and let X_j be exponentially distributed with mean $(j\mu)^{-1}$. Let $S_n = X_1 + \cdots + X_n$. Show that S_n has distribution function $P\{S_n \leq t\} = (1 - e^{-\mu t})^n$. [*Hint:* No calculation is necessary; compare with the maximum of n exponential variables.]

8. Find the probability generating function $P_k(z, t)$ for the system (4.20) subject to the initial condition that at $t = 0$ there are k customers in service, where service times are mutually independent, identically distributed exponential variables, each with mean μ^{-1}. Do the state probabilities form a Poisson distribution for any finite $t \geq 0$? Find the statistical equilibrium distribution and show that it is independent of the initial conditions.

Answer: $P_k(z, t) = (1 - e^{-\mu t} - e^{-\mu t} z)^k P(z, t)$, where $P(z, t)$ is given by equation (4.25).

9. Customers request service from a group of s servers according to a Poisson process with mean interarrival time λ^{-1}. Service times are mutually independent exponentially distributed random variables with common mean μ^{-1}. At time $t = 0$ an observer samples the system and finds all s servers occupied and no customers waiting.

   a. Find the probability that the next arriving customer is blocked.

   $$Answer: \frac{\lambda}{\lambda + s\mu}.$$

   b. Let N be the number of customers that arrive prior to the first completion of a customer in service. Find $P\{N = j\}$.

   $$Answer: \left(\frac{\lambda}{\lambda + s\mu}\right)^j \left(\frac{s\mu}{\lambda + s\mu}\right).$$

   c. Find the probability that the next arriving customer finds at least two idle servers.

   $$Answer: \left(\frac{s\mu}{\lambda + s\mu}\right) \left(\frac{(s - 1)\mu}{\lambda + (s - 1)\mu}\right).$$

10. Let $\{X_j\}$ be a sequence of identically distributed mutually independent Bernoulli variables with $P\{X_j = 1\} = p$. Let $S_N = X_1 + \cdots + X_N$ be the sum of a random number N of the random variables $\{X_j\}$, where N has the Poisson distribution with mean λ. Prove that S_N has the Poisson distribution with mean λp. [In general, the distribution of a sum of a random number of independent random variables is called a *compound* distribution. It can be shown (see, for example, Chapter XII of Feller [1968]) that if the $\{X_j\}$ have probability generating function $f(z)$ and N has probability generating function $g(z)$, then S_N has probability generating function $g[f(z)]$. Our result is then an easy consequence.]

11. Suppose customers arrive at instants $T_1, T_2, \ldots$, where the interarrival times are independent and have common distribution function $P\{T_j - T_{j-1} \le x\} = G(x)$ $(j = 1, 2, \ldots; T_0 = 0)$. (This is called *recurrent input*.) Let $P_j(x)$ be the probability of j arrivals in an interval of length x. Use the fact that

$$P_j(x) = \int_0^x P_{j-1}(x - \xi) \, dG(\xi) \qquad (j = 1, 2, \ldots)$$

with

$$P_0(x) = 1 - G(x)$$

to prove again: When customer interarrival times are mutually independent random variables, each with the negative exponential distribution with mean interarrival time λ^{-1}, then the number of customers arriving in a fixed interval of length x has the Poisson distribution with mean λx.

12. At $t = 0$ customer A places a request for service and finds all s servers busy and n other customers waiting for service. All customers wait as long as necessary for service, waiting customers are served in order of arrival, and no new requests for service are permitted after $t = 0$. Service times are assumed to be mutually independent, identically distributed, exponential random variables, each with mean duration τ.

  a. Find the expected length of time customer A spends waiting for service in the queue.

  b. Find the expected length of time from the arrival of customer A at $t = 0$ until the system becomes completely empty (all customers complete service).

  c. Find the expected lengths of the shortest service time and the longest service time of the $s + n + 1$ customers.

  d. Let X be the order of completion of service of customer A; that is, $X = m$ if A is the mth customer to complete service after $t = 0$. Find $P\{X = m\}$ $(m = 1, 2, \ldots, s + n + 1)$.

  e. Find the probability that customer A completes service before the customer immediately ahead of him on the queue.

  f. Let W be the amount of time customer A waits for service. Find $P\{W > x\}$.

13. Consider a Poisson process where $N(t)$ is the number of arrivals in $(0, t)$ and $T_1, T_2, \ldots$ are the arrival epochs. Show that

$$P\{T_1 \leq x_1, \ldots, T_n \leq x_n \mid N(t) = n\}$$
$$= P\{T_1 \leq x_1, \ldots, T_n \leq x_n \mid T_{n+1} = t\}.$$

14. A sequence of events is generated according to a Poisson process. An observer views (samples) this process at an arbitrary instant. Let X be the duration of time separating the last event prior to the sampling instant and the first event subsequent to the sampling instant. Show that the distribution function of X is the two-phase Erlangian.

15. Suppose that customers arrive in batches, where the batch arrival epochs constitute a Poisson process with rate λ, and where the number of customers in each batch is a random variable with probability generating function $h(z)$. Assume that the batch sizes are independent of the arrival epochs and each other.

     a. Show that the number of customers arriving in an interval of fixed length t has probability generating function

$$f(z, t) = e^{-\lambda t[1 - h(z)]}.$$

     b. Consider a time interval $(0, X)$ whose length has distribution function $P\{X \leq x\} = F(x)$ with Laplace–Stieltjes transform $\phi(s)$. Let $g(z)$ be the probability generating function of the number of customers ariving in $(0, X)$. Show that

$$g(z) = \phi[\lambda - \lambda h(z)].$$

16. Let N_1 and N_2 be independent, identically distributed, nonnegative integer-valued random variables. We consider two different procedures for distributing $N_1 + N_2$ balls into two cells. In procedure (a), we place N_1 balls into the first cell and N_2 balls into the second cell. In procedure (b), we consider the $N_1 + N_2 = N$ balls together, and independently place each of the N balls into a cell, with each ball having probability $\frac{1}{2}$ of being placed into the first cell, and probability $\frac{1}{2}$ of being placed into the second cell. Denote by M_ν ($\nu = 1, 2$) the number of balls placed into the νth cell according to procedure (b).

     a. Let N_ν have the Poisson distribution

$$P\{N_\nu = j\} = \frac{\left(\frac{\lambda}{2}\right)^j}{j!} \, e^{-\lambda/2} \qquad (\nu = 1, 2; j = 0, 1, \ldots).$$

     Show that

$$P\{N_1 = j_1, N_2 = j_2\} = P\{M_1 = j_1, M_2 = j_2\}.$$

     b. Let N_ν have the geometric distribution

$$P\{N_\nu = j\} = (1 - p)^j p \qquad (\nu = 1, 2; j = 0, 1, \ldots).$$

Show that

$$P\{N_1 = 0\} = p \neq \frac{p^2}{\left(\dfrac{1+p}{2}\right)^2} = P\{M_1 = 0\}.$$

c. Define the generating functions

$$g(z) = \sum_{j=0}^{\infty} P\{N_v = j\}z^j \qquad (v = 1, 2).$$

Show that if procedures (a) and (b) are equivalent, then

$$g(x)g(y) = g^2\left(\frac{x+y}{2}\right). \qquad (16.1)$$

[*Hint:* Use the method of collective marks: Let x be the probability that a ball in cell 1 is not marked, and let y be the probability that a ball in cell 2 is not marked. Show that the probability that there are no marked balls in either cell is $g(x)g(y)$ under procedure (a) and $g^2[(x+y)/2]$ under procedure (b).]
  d. Conclude that procedures (a) and (b) are equivalent if and only if N_v has a Poisson distribution. [*Hint:* Make the substitution $x = x + y$, $y = 0$ in equation (16.1), and let $g(x) = g(0)u(x)$ to obtain equation (5.22) of the text.]
17. Consider the single-server queue with an unlimited number of waiting positions. Assume that the input process is Poisson with rate λ. Let the service time distribution function $H(\xi)$ be arbitrary, with Laplace–Stieltjes transform $\eta(s)$,

$$\eta(s) = \int_0^\infty e^{-s\xi}\, dH(\xi)$$

and with mean τ and variance σ^2. Denote by $W(\xi)$ the waiting time distribution function, and by $\omega(s)$ its Laplace–Stieltjes transform,

$$\omega(s) = \int_0^\infty e^{-s\xi}\, dW(\xi).$$

a. Let $g(z) = \sum_{j=0}^\infty \Pi_j^* z^j$ be the equilibrium probability generating function of the number of customers left behind in the system at the instant an arbitrary customer completes service and departs from the system. Define the departing customer's *sojourn time* as the length of time spent in the system from the instant of arrival to the instant of departure, and let the Laplace–Stieltjes transform of the sojourn time distribution function be denoted by $\phi(s)$. Show that, if customers are served in order of arrival, then $g(z)$ and $\phi(s)$ are related as follows:

$$g(z) = \phi(\lambda - \lambda z). \tag{17.1}$$

b. It can (and in Chapter 5 will) be shown that the distribution $\{\Pi_j^*\}$ satisfies the equations

$$\Pi_j^* = p_j \Pi_0^* + \sum_{i=1}^{j+1} p_{j-i+1} \Pi_i^* \qquad (j = 0, 1, \ldots), \tag{17.2}$$

where

$$p_j = \int_0^\infty \frac{(\lambda\xi)^j}{j!} e^{-\lambda\xi} \, dH(\xi). \tag{17.3}$$

Starting with equation (17.2), show that

$$g(z) = \frac{(z - 1)\eta(\lambda - \lambda z)}{z - \eta(\lambda - \lambda z)} \Pi_0^*. \tag{17.4}$$

c. Show that the normalization equation

$$\sum_{j=0}^\infty \Pi_j^* = 1 \tag{17.5}$$

implies

$$\Pi_0^* = 1 - \rho, \tag{17.6}$$

where $\rho = \lambda\tau < 1$, so that equation (17.4) becomes

$$g(z) = \frac{(z - 1)\eta(\lambda - \lambda z)}{z - \eta(\lambda - \lambda z)} (1 - \rho) \qquad (\rho < 1). \tag{17.7}$$

d. Give a physical interpretation of the requirement $\rho < 1$.

e. Deduce from equations (17.1) and (17.7) the *Pollaczek–Khintchine formula* for the Laplace–Stieltjes transform of the order-of-arrival waiting time distribution function:

$$\omega(s) = \frac{s(1 - \rho)}{s - \lambda[1 - \eta(s)]}. \tag{17.8}$$

f. Show that the expected value of the waiting time W is given by

$$E(W) = \frac{\rho\tau[1 + (\sigma^2/\tau^2)]}{2(1 - \rho)}. \tag{17.9}$$

g. Compare the mean waiting time when service times are constant to the mean waiting time when service times are exponentially distributed.

h. Show that when service times are exponentially distributed, the Pollaczek–Khintchine formula (17.8) yields

$$P\{W > t\} = \rho e^{-(1-\rho)t/\tau}. \tag{17.10}$$

[*Hint*:

$$\int_0^\infty e^{-st}\, dW(t) = W(0) + \int_{0+}^\infty e^{-st} W'(t)\, dt.]$$

i. Let Π_0 be the equilibrium probability that an arbitrary arriving customer finds the system empty. Show that, in general, $\Pi_0 = \Pi_0^*$. [*Hint:* Every customer who leaves the system empty is followed by a customer who finds the system empty. (Under very general conditions, the equilibrium distribution $\{\Pi_j^*\}$ of the number of customers left behind by a departure, and the equilibrium distribution $\{\Pi_j\}$ of the number of customers found by an arrival, are equal. This phenomenon will be discussed in detail in Chapter 5.)] This result implies that $P\{W > 0\} = \rho = \lambda\tau$ for any service time distribution function with mean τ; the form of $H(\xi)$ does not affect the probability of blocking, but does affect the waiting time distribution function and the mean waiting time, as part **g** illustrates.

Birth-and-Death Queueing Models

$$3$$

3–1. Introduction

In Chapter 1 we discussed the characteristics of a queueing model, and in Chapter 2 we discussed the birth-and-death process. In this chapter we shall develop a correspondence between certain queueing models and certain birth-and-death processes, and then specialize the results of our previous birth-and-death analysis to provide an analysis of these queueing models.

Recall from Chapter 1 that a queueing model is defined in terms of three characteristics: the input process, the service mechanism, and the queue discipline. The *input process* describes the sequence of requests for service. For example, a common assumption for the input process, and one that we shall make in this chapter, is that of *Poisson* (or *random*) *input*, where the customers are assumed to arrive according to a Poisson process. Another input process we shall study in this chapter is called *quasirandom input*, where each idle source generates requests independently and with the same exponentially distributed interrequest time.

The *service mechanism* is the category that includes such characteristics as the number of servers and the lengths of time that customers hold the servers. In this chapter we will study models with an arbitrary number of parallel servers and with independent, identically distributed *exponential service times*.

The *queue discipline* specifies the disposition of blocked customers (customers who find all servers busy). In this chapter we will consider three different queue disciplines. When blocked customers do not wait, but return immediately to their prerequest state, the queue discipline is said to be *blocked customers cleared* (BCC). When blocked customers wait as long as necessary for service, the queue discipline is said to be *blocked customers delayed* (BCD). And when customers are assumed to stay in the system for a time duration (sojourn time) that is independent of the state of the system, the queue discipline is said to be *blocked customers held* (BCH).

Poisson input can be considered a special case of quasirandom input. But it is more instructive to study Poisson input as an important input process in its own right, so we shall proceed by first discussing each of the three queue disciplines in the context of Poisson input. Then we shall discuss each of these queue disciplines in the context of quasirandom input, while simultaneously showing the relationship between the two.

We shall now show that certain queueing processes are birth-and-death processes. Let $N(t)$ be the number of customers in the system (waiting and in service) at time t, and denote by E_j the state of the system at time t if $N(t) = j$. We assume that if at any time t the system is in state E_j, the conditional probability that a customer will arrive during $(t, t + h)$ is $\lambda_j h + o(h)$ as $h \to 0$, and the conditional probability that a customer will depart (either through service completion or defection from the system) in $(t, t + h)$ is $\mu_j h + o(h)$ as $h \to 0$. The probability that during $(t, t + h)$ more than one arrival and/or departure occurs is assumed to be $o(h)$ as $h \to 0$.

Comparison with the postulates of Section 2–2 for the birth-and-death process shows that such a queueing process is indeed a birth-and-death process.

Most of the remainder of this chapter will be devoted to the development of particular birth-and-death queueing models, that is, to the development of queueing models that are birth-and-death processes, and for which the input process, the service mechanism, and the queue discipline can be specified through choice of the birth rates $\{\lambda_j\}$ and the death rates $\{\mu_j\}$.

The statistical equilibrium state probabilities for the birth-and-death process (or queue) are given by equations (3.17) and (3.18) of Chapter 2. For convenience, we repeat those results:

$$
P_j = \begin{cases} \dfrac{\lambda_0 \lambda_1 \cdots \lambda_{j-1}/\mu_1 \mu_2 \cdots \mu_j}{1 + \sum\limits_{k=1}^{\infty} (\lambda_0 \lambda_1 \cdots \lambda_{k-1}/\mu_1 \mu_2 \cdots \mu_k)} & (j = 1, 2, \ldots) \\[4ex] \dfrac{1}{1 + \sum\limits_{k=1}^{\infty} (\lambda_0 \lambda_1 \cdots \lambda_{k-1}/\mu_1 \mu_2 \cdots \mu_k)} & (j = 0). \end{cases} \tag{1.1}
$$

Before proceeding to the application of equation (1.1) to queues with particular choices of the input process, service mechanism, and queue discipline, we shall direct our attention to the relationship between the probabilities given by equation (1.1), which describe the system at an arbitrary instant during equilibrium, and the probabilities that describe the system at the instants at which the customers arrive.

3–2. Equality of the Outside Observer's Distribution and the Arriving Customer's Distribution for Systems with Poisson Input

We have shown that the equilibrium birth-and-death probabilities $\{P_j\}$ given by (1.1) can be interpreted as state probabilities for some queueing models. The distribution $\{P_j\}$ was derived from equations that express how the durations of time the system spends in various states relate to each other. Therefore, as discussed in Chapter 2, for systems in equilibrium, P_j may be interpreted either as the proportion of time that the system spends in state E_j or as the probability that the system is in state E_j at an arbitrary instant. For any (not necessarily birth-and-death) queue, we call the distribution $\{P_j\}$ of time the system spends in each state the *outside observer's distribution*.

Now consider the state distribution that an arriving customer would see, that is, the state distribution with respect to only those instants at which requests for service occur. We denote this distribution by $\{\Pi_j\}$, and call it the *arriving customer's distribution*. It is important to realize that, in general, the outside observer's distribution $\{P_j\}$ and the arriving customer's distribution $\{\Pi_j\}$ are different.

For example, consider a single-server system in which the interarrival times are constant; that is, suppose that requests for service occur at instants $\tau_1, \tau_2, \ldots, \tau_i, \ldots$, where $\tau_{i+1} - \tau_i = \tau$ $(i = 1, 2, \ldots)$. Suppose further that service times are of constant length $\tau - \varepsilon$, with $\varepsilon > 0$. Clearly, the states of the system as seen by an outside observer are described by $P_0 = \varepsilon/\tau$ and $P_1 = (\tau - \varepsilon)/\tau$, where $P_0 \to 0$ and $P_1 \to 1$ as $\varepsilon \to 0$. Arriving customers, on the other hand, see the system states with probabilities $\Pi_0 = 1$ and $\Pi_1 = 0$ (independent of the value of ε). (Note: the queue of this example is not a birth-and-death queue.)

Suppose that for some arbitrary queue we know the outside observer's distribution $\{P_j\}$. Clearly, the distribution of interest in evaluating the quality of service provided by the system is the arriving customer's distribution $\{\Pi_j\}$. Thus we would like to be able to obtain the arriving customer's distribution $\{\Pi_j\}$ from the known outside observer's distribution $\{P_j\}$. It is a most important fact that for systems with Poisson input these two distributions are identical:

$$\Pi_j = P_j \qquad (j = 0, 1, \ldots). \tag{2.1}$$

(Note: a queue with Poisson input is not necessarily a birth-and-death queue, and vice versa.)

To prove equation (2.1), recall from the discussion in Chapter 2 of the Poisson process that the duration of time separating an arbitrary instant and the preceding arrival epoch has the same (exponential) distribution as does the time separating successive arrival epochs. Since the state of any system at any epoch is completely determined by the sequence of arrivals and service times prior to the epoch, it follows that, when the input process is Poisson, no inference about the state of the system at an epoch can be drawn from knowledge of whether or not the epoch in question is an arrival epoch. That is, for systems with Poisson input, the equilibrium state distribution $\{P_j\}$ at an arbitrary epoch is the same as the equilibrium state distribution $\{\Pi_j\}$ at an arrival epoch.

An intuitive interpretation of this result is this: Since Poisson arrivals occur randomly in time, the proportion Π_j of arrivals that occur during state E_j should equal the proportion P_j of time the system spends in state E_j.

Although we are concerned here only with systems in equilibrium, a slight modification of the above argument is sufficient to show (see Exercise 1) for systems with Poisson input that, for all $t \geq 0$, the outside observer's distribution $\{P_j(t)\}$ and the arriving customer's distribution $\{\Pi_j(t)\}$ are equal:

$$\Pi_j(t) = P_j(t) \qquad (t \geq 0; j = 0, 1, \ldots). \tag{2.2}$$

We now turn our attention to some particular birth-and-death queueing models.

3–3. Poisson Input, s Servers, Blocked Customers Cleared: The Erlang Loss Formula

We assume that customer arrivals follow a Poisson process with rate λ; that service times are exponentially distributed with mean service time μ^{-1}, independent of each other and the arrival process; and that customers who find all s servers busy leave the system and have no effect upon it, that is, *blocked customers cleared* (BCC). (However, the assumption of exponential service times will be seen to be unnecessary.) An application of the BCC assumption arises in telephone traffic engineering, where calls that find all trunks busy are given a busy signal. Other applications should be apparent.

Since customers arrive at random with rate λ, but effect state changes only when $j < s$ (because blocked customers are cleared), we may write

$$\lambda_j = \begin{cases} \lambda & \text{when } j = 0, 1, \ldots, s-1 \\ 0 & \text{when } j = s. \end{cases} \qquad (3.1)$$

Because service times are exponential, when there are j customers in service the rate μ_j at which service completions occur is

$$\mu_j = j\mu \qquad (j = 0, 1, \ldots, s). \qquad (3.2)$$

The rates (3.1) and (3.2), in conjunction with (1.1), give for the statistical equilibrium probability of j busy servers

$$P_j = \frac{(\lambda/\mu)^j/j!}{\sum\limits_{k=0}^{s} (\lambda/\mu)^k/k!} \qquad (j = 0, 1, \ldots, s) \qquad (3.3)$$

and $P_j = 0$ for $j > s$. The distribution (3.3) is called the *truncated Poisson distribution*.

Note first that the rates λ and μ appear in (3.3) only through the ratio λ/μ. This is characteristic of many queueing formulas. The ratio λ/μ is called the *offered load* and is often given the symbol a. The mean service time is μ^{-1}, so that the offered load $a = \lambda/\mu$ is a dimensionless quantity numerically equal to the mean number of arrivals that occur during a service time. The offered load a is thus a measure of the demand placed on the system. The numerical values of a are expressed in units called *erlangs*, (*erl*). The offered load per server, given by the ratio a/s, is often called the *traffic intensity*.

More generally, suppose that the service time distribution function is $H(t)$, with mean

$$\int_0^\infty t \, dH(t) = \tau, \qquad (3.4)$$

and suppose that customers arrive according to some (not necessarily Poisson) process with rate λ. Then the average number of arrivals occurring during an interval of length t is λt; therefore, the average number a of arrivals during an arbitrary service time is

$$a = \int_0^\infty \lambda t \; dH(t) = \lambda \tau. \qquad (3.5)$$

Therefore let us define the *offered load a*, in general, as the mean number of requests per service time.

Returning to the state probabilities (3.3), we see that the probability that all s servers are busy is given by (3.3) with $j = s$. Formula (3.3) with $j = s$ is called the *Erlang loss formula* in the United States and is denoted by

$$B(s, a) = \frac{a^s/s!}{\displaystyle\sum_{k=0}^{s} (a^k/k!)}. \qquad (3.6)$$

Likewise, the truncated Poisson distribution (3.3) is also known as the *Erlang loss distribution*. In Europe, the right-hand side of (3.6) is called *Erlang's first formula* and is denoted by $E_{1,s}(a)$. Formula (3.6) was first derived by Erlang in 1917. (See Brockmeyer et al. [1948].) As already suggested, the Erlang loss formula has found extensive application in the field of telephone traffic engineering. Curves of formula (3.6) for fixed values of s are plotted against increasing values of a in Figures A–1 and A–2 of Appendix A. Formula (3.6) is also tabulated in Dietrich et al. [1966].

It is important to note that (3.6) gives both the proportion of time that all s servers are busy and the proportion of arriving customers who find all s servers busy (and thus are lost). Note also that formula (3.6), which we have derived from first principles, is the same as formula (1.6) of Chapter 1, which was derived through a heuristic argument. We have now answered some, but not all, of the questions raised in Chapter 1 about the validity of this formula.

Another useful quantity is the *carried load a'*, which is defined in general for systems in statistical equilibrium as the mean number of busy servers:

$$a' = \sum_{j=1}^{s-1} jP_j + s \sum_{j=s}^{\infty} P_j. \qquad (3.7)$$

The first sum on the right-hand side of (3.7) reflects the assumption that, if the number of customers in the system is less than the number of servers, then all these customers will be in service; the second sum reflects the fact that all s servers will be busy if and only if there are at least s customers in the system.

For the queue discipline of blocked customers cleared (in which $P_j = 0$ when $j > s$), substitution of (3.3) into (3.7) yields, after some simplification,

$$a' = a[1 - B(s, a)]. \tag{3.8}$$

It is immediately evident from (3.8) that the offered load a is the load that would be carried if the number of servers were infinite; and, in fact, the carried load is just that portion of the offered load that is not cleared (lost) from the system.

In general, whenever the input process is not influenced by the system states, the offered load (the mean number of arrivals in a service time) equals the mean number of customers in service simultaneously on an infinite-server group in statistical equilibrium. With an existing server group, the carried load a' lends itself to direct measurement, and formula (3.8) permits estimation of the offered load a and the probability of blocking. Statistical questions arising from consideration of traffic measurements are often quite difficult, and discussion of these questions is beyond the scope of this text.

We define the *server occupancy* ρ as the load carried per server in equilibrium,

$$\rho = \frac{a'}{s}. \tag{3.9}$$

The server occupancy ρ measures the degree of utilization of a group of servers (and is sometimes called the *utilization factor*). Clearly we must always have $\rho \leq 1$.

Investigation of formulas (3.6), (3.8), and (3.9) leads to the following important conclusion: as the number of servers is increased and the offered load is increased such that the probability of blocking remains constant, the server occupancy increases. This is often expressed by the statement, Large server groups are more efficient than small ones.

Unfortunately, in practice hardware limitations sometimes preclude exploitation of this fact. Moreover, high-occupancy server groups are more vulnerable to service degradation during periods of overload than are smaller server groups with the same blocking probability but lower occupancy.

For a server group of fixed size, occupancy increases with increasing load, thereby increasing server group efficiency; unfortunately, the probability of blocking also increases with increasing load. Hence, efficient use of equipment must be balanced against the provision of acceptable service for the customers.

An important theorem is that all of the results derived above are true for any service time distribution function with finite mean, even though the Markov property of the exponential distribution function was used explicitly in the above derivation. (Specifically, in using the birth-and-death formulation we have assumed that if at any instant t there are j customers in service, each with mean service time μ^{-1}, the probability that a customer will complete service in $(t, t + h)$ is $j\mu h + o(h)$ as $h \to 0$, independent of the value of t and the lengths of time that the customers have been in service.) We shall call systems with Poisson input and blocked customers cleared—whose state probabilities are given by (3.3)—*Erlang loss systems*.

The remarkable fact that the truncated Poisson distribution (3.3) is valid for an arbitrary service time distribution function was conjectured by Erlang himself in 1917. Subsequently, many investigators studied this problem, and a variety of proofs have been offered. (See pp. 271–278 of Syski [1960]; and see also Takács' paper [1969].) A proof for the special case where the service time is a sum of exponentially distributed phases is given in Exercise 5 of Chapter 4.

It is worthwhile at this point to give a proof for the special case $s = 1$. We suppose that customers arrive according to a Poisson process with rate λ. An arrival who finds the server idle will hold it for a time interval whose duration is a random variable with mean τ. An arrival who finds the server occupied will leave the system immediately. Hence the server alternates between busy and idle states, each busy period of mean length τ, and each idle period of mean length λ^{-1}. This is illustrated in Figure 3–1.

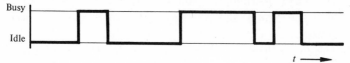

Figure 3–1.

Consider a single cycle composed of an idle period and an adjacent busy period. The cycle has mean length $\lambda^{-1} + \tau$, and thus the ratio of the mean busy period to the mean cycle length is

$$\frac{\tau}{\lambda^{-1} + \tau} = \frac{a}{1 + a},$$

which is the Erlang loss formula (3.6) with $s = 1$. Since the ratio of mean values $\tau/(\lambda^{-1} + \tau)$ is indeed the same as the proportion of time that the server is busy, we have the required result.

Let us consider this single-server model again, this time from the point of view of arriving customers. We have already argued that the proportion of time (or probability) the server is busy is $a/(1 + a)$, that is, $P_0 = 1/(1 + a)$ and $P_1 = a/(1 + a)$, and we know that for systems with Poisson input $\{\Pi_j\} = \{P_j\}$. We now calculate Π_0 and Π_1 directly by a similar heuristic argument; we form the ratio of the mean number of customers blocked per cycle to the mean number of customers arriving per cycle. The number of customers blocked during a cycle is the number that arrive when the server is busy; the mean number of arrivals per busy period (service time) is, by definition, a. The number of customers who arrive per cycle is the sum of the number who arrive during the busy period and the number who arrive during the idle period. But the latter is simply 1; the first customer to arrive during an idle period seizes the server and initiates a busy period. Hence the required ratio is $\Pi_1 = a/(1 + a)$ so that, as promised, $\Pi_1 = P_1$, and, since $\Pi_0 + \Pi_1 = 1$, therefore $\Pi_0 = 1/(1 + a) = P_0$.

Consider a server group that serves two independent streams of Poisson traffic (for example, a telephone trunk group serving eastbound and westbound traffic) on a BCC basis. That is, suppose that arrivals from stream i occur according to a Poisson process with rate λ_i, and assume first that the customers in each stream have a common (but arbitrary) service time distribution function with mean τ. Then the two streams can be viewed as comprising a single Poisson stream with rate $\lambda_1 + \lambda_2$, so that the outside observer's distribution $\{P_j\}$ is given by (3.3) with $\lambda = \lambda_1 + \lambda_2$. Since each stream is Poisson, each stream sees the (same) outside observer distribution, and hence each stream sees the same arriving customer distribution; thus the probability of blocking is the same for each stream.

Suppose now that the (arbitrary) service time distribution functions of the two Poisson streams are not identical, with stream i having mean service time τ_i. Let $a_i = \lambda_i\tau_i$ and $a = a_1 + a_2$. Arrivals still occur according to a Poisson process with rate $\lambda_1 + \lambda_2$. It follows from our previous result that, regardless of the form of the composite service time distribution function, the state probabilities are still given by (3.3), where the composite mean service time τ remains to be determined. Again, since each stream is Poisson, each stream sees the same state distribution. Thus, given that an arbitrary customer is served, the probability that he comes from stream i is simply λ_i/λ. Therefore, the (composite) mean service time τ for all customers who are served is

$$\tau = \frac{\lambda_1}{\lambda} \tau_1 + \frac{\lambda_2}{\lambda} \tau_2.$$

Multiplying through by λ we obtain

$$a = a_1 + a_2.$$

We conclude that when two streams of Poisson traffic of magnitudes a_1 erl and a_2 erl are offered to a single group of s servers on a BCC basis, each stream suffers a blocking probability given by the Erlang loss formula (3.6) with $a = a_1 + a_2$. The generalization of this result to include an arbitrary number of Poisson streams is clearly true.

3–4. Poisson Input, s Servers with Exponential Service Times, Blocked Customers Delayed: The Erlang Delay Formula

Consider now the case in which customers who find all s servers busy join a queue and wait as long as necessary for service, that is, *blocked customers delayed* (BCD). No server can be idle if a customer is waiting. The number of waiting positions in the queue is assumed to be infinite. Applications of this model should be self-evident. (We note for future reference that in the terminology of queueing theory, the s-server BCD queue with Poisson input and exponential service times is called the $M/M/s$ queue. This terminology will be discussed in Chapter 5.) Since customers arrive according to a Poisson process with rate λ, and every arrival effects a change of system state, we have

$$\lambda_j = \lambda \qquad (j = 0, 1, \ldots). \tag{4.1}$$

The assumption of exponential service times implies that if at any time all the j customers in the system are in service, the rate at which service completions occur is $j\mu$; if all s servers are busy, only those customers that are in service are eligible to leave, so that the service completion rate is $s\mu$. Hence

$$\mu_j = \begin{cases} j\mu & (j = 0, 1, \ldots, s) \\ s\mu & (j = s, s + 1, \ldots). \end{cases} \tag{4.2}$$

Using (4.1) and (4.2) in equation (1.1) we can write

$$P_j = \frac{a^j}{j!} P_0 \qquad (j = 0, 1, \ldots, s) \qquad (4.3)$$

and

$$P_j = \frac{a^j}{s! \, s^{j-s}} P_0 \qquad (j = s, s + 1, \ldots), \qquad (4.4)$$

where $a = \lambda/\mu$ and where P_0 is given by

$$P_0 = \left(\sum_{k=0}^{s-1} \frac{a^k}{k!} + \sum_{k=s}^{\infty} \frac{a^k}{s! \, s^{k-s}} \right)^{-1}.$$

If $a < s$ the infinite geometric sum on the right converges, and

$$P_0 = \left(\sum_{k=0}^{s-1} \frac{a^k}{k!} + \frac{a^s}{(s - 1)! \, (s - a)} \right)^{-1} \qquad (0 \leq a < s). \qquad (4.5)$$

If $a \geq s$, the infinite geometric sum diverges to infinity. Then $P_0 = 0$ and hence $P_j = 0$ for all finite j. For $a \geq s$, therefore, the queue length is infinite (greater than any prespecified finite value) with probability 1. In this case, we say that no statistical equilibrium distribution exists.

The probability that all servers are occupied,

$$\sum_{j=s}^{\infty} P_j = \frac{a^s}{s!} \frac{s}{s - a} P_0 \qquad (0 \leq a < s), \qquad (4.6)$$

is given by the *Erlang delay formula*, $C(s, a) = \sum_{j=s}^{\infty} P_j$, (so called because blocked customers are delayed until service commences):

$$C(s, a) = \frac{a^s/[(s - 1)! \, (s - a)]}{\sum\limits_{k=0}^{s-1} (a^k/k!) + a^s/[(s - 1)! \, (s - a)]} \qquad (0 \leq a < s). \qquad (4.7)$$

We call systems described by probabilities (4.3), (4.4), (4.5), and (4.7) *Erlang delay systems*. In Europe the right-hand side of (4.7) is called *Erlang's second formula* and is denoted by $E_{2,s}(a)$. Curves for formula (4.7) are given in Figures A–3 and A–4 of Appendix A. See also Dietrich et al. [1966] and Descloux [1962].

Since we have Poisson input, the arriving customer's distribution $\{\Pi_j\}$ is identical to the calculated outside observer's distribution $\{P_j\}$.

Unlike the Erlang loss probabilities, the Erlang delay probabilities are not valid for an arbitrary service time distribution function.

Again unlike the Erlang loss probabilities, the Erlang delay probabilities comprise a proper distribution only when the offered load is less than the number of servers. This restriction follows mathematically from the convergence criterion for the infinite geometric sum and does not apply if the number of queue positions is finite (so that customers finding all queue positions busy are cleared from the system).

From the definition (3.7) of carried load we calculate directly that

$$a' = a; \tag{4.8}$$

that is, the carried and offered loads are equal (or, equivalently, the utilization factor or server occupancy and the traffic intensity are equal). This is intuitively clear, because in the Erlang delay model all blocked customers wait as long as necessary for service, and therefore all arriving customers are served. Indeed, (4.8) provides an intuitive partial explanation for the restriction $a < s$ (or, equivalently, $\rho < 1$), for $a > s$ would require the carried load (the mean number of busy servers) to exceed the number of servers, which is clearly impossible.

Let us briefly consider the single-server case without the requirements of Poisson input and exponential service times. We have argued that the carried load equals the offered load by virtue of the assumption that all customers wait until served (BCD), and this is true for arbitrary interarrival time and service time distribution functions. Also, by the definition (3.7), in the single-server case the carried load equals the proportion of time the server is busy, $a' = \sum_{j=1}^{\infty} P_j$ (where, in general, we may not know how to calculate the $\{P_j\}$). We conclude that the proportion of time that a single-server BCD system is busy is always equal to the offered load $a = \lambda\tau$. [As a check, note that $C(1, a) = a$.]

A quantity of some interest for the single-server queue is the *busy period*, defined as the length of time from the instant the (previously idle) server is seized until it next becomes idle and there is no one waiting in the queue. The calculation of this quantity is difficult in general, and we shall investigate it in some detail in Chapter 5. But with the simple tools presently at hand, we can easily calculate the mean busy period for systems with Poisson input (and arbitrary distribution of service times). Denote by b the mean length of the busy period. Then the ratio of the mean busy period to the total cycle time (contiguous idle period and busy period) is $b/(\lambda^{-1} + b)$. But this ratio, which is independent of the form of the service time distribution function, is simply the proportion of time $a = \lambda\tau$ the server is busy:

$$\lambda\tau = \frac{b}{\lambda^{-1} + b}.$$

Solving for b yields

$$b = \frac{\tau}{1 - a} \qquad (0 \le a < 1), \tag{4.9}$$

where τ is the mean service time.

3–5. Order-of-Arrival Waiting Time Distribution Function for the Erlang Delay Model

When customers who find all s servers busy wait until served, it is often required to know the distribution of the time that the customers spend waiting for service to commence. We shall discuss waiting time distribution functions for various queue disciplines in detail in Chapter 6. Because of its simplicity and obvious importance, we derive here the waiting time distribution function for the Erlang delay system (Poisson input, exponential service times, BCD) in which the queue discipline is service in order of arrival.

Let W be the wait or delay experienced by an arbitrary request for service; that is, the random variable W is the length of time (which may be zero) that an arbitrary customer spends waiting in the queue. We wish to determine for all $t \ge 0$ the complementary waiting time distribution function $P\{W > t\}$. Since it is most convenient to work directly with the conditional complementary waiting time distribution function $P\{W > t \mid W > 0\}$, let us write

$$P\{W > t\} = P\{W > 0\}P\{W > t \mid W > 0\}, \tag{5.1}$$

where

$$P\{W > 0\} = C(s, a) = \frac{a^s}{s!} \frac{s}{s - a} P_0. \tag{5.2}$$

Note that (5.2) is true for any Erlang delay system in which the order of service of waiting customers is independent of the particular service time values. We shall use the word *nonscheduled* to describe any queue discipline in which customers are selected for service from among those waiting without regard to the lengths of service required by the waiting customers. Examples of nonscheduled queue disciplines are service in order of arrival, service in random order, and service in reverse order of arrival. On the other hand, for example, if the waiting customer with the shortest service time is always the next one to receive service, then the queue discipline is not nonscheduled. We assume throughout this text that every queue discipline is nonscheduled unless specified otherwise.

If N is the number of customers in the system found by an arbitrary arrival, then, applying the law of total probability, we can write

$$P\{W > t\} = \sum_{j=0}^{\infty} P\{W > t \mid N = j + s\} P\{N = j + s\}. \qquad (5.3)$$

Both equations (5.1) and (5.3) are true for queueing systems in general. In the particular system under consideration

$$P\{N = j + s\} = \Pi_{j+s} = P_{j+s} = \frac{a^s}{s!} \left(\frac{a}{s}\right)^j P_0, \qquad (5.4)$$

the equalities in (5.4) holding by definition, the equality of the arriving customer's distribution and the outside observer's distribution for systems with Poisson input, and equation (4.4), respectively. Equations (5.1) through (5.4) together give

$$P\{W > t \mid W > 0\} = (1 - \rho) \sum_{j=0}^{\infty} \rho^j P\{W > t \mid N = j + s\}, \qquad (5.5)$$

where $\rho = a/s$ is the server occupancy or utilization factor. Equation (5.5) is valid for any nonscheduled order of service in an Erlang delay system.

It remains to calculate $P\{W > t \mid N = j + s\}$ for order-of-arrival service. Suppose that a customer (the *test customer*) arrives at time T_c and finds all servers busy and $j \geq 0$ other customers in line ahead of him. Let X_1 be the elapsed time from T_c until the first service completion epoch, let X_i $(i = 2, \ldots, j)$ be the length of time that the ith ordered customer in the queue waits at the head of the queue, and let X_{j+1} be the length of time that the test customer spends at the head of the queue. Then the test customer's wait in the queue is the sum $X_1 + \cdots + X_{j+1}$.

By virtue of the Markov property of the exponential distribution function, the random variables X_i $(i = 1, 2, \ldots, j + 1)$ are mutually independent, identically distributed negative exponential random variables with common mean $(s\mu)^{-1}$. Thus the distribution function of the length of time spent waiting in the queue by a blocked customer who finds $j \geq 0$ other customers ahead of him is the $(j + 1)$-fold self-convolution of the exponential distribution function, that is, the j-phase Erlangian (gamma) distribution (see Exercise 12f of Chapter 2 and Exercise 12h of this chapter):

$$P\{W > t \mid N = j + s\} = e^{-s\mu t} \sum_{k=0}^{j} \frac{(s\mu t)^k}{k!}. \qquad (5.6)$$

Note that equation (5.6) is valid for any input process, not just Poisson input.

Insertion of (5.6) into (5.5) and interchange of the order of summation yields the important result:

$$P\{W > t \mid W > 0\} = e^{-(1-\rho)s\mu t} \qquad (t \geq 0, \rho < 1). \qquad (5.7)$$

(For another derivation of this result see Exercise 12.)

We conclude that for the Erlang delay system, the order-of-arrival conditional waiting time distribution function is negative exponential.

Equation (5.7) is particularly suited to graphical presentation; for each value of ρ, equation (5.7) gives a straight line when $P\{W > t \mid W > 0\}$ is plotted against $s\mu t$ on semilog paper, as in Figure 7 of Appendix A. The unconditional waiting time probability $P\{W > t\}$ is easily obtained from equations (5.1), (5.2), and (5.7):

$$P\{W > t\} = C(s, a)e^{-(1-\rho)s\mu t} \qquad (t \geq 0, \rho < 1) \qquad (5.8)$$

where $\rho = a/s$. Numerically, we can easily calculate $P\{W > t\}$ by evaluating the term $e^{-(1-\rho)s\mu t}$ from its graph in Appendix A, evaluating $C(s, a)$ from its graph in Appendix A or from one of the tabulations of the Erlang delay formula, and forming the required product.

Since the conditional waiting time for blocked customers is exponentially distributed according to (5.7), it follows that the conditional mean waiting time $E(W \mid W > 0)$ (the mean wait suffered by those customers who are blocked) is given by

$$E(W \mid W > 0) = \frac{1}{(1 - \rho)s\mu} \qquad (5.9)$$

and thus the overall mean waiting time $E(W)$ is given by

$$E(W) = \frac{C(s, a)}{(1 - \rho)s\mu}. \qquad (5.10)$$

These formulas are tabulated or plotted in Dietrich et al. [1966] and Descloux [1962].

We note in passing the interesting result that for $s = 1$ the conditional mean waiting time (5.9) equals the mean busy period (4.9). Mathematical "coincidences" rarely occur; this apparent coincidence has, in fact, a simple explanation, which will be given in Chapter 6.

Although formulas (5.9) and (5.10) were calculated for order-of-arrival service, they are valid for any nonscheduled order of service. (We shall prove this important fact in Section 5–3.)

3–6. Poisson Input, s Servers, Blocked Customers Held: The Poisson Formula

In the BCD model blocked customers wait as long as necessary for service, and in the BCC model blocked customers wait not at all. An intermediate assumption that is particularly easy to handle is that an arriving customer is willing to spend an amount of time T (called the *sojourn time*) in the system, where T is a random variable, after which he will depart regardless of whether or not at the expiration of his sojourn time he is in service or is still waiting in the queue. In other words, a blocked customer will wait for service as long as time T; if he receives service before the expiration of T, he then holds the server for the remainder of time T. This queue discipline is called *blocked customers held* (BCH).

Suppose that the customer sojourn times are exponentially distributed with mean μ^{-1}. Then, by virtue of the Markov property of the exponential distribution, the rate at which customers leave the system when the system is in state E_j is $j\mu$ for $j < s, j = s$, and $j > s$. Hence the birth-and-death coefficients for the Poisson input, exponential sojourn time, BCH system are

$$\lambda_j = \lambda \qquad (j = 0, 1, \ldots) \tag{6.1}$$

and

$$\mu_j = j\mu \qquad (j = 0, 1, \ldots). \tag{6.2}$$

Substitution of (6.1) and (6.2) into (1.1) yields the familiar Poisson distribution

$$P_j = \frac{a^j}{j!}\, e^{-a} \qquad (j = 0, 1, \ldots). \tag{6.3}$$

Equation (6.3) is valid for all $a \geq 0$.

Note that since the customer sojourn times are (by assumption) exponentially distributed with mean μ^{-1}, then by the Markov property the length of time a customer who gets served holds the server also follows the negative exponential distribution with mean μ^{-1}. If this seems contradictory, note that among all customers, those with long sojourn times are more likely to get served, and those with short sojourn times are more likely to defect before receiving service (unless, of course, they are not blocked), so that there is no logical conflict in the statement that the sojourn time and service time distribution functions are identical.

As is now evident, the BCH state probabilities (6.3) can be viewed as the BCC state probabilities (3.3) with $s = \infty$. We should not be surprised therefore to learn that the result (6.3) gives the equilibrium state probabilities for an infinite-server group serving customers with arbitrary sojourn time distribution function with finite mean.

Returning to the interpretation of the BCH model as an s-server system with unlimited waiting space, the probability that an arriving customer will find all s servers busy is denoted by $P(s, a)$, where

$$P(s, a) = \sum_{j=s}^{\infty} \frac{a^j}{j!} e^{-a}. \tag{6.4}$$

From the definition (3.7), the carried load a' can be shown to be

$$a' = a[1 - P(s - 1, a)] + sP(s, a). \tag{6.5}$$

Tabulations of (6.3) and (6.4) are given in Dietrich et al. [1966] and Chapter 26 of Abramowitz and Stegun [1964]. Curves for (6.4) are given in Figures A–5 and A–6 of Appendix A. Note that $B(s, a) < P(s, a) < C(s, a)$ for $a > 0$ and $s = 1, 2, \ldots$ (see Exercise 15).

Finally, as promised in Chapter 2, we shall use the *method of collective marks* (see Runnenburg [1965]) to obtain the transient solution for the Poisson input, infinite-server model in the case of arbitrary service time distribution function. (Recall that the transient solution in the special case of exponential service times was obtained in Section 2–4 from the differential-difference birth-and-death equations by the use of generating functions.)

Let $P_j(t)$ be the probability that at time t there are j customers in service, and define the probability generating function

$$P(z, t) = \sum_{j=0}^{\infty} P_j(t)z^j. \tag{6.6}$$

We shall obtain the generating function by interpreting the right-hand side of (6.6) directly as a probability (method of collective marks).

Suppose that each arriving customer is given an identifying mark with probability $1 - z$. Then $P_j(t)z^j$ is the probability that at time t there are j customers in service, none of whom is marked. Therefore, $P(z, t) = \sum_{j=0}^{\infty} P_j(t)z^j$ is the probability that no marked customers are in service at time t.

To evaluate this probability, consider an arbitrary customer (the test customer) who is assumed to have arrived at some time t_0 during the interval $(0, t)$. We shall calculate the probability $p(t)$ that the test customer is still present at time t.

Let X be the service time of a customer, with distribution function $H(x)$. The test customer will be present at time t if either (a) $X > t$ or (b) $X < t$ and $t_0 + X > t$. Event (a) has probability $1 - H(t)$. To calculate the probability of event (b), note that if $X = x < t$, then event (b) holds if and only if t_0 lies in the interval $(t - x, t)$. (See Figure 3–2.)

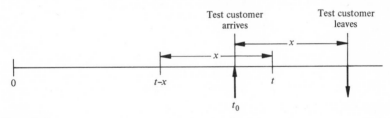

Figure 3–2.

Since by assumption the arrivals occur according to a Poisson process, it follows [see the argument surrounding equation (5.29) of Chapter 2] that the location of the arrival epoch t_0 is uniformly distributed in $(0, t)$. Therefore the probability that t_0 lies in the interval $(t - x, t)$ is x/t. Hence, event (b) has probability $\int_0^t (x/t)\, dH(x)$, and $p(t)$ is given by

$$p(t) = 1 - H(t) + \int_0^t \frac{x}{t}\, dH(x). \qquad (6.7)$$

Equation (6.7) gives the probability $p(t)$ that an arbitrary customer, who is assumed to have arrived in $(0, t)$, is still in service at time t. The probability is $(1 - z)p(t)$ that the customer is a marked customer present at time t; that is, with probability $1 - (1 - z)p(t)$ the customer is either not marked, not present, or both. The probability that k customers arrive in $(0, t)$ is, by assumption, $[(\lambda t)^k/k!]e^{-\lambda t}$. Therefore, if the system is assumed initially empty, the probability that no marked customers are present at time t is

$$P(z, t) = \sum_{k=0}^{\infty} \frac{(\lambda t)^k}{k!}\, e^{-\lambda t}[1 - (1 - z)p(t)]^k, \qquad (6.8)$$

which reduces to

$$P(z, t) = e^{-\lambda t p(t)(1-z)}. \tag{6.9}$$

According to equation (6.9), the probability generating function $P(z, t)$ is that of a Poisson distribution with mean $\lambda t p(t)$:

$$P_j(t) = \frac{[\lambda t p(t)]^j}{j!} e^{-\lambda t p(t)} \qquad (j = 0, 1, \ldots). \tag{6.10}$$

Hence, for arbitrary service time distribution function, the number of customers in service at time $t \geq 0$ has the Poisson distribution with time-dependent mean $\lambda t p(t)$. The reader should compare equation (6.10) with equation (4.26) of Chapter 2.

We now consider the statistical equilibrium distribution $P_j = \lim_{t \to \infty} P_j(t)$. It can be shown that, for any distribution function $H(x)$ $(0 \leq x < \infty)$ with finite mean $\tau = \int_0^\infty x \, dH(x)$,

$$\lim_{t \to \infty} t[1 - H(t)] = 0. \tag{6.11}$$

Then

$$\lim_{t \to \infty} t p(t) = \tau \tag{6.12}$$

so that the statistical equilibrium distribution is

$$P_j = \frac{a^j}{j!} e^{-a} \qquad (j = 0, 1, \ldots), \tag{6.13}$$

where $a = \lambda \tau$.

We conclude that the statistical equilibrium state probabilities for the Poisson input BCH model are indeed given by the Poisson distribution with mean $a = \lambda \tau$, independently of the form of the service time distribution function.

3–7. Quasirandom Input

In all the birth-and-death queueing models considered so far, we have assumed that requests for service occur according to a Poisson process with rate λ. With Poisson input, the probability that a request for service will occur in any interval $(t, t + h)$ is independent of the state of the system at time t. This important property is at the heart of the proof in Section 3–2 of the equality of the outside observer's distribution $\{P_j\}$ and the arriving customer's distribution $\{\Pi_j\}$ for systems with Poisson input.

Consider now a system in which the requests for service are generated by a finite number of sources. In such a system the probability of an arrival in an interval $(t, t + h)$ will not be independent of the system state at time t, since it will, in general, depend directly on the number of sources idle (and therefore available to generate new requests) at time t. Consequently, the outside observer's and the arriving customer's distributions are not equal.

These properties are illustrated by the finite-source system with an equal number of sources and servers. When all the servers are occupied no new requests can occur, since there are no idle sources to generate new requests. Therefore the probability of blocking is zero, whereas the proportion of time all servers are busy can take any value between zero and one.

The particular kind of finite-source input we shall consider is often called quasirandom input (as opposed to Poisson or completely random input). We say that a finite number n of (identical) sources generate *quasirandom input* if the probability that any particular source generates a request for service in any interval $(t, t + h)$ is $\gamma h + o(h)$ as $h \to 0$ if the source is idle at time t, and zero if the source is not idle (waiting or being served) at time t, independently of the states of any other sources.

It follows from this definition that, if a particular source is idle at time t, the distribution of time from t until the source next generates a request for service is exponential with mean γ^{-1}; that is, with probability $e^{-\gamma x}$ the source will not originate a request for service in $(t, t + x)$.

If the number of sources idle at time t is n, the probability that exactly j of them generate requests for service in $(t, t + x)$ is $\binom{n}{j}(1 - e^{-\gamma x})^j \times (e^{-\gamma x})^{n-j}$. [We have assumed here that each idle source can generate at most one request in $(t, t + x)$.] Now let $n \to \infty$ and $\gamma \to 0$ in such a way that $n\gamma = \lambda$. Then

$$\lim_{\substack{n \to \infty \\ \gamma \to 0 \\ n\gamma = \lambda}} \binom{n}{j}(1 - e^{-\gamma x})^j (e^{-\gamma x})^{n-j} = \frac{(\lambda x)^j}{j!} e^{-\lambda x}. \tag{7.1}$$

Thus, assuming that each idle source can generate at most one request in $(t, t + x)$, we have shown that the distribution of the number of requests generated is, in the limit, Poisson. It should be intuitively clear that because $\gamma \to 0$ the restriction of at most one request per source can be removed without affecting the conclusion. Then, more formally, we conclude:

If the number n of independent sources generating quasirandom input increases to infinity and the request rate γ per idle source decreases to zero in such a way that the overall idle-source request rate $n\gamma$ remains constant, $n\gamma = \lambda$, then in the limit the input process is Poisson with rate λ.

A formal proof of this theorem is given in Khintchine [1969]. In view of this theorem, Poisson input is often called *infinite-source input*.

In the case of Poisson input the number of sources, or potential customers, is infinite. However, the sources affect the system only when they make requests for service, that is, when they become customers. Therefore, with Poisson input, there is no need to distinguish between sources and customers. This is not true, however, in the case of finite-source input. With finite-source input, a source assumes the role of a customer when it places a request for service, and it remains a customer as long as it is either waiting for service or in service. As soon as it becomes eligible to generate a new request for service, it again assumes the role of a source. We shall refer to a source as a customer only when we wish to stress that it is making a request for service. Any source can become a customer more than once, so the number of blocked customers is the number of requests (generated by sources) that are blocked. To avoid this confusion, we shall say that a source generates a request rather than that a source becomes a customer. The meanings of the words *customer*, *source*, and *request* should be clear from the context in which they are used.

Let us consider a system with n sources, s servers, exponential service times, and quasirandom input, where each idle source generates requests for service at rate γ. If at any time t the number of idle sources is $(n - j)$, then the probability that a request for service will occur in $(t, t + h)$ is $(n - j)\gamma h + o(h)$ as $h \to 0$. Thus queueing models with quasirandom input and exponential service times can be studied in the framework of the birth-and-death process, in a manner analogous to that used for the corresponding systems with Poisson input; we simply have a different specification of the birth coefficients $\{\lambda_j\}$.

3–8. Equality of the Arriving Customer's n-Source Distribution and the Outside Observer's $(n - 1)$-Source Distribution for Birth-and-Death Systems with Quasirandom Input

We have already shown by example that in systems with finite-source input, in contrast to the infinite-source case, the outside observer's distribution $\{P_j\}$ and the arriving customer's distribution $\{\Pi_j\}$ are, in general, unequal. In the case of birth-and-death queueing models with quasirandom input, we can calculate $\{P_j\}$ directly from the birth-and-death probabilities (1.1). But $\{\Pi_j\}$ is the distribution of direct relevance to one concerned with the quality of service provided by the servers to the customers. Hopefully, the two distributions will be simply related. Happily, they are.

For example, consider the simple system composed of one source and one server. Suppose that the source generates requests at rate γ when idle and rate zero when not idle, and let the mean service time be τ. Let $\gamma\tau = \hat{a}$; $\hat{a}$ is the load offered by the source when idle. The server alternates between busy and idle states, with each busy period of mean length τ. Consider a single cycle composed of an idle period and an adjacent busy period. The cycle has mean length $\gamma^{-1} + \tau$, and thus the ratio of the mean busy period to the mean cycle length is

$$\frac{\tau}{\gamma^{-1} + \tau} = \frac{\hat{a}}{1 + \hat{a}}.$$

As we did with a similar example for Poisson input, we interpret this ratio as the proportion of time (or probability) that the server is busy when the system is in equilibrium. This ratio is not the proportion of requests blocked, which, we have already argued, is zero when, as in this example, the number of sources does not exceed the number of servers. Let $P_j[n]$ and $\Pi_j[n]$ be the n-source outside observer's and arriving customer's state probabilities, respectively. We then have $P_1[1] = \hat{a}/(1 + \hat{a})$ and $P_0[1] = 1/(1 + \hat{a})$ for the outside observer's distribution, in contrast with the arriving customer's distribution $\Pi_1[1] = 0$ and $\Pi_0[1] = 1$.

Consider now the same system with the addition of an identical source. Since blocking can occur in this two-source one-server system, we must consider the disposition of blocked requests. Let us assume that blocked customers are cleared. (That is, any source that finds all servers busy when placing a request returns immediately to its previous state as an idle source.) The server again alternates between busy and idle states. The busy period still has mean length τ. But since there are now two sources, each bidding for service at rate γ when idle, the overall bid rate when both sources are idle is 2γ, and the idle portion of the cycle has mean length $(2\gamma)^{-1}$. Forming the ratio of the mean busy period to the mean cycle length, we obtain

$$\frac{\tau}{(2\gamma)^{-1} + \tau} = \frac{2\hat{a}}{1 + 2\hat{a}}.$$

Thus the outside observer's distribution is $P_1[2] = 2\hat{a}/(1 + 2\hat{a})$ and $P_0[2] = 1/(1 + 2\hat{a})$.

Blocking can occur only when the server is occupied by one of the sources. The number of requests blocked during a cycle is the number generated by the idle source during the service time of the busy source. Since we have assumed blocked customers cleared, the mean number of requests generated by a source during the service time of the other source is $\tau/\gamma^{-1} = \hat{a}$. On the other hand, the total number of requests generated during a cycle is simply the sum of the number generated during the busy period plus the number generated during the idle period. The latter number is 1, namely, that arrival who finds the server idle, ending the idle period and starting the busy period. Forming the ratio of the mean number of requests blocked to the mean number generated per cycle, we obtain $\hat{a}/(1 + \hat{a})$. That is, $\Pi_1[2] = \hat{a}/(1 + \hat{a})$ and $\Pi_0[2] = 1/(1 + \hat{a})$.

Comparison with our calculations for the one-source case shows that $\Pi_0[2] = P_0[1]$ and $\Pi_1[2] = P_1[1]$. In other words, the state distribution seen by a source in the two-source system when placing a request is the same as the state distribution the source would see if it placed no requests but instead acted the part of an outside observer of the one-source system.

It is true in general that for equilibrium n-source birth-and-death systems with quasirandom input, the state distribution seen by a source when placing a request is the same as if that source were not contributing load to the servers, but instead were only observing the corresponding $(n - 1)$-source system continuously or at random instants. For many years the $(n - 1)$-source outside observer's viewpoint was considered only an approximation to the n-source arriving customer's viewpoint since, it was argued, no account is taken of the fact that the particular source places a load on the system, interacting with other sources, and thus affecting the state distribution. This argument neglects to mention that the requests generated by any particular source do not follow a Poisson process (why?); apparently these two effects cancel each other exactly.

We now give a formal proof of the general theorem: In any equilibrium n-source birth-and-death queueing system with quasirandom input, the arriving customer's distribution is the same as the outside observer's distribution for the corresponding $(n - 1)$-source system.

We consider a system with n sources, each source originating requests at rate γ when idle and rate 0 otherwise (quasirandom input). Then the request rate when j sources are busy (in service or waiting for service) is

$$\lambda_j = (n - j)\gamma \qquad (j = 0, 1, \ldots, n). \tag{8.1}$$

Over a long time interval $(0, t)$, throughout which statistical equilibrium is assumed to prevail, the average number of requests for service that occur when the system is in state E_j is $\lambda_j t P_j[n]$. As $t \to \infty$, the proportion of all requests for service in $(0, t)$ who find the system in state E_j is therefore the ratio $\lambda_j t P_j[n]/\sum_{k=0}^{n} \lambda_k t P_k[n]$. Thus, using equation (8.1), the probability $\Pi_j[n]$ that a customer who requests service finds the system in state E_j is given by

$$\Pi_j[n] = \frac{(n - j)P_j[n]}{\sum_{k=0}^{n-1} (n - k)P_k[n]} \qquad (j = 0, 1, \ldots, n - 1). \qquad (8.2)$$

According to equations (1.1) and (8.1), the outside·observer's distribution can be written

$$P_j[n] = \frac{n(n - 1) \cdots (n - j + 1)\gamma^j}{\mu_1\mu_2 \cdots \mu_j} P_0[n] \qquad (j = 1, 2, \ldots, n) \qquad (8.3)$$

and

$$P_0[n] = \left(1 + \sum_{k=1}^{n} \frac{n(n - 1) \cdots (n - k + 1)\gamma^k}{\mu_1\mu_2 \cdots \mu_k}\right)^{-1}. \qquad (8.4)$$

Substitution of (8.3) into (8.2) yields

$$\Pi_j[n] = \frac{\dfrac{n(n - 1) \cdots (n - j + 1)(n - j)\gamma^j}{\mu_1\mu_2 \cdots \mu_j} P_0[n]}{nP_0[n] + \sum_{k=1}^{n-1} \dfrac{n(n - 1) \cdots (n - k + 1)(n - k)\gamma^k}{\mu_1\mu_2 \cdots \mu_k} P_0[n]}$$

$$(j = 1, 2, \ldots, n - 1). \qquad (8.5)$$

After cancellation of the factor $nP_0[n]$ in (8.5), we have

$$\Pi_j[n] = \frac{(n - 1) \cdots (n - j)\gamma^j/\mu_1\mu_2 \cdots \mu_j}{1 + \sum_{k=1}^{n-1} (n - 1) \cdots (n - k)\gamma^k/\mu_1\mu_2 \cdots \mu_k}$$

$$(j = 1, 2, \ldots, n - 1). \qquad (8.6)$$

Comparison of equation (8.6) with (8.3) and (8.4) shows that $\Pi_j[n] = P_j[n - 1]$ for $j = 1, 2, \ldots, n - 1$. Since we must have

$$\sum_{k=0}^{n-1} \Pi_k[n] = 1$$

we conclude that

$$\Pi_j[n] = P_j[n-1] \qquad (j = 0, 1, \ldots, n-1). \tag{8.7}$$

The theorem is proved. For further discussion, see Exercise 16 of Chapter 4 and Exercise 1 of Chapter 5.

Taking limits through (8.7) as $n \to \infty$ and $\gamma \to 0$ such that $n\gamma = \lambda$, the dependence on n vanishes and, since quasirandom input becomes Poisson input in the limit, we again illustrate the equality of the arriving customer's distribution and the outside observer's distribution for systems with Poisson input.

3–9. Quasirandom Input, s Servers, Blocked Customers Cleared: The Engset Formula

We assume that the number of sources is $n \geq s$ and that each source independently generates requests at rate γ when idle and rate zero otherwise. Since blocked customers are assumed cleared, a new request will effect a change of state only when at least one server is idle. Hence, we have birth rates

$$\lambda_j = \begin{cases} (n-j)\gamma & (j = 0, 1, \ldots, s-1) \\ 0 & (j = s). \end{cases} \tag{9.1}$$

Let us assume for the present that service times are exponential. Then we have death rates

$$\mu_j = j\mu \qquad (j = 0, 1, \ldots, s), \tag{9.2}$$

where μ^{-1} is the mean service time. As with the BCC Poisson input case, the assumption of exponential service times can be shown to be superfluous.

The rates (9.1) and (9.2), in conjunction with formula (1.1), give for the statistical equilibrium probability of j busy servers (where $\hat{a} = \gamma/\mu$)

$$P_j[n] = \frac{\binom{n}{j} \hat{a}^j}{\sum_{k=0}^{s} \binom{n}{k} \hat{a}^k} \qquad (j = 0, 1, \ldots, s) \tag{9.3}$$

and $P_j[n] = 0$ for $j > s$. If the substitution

$$\hat{a} = \frac{p}{1 - p} \tag{9.4}$$

is made in (9.3), then, after multiplication of numerator and denominator by $(1 - p)^n$, equation (9.3) takes the form of the *truncated binomial distribution*,

$$P_j[n] = \frac{\binom{n}{j} p^j (1 - p)^{n-j}}{\sum_{k=0}^{s} \binom{n}{k} p^k (1 - p)^{n-k}} \qquad (j = 0, 1, \ldots, s). \tag{9.5}$$

Solving (9.4) for p gives

$$p = \frac{\hat{a}}{1 + \hat{a}}, \tag{9.6}$$

which is immediately recognized as $P_1[1]$. In other words, p is the probability that an arbitrary source would be busy if there were no interaction among the sources. If $n = s$, in which case each source assumes busy and idle states unaffected by the states of the other sources, then the denominator on the right-hand side of (9.5) sums to unity, and the distribution of the number of customers in service is the simple binomial.

Expression (9.3)—or (9.5)—gives the proportion of time the system spends in each state E_j. The probability $\Pi_j[n]$ that one of the n sources finds the system in state E_j when placing a request is obtained by replacing n by $n - 1$ in (9.3):

$$\Pi_j[n] = \frac{\binom{n-1}{j} \hat{a}^j}{\sum_{k=0}^{s} \binom{n-1}{k} \hat{a}^k} \qquad (j = 0, 1, \ldots, s). \tag{9.7}$$

In particular, the proportion of requests that find all s servers busy is $\Pi_s[n]$; the right-hand side of (9.7) with $j = s$ is often called the *Engset formula*.

In Section 3–3 we defined the offered load as the mean number of customers arriving during a service time. For systems with Poisson input with rate λ, the offered load a (in erlangs) is given by $a = \lambda/\mu$ where μ^{-1} is the mean service time. With Poisson input, the arrival rate λ, and hence the offered load a, is independent of the system to which it is offered and thus provides a simple characterization of the amount of traffic that is to be handled by any system that may be provided to handle it. The same is not true of quasirandom input, because the instantaneous arrival rate λ_j depends on the state of the system, and the proportion of time the system spends in each state depends on the number of servers and the disposition of blocked customers. Therefore, although the traffic can be characterized by the number of sources n and the idle request rate γ per source, independently of the system to which it is offered, the mean number of requests per service time (the offered load a) that a system receives depends directly on the characteristics of the particular system that receives it.

We shall derive a relationship between the *offered load per idle source* $\hat{a} = \gamma/\mu$ and the total offered load a. Unfortunately, this relationship involves state probabilities that depend on the number of servers.

The general "rate up equals rate down" equations for the system with quasirandom input and exponential service times are

$$\lambda_{j-1}P_{j-1}[n] = \mu_j(s)P_j[n] \tag{9.8}$$

where

$$\mu_j(s) = \begin{cases} j\mu & (j = 0, 1, \ldots, s) \\ s\mu & (j = s+1, s+2, \ldots). \end{cases} \tag{9.9}$$

The disposition of blocked customers is specified by the coefficients $\{\lambda_j\}$.

Since, by definition, the carried load a' is given by

$$a' = \sum_{j=1}^{s} jP_j[n] + s \sum_{j=s+1}^{n} P_j[n], \tag{9.10}$$

it follows upon summing equations (9.8) for $j = 1, 2, \ldots, n$ that

$$\frac{1}{\mu} \sum_{j=0}^{n-1} \lambda_j P_j[n] = a'. \tag{9.11}$$

When blocked customers are cleared, the left-hand side of equation (9.11) becomes

$$\frac{1}{\mu} \sum_{j=0}^{n-1} \lambda_j P_j[n] = \hat{a}\{n(1 - P_s[n]) - (a' - sP_s[n])\}. \tag{9.12}$$

Equations (9.11) and (9.12) imply

$$\hat{a} = \frac{a'}{n(1 - P_s[n]) - a' + sP_s[n]}.$$ (9.13)

In view of the fact that the carried load a' is that portion of the offered load a that is not cleared, we have

$$a' = a(1 - \Pi_s[n]).$$ (9.14)

Equations (9.13) and (9.14) give the following relationship between the offered load per idle source $\hat{a} = \gamma/\mu$ and the total offered load a:

$$\hat{a} = \frac{a(1 - \Pi_s[n])}{n(1 - P_s[n]) - a(1 - \Pi_s[n]) + sP_s[n]}.$$ (9.15)

Thus the offered load in erlangs generated by a finite number of sources cannot be specified without first calculating its effect on the particular system to which it is offered.

To partially rectify this situation, we consider the *intended offered load* a^*, defined as the load that the sources would offer to a system with sufficient servers such that no blocking occurs (that is, $s = n$). In this case the offered and carried loads are equal. When $s = n$, the distribution (9.5) is the binomial distribution with mean np. Hence

$$a^* = n \frac{\hat{a}}{1 + \hat{a}}.$$ (9.16)

With BCC, the offered load a is bounded from below by the intended offered load a^* (why?), which provides an approximation to a when the probability of blocking is small.

The point to be made here is simply that the offered load a is a most useful and simple measure of demand for Poisson traffic, but not nearly so useful or simple for quasirandom input.

The above results were calculated here on the assumption of exponential service times. But, as with Poisson input, when blocked customers are cleared the birth-and-death relations are valid for any service time distribution function with finite mean τ. (Note that in the heuristic discussion of single-server systems with one and two sources, no assumption was made about the form of the service time distribution function.)

Cohen [1957] (see also pp. 278–84 of Syski [1960]) has derived a "generalized Engset formula," which shows that for finite-source BCC systems with nonidentical sources, the state probabilities depend only on the mean service times and mean idle-source interarrival times for each source, and not on the forms of their respective distribution functions.

3–10. Quasirandom Input, s Servers with Exponential Service Times, Blocked Customers Delayed: State Probabilities and Order-of-Arrival Waiting Time Distribution Function

We consider now the case in which customers who find all s servers busy wait as long as necessary for service. Since every arrival effects a change of state, we have

$$\lambda_j = (n - j)\gamma \qquad (j = 0, 1, \ldots, n), \qquad (10.1)$$

where n is the number of sources and γ is the request rate for an idle source. The rate μ_j at which busy sources become idle is

$$\mu_j = \begin{cases} j\mu & (j = 0, 1, \ldots, s) \\ s\mu & (j = s, s + 1, \ldots, n), \end{cases} \qquad (10.2)$$

where μ^{-1} is the mean service time.

With $\hat{a} = \gamma/\mu$ the rates (10.1) and (10.2), in conjunction with equation (1.1), give for the statistical equilibrium probability of j busy servers

$$P_j[n] = \begin{cases} \binom{n}{j} \hat{a}^j P_0[n] & (j = 0, 1, \ldots, s) \\ \dfrac{n!}{(n - j)! \, s! \, s^{j-s}} \hat{a}^j P_0[n] & (j = s, s + 1, \ldots, n) \end{cases} \qquad (10.3)$$

where $P_0[n]$ is given by

$$P_0[n] = \left(\sum_{k=0}^{s} \binom{n}{k} \hat{a}^k + \sum_{k=s+1}^{n} \frac{n!}{(n - k)! \, s! \, s^{k-s}} \hat{a}^k \right)^{-1}. \qquad (10.4)$$

Note that, in contrast with the infinite-source Erlang delay model, the number of terms in the second summation on the right-hand side of (10.4) is finite. Therefore the equilibrium state distribution (10.3) and (10.4) is nondegenerate for all values of the parameters γ and μ. That is, since the number of sources n is finite, the number of customers waiting for service can never exceed the finite value $n - s$, so that ever-increasing queue lengths cannot occur. In effect, finite-source systems are self-regulating, since the request rate gets smaller as the system gets busier, and the stream of requests shuts off completely when there are no idle sources available to generate new requests.

The probability $P\{W > 0\}$ that a customer must wait for service is the probability that a source finds all servers busy when placing a request. Therefore

$$P\{W > 0\} = \sum_{j=s}^{n-1} \Pi_j[n] = \sum_{j=s}^{n-1} P_j[n - 1]. \qquad (10.5)$$

To calculate the waiting time distribution function, we can write [see equation (5.3)]

$$P\{W > t\} = \sum_{j=0}^{n-s-1} P\{W > t \mid N = j + s\}P\{N = j + s\}. \qquad (10.6)$$

$P\{N = j + s\}$ is the probability that a source finds all s servers busy and j other sources waiting for service when it places a request for service. Hence

$$P\{N = j + s\} = \Pi_{j+s}[n] = P_{j+s}[n - 1]. \qquad (10.7)$$

If requests are served in order of arrival, the conditional probability $P\{W > t \mid N = j + s\}$ that a customer waits beyond t when placing a request, given that he finds $j + s$ other customers waiting, is exactly the same in a finite-source system as in its infinite-source counterpart; the waiting time of a customer who finds all s servers busy and j other waiting customers ahead of him is the sum of the lengths of time that each of the $j + 1$ customers spends at the head of the queue. Since these time intervals are independent exponential variables with common mean $(s\mu)^{-1}$, we have [see equation (5.6) and Exercise 12]

$$P\{W > t \mid N = j + s\} = e^{-s\mu t} \sum_{k=0}^{j} \frac{(s\mu t)^k}{k!}. \qquad (10.8)$$

By the same argument

$$E(W \mid N = j + s) = \frac{j + 1}{s\mu}. \qquad (10.9)$$

Substituting (10.7) and (10.8) into (10.6) we obtain, after some simplification,

$$P\{W > t\} = c \sum_{j=0}^{n-s-1} \frac{[\phi(t)]^j}{j!} e^{-\phi(t)}, \tag{10.10}$$

where

$$\phi(t) = \frac{s\mu}{\gamma} + s\mu t \tag{10.11}$$

and

$$c = \Pi_0[n] \frac{(n-1)! \, \hat{a}^s}{s!} \left(\frac{\hat{a}}{s}\right)^{n-s-1} e^{s\mu/\gamma}. \tag{10.12}$$

Using (10.9), the mean wait for service (for arbitrary order of service) suffered by an arbitrary customer when placing a request can be calculated directly from the formula

$$E(W) = \sum_{j=0}^{n-s-1} E(W \mid N = j + s)P\{N = j + s\}. \tag{10.13}$$

As was true in the BCC case, the offered load a cannot be specified in the BCD case without first calculating its effects on the particular system to which it is offered. With BCD, the left-hand side of equation (9.11) becomes

$$\frac{1}{\mu} \sum_{j=0}^{n-1} \lambda_j P_j[n] = \hat{a} \left(n - \sum_{j=1}^{n} j P_j[n]\right). \tag{10.14}$$

Equations (9.11) and (10.14) imply

$$\hat{a} = \frac{a'}{n - \sum_{j=1}^{n} j P_j[n]}. \tag{10.15}$$

In BCD systems, the carried load a' and the offered load a are equal,

$$a' = a. \tag{10.16}$$

Equations (10.15) and (10.16) give the following relationship between the offered load per idle source $\hat{a} = \gamma/\mu$ and the total offered load a:

$$\hat{a} = \frac{a}{n - \sum_{j=1}^{n} j P_j[n]}. \tag{10.17}$$

Note that (10.17) could have been anticipated on intuitive grounds: the total offered load a is the product of the offered load per idle source $\hat{a}$ and the average number $n - \sum_{j=1}^{n} jP_j[n]$ of idle sources.

It can be shown (see Exercise 27) that

$$\sum_{j=1}^{n} jP_j[n] = a \left(1 + \frac{E(W)}{\mu^{-1}}\right). \qquad (10.18)$$

[Equation (10.18) is a special case of a well-known formula, from which it can be written down with no calculation. This particular case is used as an illustrative example in a discussion of this formula in Section 5–3.] Thus the offered load $\hat{a}$ per idle source, the total offered load a, the mean wait $E(W)/\mu^{-1}$ for service in units of mean service time, and the number n of sources are related according to the equation

$$\hat{a} = \frac{a}{n - a[1 + \mu E(W)]}. \qquad (10.19)$$

The offered load a is bounded from above by the intended offered load $a^* = n[\hat{a}/(1 + \hat{a})]$ (why?), which provides an approximation to a when the probability of blocking is small.

As was true in the case of Poisson input, when the input is quasirandom and blocked customers are delayed, the state distribution $\{P_j\}$ depends on the form of the service time distribution function; the above results are valid for exponential service times only.

The order-of-arrival waiting time distribution function (10.10) and some related quantities have been tabulated by Descloux [1962], who also gives a concise theoretical discussion covering much of the same material presented here. Tabulations are also available in Peck and Hazelwood [1958].

3–11. Quasirandom Input, *s* Servers, Blocked Customers Held

The blocked customers held (BCH) assumption is that a blocked customer is willing to spend an amount of time (sojourn time) as a customer, after which he will again become an idle source, whether or not he is in service or is still waiting in the queue.

With quasirandom input and exponential sojourn times the birth-and-death coefficients are

$$\lambda_j = (n - j)\gamma \qquad (j = 0, 1, \ldots, n) \tag{11.1}$$

and

$$\mu_j = j\mu \qquad (j = 0, 1, \ldots, n). \tag{11.2}$$

Substitution of (11.1) and (11.2) into (1.1) gives

$$P_j[n] = \binom{n}{j} p^j (1 - p)^{n-j} \qquad (j = 0, 1, \ldots, n), \tag{11.3}$$

where $p = \hat{a}/(1 + \hat{a})$ and $\hat{a} = \gamma/\mu$.

The result (11.3) could have been obtained immediately from the BCC state probabilities (9.5) by setting $s = n$; that is, in complete analogy with the Poisson input case, the BCH distribution is that which would obtain if the number of servers were "infinite." Again, (11.3) follows directly from the observation that with BCH the sources become busy and idle independently of each other. Since $p = \hat{a}/(1 + \hat{a})$ is the probability that the source is busy in a one-source one-server system (for arbitrary service time distribution function), the binomial (11.3) follows immediately as the probability that exactly j out of n sources are busy at an arbitrary instant. The latter statement also implies that, as was true with Poisson input, the BCH distribution is valid for any service time distribution function with finite mean.

Since the sources have no effect on each other, the (actual) offered load a and the intended offered load a^* (defined in Section 3–9 as the load that would be offered if the number of sources and servers were equal) are equal (to the mean number of busy sources):

$$a = a^* = np. \tag{11.4}$$

3–12. Summary

In this chapter we have shown that certain queueing models can be treated within the framework of the birth-and-death process. In particular, we have studied six queueing models with two types of input (Poisson and quasirandom), three different queue disciplines (BCC, BCD, and BCH), and exponential service times. We have stated that although the assumption of exponential service times was used to justify the formulation as a birth-and-death process, the results derived for BCC and BCH are valid for any service time distribution function with finite mean. We have also derived the waiting time distribution function for the BCD case in which customers are served in their order of arrival. Each model was discussed in detail, and ways in which the various models relate to each other were pointed out.

Systems with quasirandom input differ in some basic respects from systems with Poisson input (even though every Poisson input model can be obtained, by a limiting process, directly from its quasirandom input counterpart). In particular, in contrast to systems with Poisson input, (a) finite-source systems can admit only a finite number of states, so that questions of convergence do not arise; (b) the magnitude of the offered load depends on the state probabilities of the system to which it is offered; and (c) the arriving customer's distribution and the outside observer's distribution are unequal, but the former agrees with the latter for the corresponding system with one less source.

Finite-source models are discussed in detail by Syski [1960], who covers most of the material given here, including a summary of Cohen's paper on the generalization of the Engset formula. (As previously mentioned, tabulations of finite-source formulas are given in Descloux [1962] and Peck and Hazelwood [1958].)

Poisson input models have been more widely studied. Several references were given in this chapter, and many others are available. Of particular historical interest, Fry [1928, second edition 1965] discusses both Poisson and finite-source models in the context of teletraffic theory.

From a practical viewpoint, the Erlang loss and Erlang delay models are the most important, and situations for which they may be realistic models should be self-evident. The finite-source models are of interest largely for theoretical reasons, but there are some direct applications. Common examples are in telephony, where a small number of lines (sources) in a central office have access to a common outgoing trunk group (servers), and in reliability engineering, where a small number of machines (sources) are serviced when they break down by a smaller number of repairmen (servers). The BCH (or infinite-server) models are of interest because of their formal mathematical simplicity; because they provide a model that is, in a sense, intermediate between the BCC and BCD models; and because they provide useful models in epidemiology (see Exercise 17) and other areas.

Some of the material presented in this chapter is not well known outside of the literature of teletraffic theory. In particular, the concepts of offered load and carried load, the BCH queue discipline, and the relationship between the arriving customer's distribution and the outside observer's distribution have not received the attention in the general literature of queueing theory that they seem to warrant.

Exercises

1. Prove equation (2.2). [*Hint:* See Exercise 13 of Chapter 2.]
2. Customers arrive at a two-chair shoe shine stand at rate 10 per hour. The average length of a shoe shine is 6 minutes. There is only one attendant so that one chair is used as a waiting position. Customers who find both chairs occupied go away.
   a. Assuming Poisson input and exponential service times, write and solve the statistical equilibrium probability state equations.
   b. Find the mean number of customers served per hour.
   c. Repeat the analysis to calculate the mean number of customers served per hour when there are two attendants at the stand (and no waiting positions).
   d. Which of the input and service time assumptions made above are necessary for the validity of the results obtained in parts **a** and **b**? In part **c**?
3. Consider an Erlang loss system with ordered hunt: The servers are numbered $1, 2, \ldots, s$, and arriving customers take the lowest-numbered idle server.
   a. Show that the load $a'_{BCC}(m)$ carried by the mth ordered server in a BCC system is given by

   $$a'_{BCC}(m) = a[B(m-1, a) - B(m, a)] \qquad (m = 1, 2, \ldots, s).$$

   b. Find the probability (proportion of time) that the mth server is busy.
   c. Show that the probability that an arbitrary customer will be served by the mth server equals $a'_{BCC}(m)/a$.
   d. Verify that

   $$a' = \sum_{m=1}^{s} a'_{BCC}(m).$$

   e. It should be intuitively obvious that in the limit as $a \to \infty$, then $a'_{BCC}(m) \to 1$ $(m = 1, 2, \ldots, s)$. Prove it.

    f. Prove that the variance v of the equilibrium distribution of the number of customers in progress on the s-server group is given by

$$v = a'[1 - a'_{BCC}(s)]$$

where a' is the total load carried by the s-server group and $a'_{BCC}(s)$ is the load carried by the last server. Draw graphs of v versus a and v versus a'.

4. Consider an equilibrium s-server Erlang loss system with exponential service times and offered load a erl. A statistician observes the system at a random instant and waits until the next customer arrives. Show that the probability p that this customer is blocked is

$$p = \frac{a}{a + s} B(s, a).$$

Explain why $p \neq B(s, a)$.

5. Verify equation (4.8).

6. Consider an Erlang loss system with *retrials*. Any customer who finds all s servers busy will return and place another request for service at some later time, and will persist in this manner until he receives service. Let $a = \lambda\tau$, where τ is the average service time, and λ is the rate at which the original requests for service occur. (That is, λ is the arrival rate with retrials not counted.) Since all customers are served, the carried load equals the original offered load $a = \lambda\tau$. Therefore, the probability of blocking (the probability that a customer requesting service will find all s servers busy and be forced to retry) is given by $B(s, \hat{a})$, where $\hat{a}$ satisfies the equation

$$\hat{a}[1 - B(s, \hat{a})] = a.$$

Discuss the strengths and weaknesses of this approximate analysis of the Erlang loss system with retrials. (See Riordan [1962].)

7. Show that in the Erlang delay system with order-of-arrival service, the customer waiting time distribution function has variance

$$V(W) = \frac{C(s, a)[2 - C(s, a)]}{(s\mu)^2(1 - \rho)^2}.$$

8. a. Consider an Erlang delay system, and denote by L the mean queue length, W the mean waiting time for service, and λ the arrival rate.

Verify the equation $L = \lambda W$. (This well-known equation is true under very general conditions, and is often written using the present symbols. See Section 5–3.)

  b. Redefine L to be the mean number of customers in the system (waiting and in service) and W to be the mean time spent in the system. (W is the mean sojourn time.) Verify $L = \lambda W$ using these redefinitions.

 9. Find the distribution function for the remaining waiting time of a customer who has already waited a length of time $x > 0$ in an Erlang delay system with order-of-arrival service.

10. Prove that in an Erlang delay system with order-of-arrival service, the conditional probability that a blocked customer will still be waiting in the queue when the next arrival occurs is equal to the server occupancy or utilization factor ρ. (This is a special case of a more general result. See Exercise 23 of Chapter 5.)

11. Let W be the waiting time and T the sojourn time (waiting time plus service time) of an arbitrary customer. Show that in the single-server Erlang delay system with service in order of arrival,

$$P\{T > t\} = P\{W > t \mid W > 0\}.$$

12. Consider the differential-difference equations

$$\frac{d}{dt} F_j(t) = cF_{j-1}(t) - cF_j(t)$$

$$[t \geq 0; j = 0, 1, \ldots; F_{-1}(t) = 0], \qquad (12.1)$$

where c is an arbitrary constant. Define

$$F(x, t) = \sum_{j=0}^{\infty} F_j(t)x^j. \qquad (12.2)$$

 a. Show that $F(x, t)$ satisfies

$$\frac{\partial}{\partial t} F(x, t) = c(x - 1)F(x, t), \qquad (12.3)$$

which has solution

$$F(x, t) = F(x, 0)e^{-(1-x)ct}. \qquad (12.4)$$

b. Let $N(t)$ be the number of events occurring in $(0, t)$ according to a Poisson process with rate λ. Then, according to equation (2.5) of Chapter 2, we can set $F_j(t) = P\{N(t) = j\} = P_j(t)$ and $c = \lambda$ in equation (12.1). Show that equation (12.4) yields the Poisson distribution,

$$P_j(t) = \frac{(\lambda t)^j}{j!} e^{-\lambda t} \qquad (j = 0, 1, \ldots).$$

c. In an Erlang delay system with s servers, mean service time μ^{-1}, and service in order of arrival, let N be the number of customers waiting or in service when an arbitrary customer (the test customer) arrives, let W be the test customer's waiting time, and define $W_j(t) = P\{W > t \mid N = j + s\}$. Show that

$$\frac{d}{dt} W_j(t) = s\mu W_{j-1}(t) - s\mu W_j(t)$$

$$[t \geq 0; j = 0, 1, \ldots; W_{-1}(t) = 0]. \qquad (12.5)$$

d. Define

$$W(x, t) = \sum_{j=0}^{\infty} W_j(t) x^j \qquad (12.6)$$

and show by comparison with equation (12.4) that

$$W(x, t) = W(x, 0) e^{-(1-x)s\mu t}. \qquad (12.7)$$

e. Show that

$$W(x, 0) = \frac{1}{1 - x}. \qquad (12.8)$$

f. Show that equation (5.5) implies (Riordan [1962])

$$P\{W > t \mid W > 0\} = (1 - \rho) W(\rho, t). \qquad (12.9)$$

g. Deduce from equations (12.7)–(12.9) that

$$P\{W > t \mid W > 0\} = e^{-(1-\rho)s\mu t}. \qquad (12.10)$$

Compare with equation (5.7).

h. Show directly from equations (12.6)–(12.8) that

$$W_j(t) = \sum_{k=0}^{j} \frac{(s\mu t)^k}{k!} e^{-s\mu t}. \qquad (12.11)$$

Compare equation (12.11) with equations (5.6) and (10.8).

13. Verify equation (6.5).

14. For the BCH system with Poisson input, exponential sojourn times, and service of waiting customers in order of arrival, find the probability that an arrival who finds all s servers busy and $n \geq 0$ other customers waiting in the queue ever gets served.

15. Prove that $B(s, a) < P(s, a) < C(s, a)$ $(a > 0, s = 1, 2, \ldots)$. Give a physical explanation of this fact.

16. Show that

a.
$$C(s, a) = \frac{(s/a)B(s, a)}{[(s/a) - 1] + B(s, a)}.$$

b.
$$C(s, a) = \frac{1}{[(s - a)/aB(s - 1, a)] + 1}.$$

c.
$$B(s, a) = \frac{aB(s - 1, a)}{s + aB(s - 1, a)}.$$

d.
$$C(s, a) = \frac{1}{1 + \left(\dfrac{s - a}{a}\right)\dfrac{s - 1 - aC(s - 1, a)}{(s - 1 - a)C(s - 1, a)}}.$$

How might these formulas be computationally useful?

17. Consider a population large enough to be considered infinite, in which members contract a certain disease that disables them for a time interval whose duration has distribution function $H(t)$ with mean τ. Assume that the probability $p(k; \xi)$ that k people contract the disease in any interval of length ξ is $p(k; \xi) = [(\lambda\xi)^k/k!] \, e^{-\lambda\xi}$ $(k = 0, 1, \ldots)$. Find the probability generating function for the number of disabled people at any time $t \geq 0$. Find the equilibrium distribution of the number of disabled people.

18. *The j factor* (R. I. Wilkinson [1937, unpublished]). Consider the birth-and-death model defined by

$$\lambda_n = \lambda \qquad\qquad (n = 0, 1, \ldots)$$

$$\mu_n = n\mu \qquad\qquad (n = 0, 1, \ldots, s)$$

and

$$\mu_n = [s + j(n - s)]\mu \qquad (n = s, s + 1, \ldots).$$

Show that this model includes the Erlang loss, Erlang delay, and Poisson formulas as special cases. What is the significance of the j factor, and how might this model be useful?

19. *Priority reservation.* A group of s telephone trunks is offered a_1 erl of eastbound Poisson traffic and a_2 erl of westbound Poisson traffic. Both eastbound and westbound call holding times are exponentially distributed with common mean. To give the eastbound traffic better service than the westbound traffic, any westbound call that finds less than $n + 1$ $(n < s)$ trunks idle is cleared, whereas eastbound requests are cleared only when all s trunks are busy.

   a. Write the state equations that determine P_j, the statistical equilibrium probability that j calls are in the system $(j = 0, 1, 2, \ldots, s)$. Include all boundary conditions.

   b. Solve the equations for P_j $(j = 0, 1, 2, \ldots, s)$.

   c. Write the expressions (in terms of P_j) for the proportions of eastbound and westbound calls lost.

20. Show that for an s-server birth-and-death queueing system, the statistical equilibrium conditional probability that j customers are in service, given that $j \leq s$, is the same as the corresponding unconditional probability with blocked customers cleared.

21. Customers request service from a group of s servers with n waiting positions. Customers who find all waiting positions occupied are cleared; all others wait until served. The input is Poisson with rate λ, and the service times are exponential with mean μ^{-1}. Find

   a. The probability that a customer obtains service immediately.

   b. The probability that a customer will be lost (cleared).

   c. The carried load.

22. Customers arrive according to a Poisson process with rate λ at a single server with n waiting positions. Customers who find all waiting positions occupied are cleared; all other customers wait as long as necessary for service. The mean service time is τ, and $\lambda\tau = a$.

   a. Assume exponential service times, and show that

$$P_j = \frac{(1 - a)a^j}{1 - a^{n+2}} \qquad (j = 0, 1, \ldots, n + 1). \qquad (22.1)$$

   b. Make no assumption about the form of the service time distribution function, and show that

$$\frac{1 - P_0}{1 - P_{n+1}} = a.$$

23. Customers with exponential service times with mean μ^{-1} arrive at a single server according to a Poisson process with rate λ. An arrival

who finds j other customers will join the queue and wait until served with probability $1/(j + 1)$ and with probability $1 - [1/(j + 1)]$ will immediately be cleared from the system.

a. Find the offered load.

b. What condition must the offered load satisfy to ensure the existence of a statistical equilibrium distribution?

c. Find the carried load.

d. Find the proportion of customers cleared from the system.

24. *Queue with feedback.* Customers request service on a BCD basis from a group of s servers according to a Poisson process with rate λ. Upon seizing an idle server, a customer holds it for an exponentially distributed length of time with mean μ^{-1}. Upon leaving the server, the customer rejoins the queue (as if he were a new arrival) with probability p, and leaves the system with probability $1 - p$.

a. What condition is required for the existence of a statistical equilibrium distribution?

b. Find the statistical equilibrium probability that a new arrival finds all servers busy.

c. Find the carried load.

d. Find the offered load.

[*Hint:* What is the distribution function of total service time for a customer?]

25. A single server serves customers of two priority classes on a pre-emptive basis: high-priority customers will preempt the server from low-priority customers, so that no low-priority customer is ever served when a high-priority customer is present. High-priority customers arrive according to a Poisson process at rate λ_1 and have exponential service times with mean μ_1^{-1}. Low priority customers arrive according to a Poisson process at rate λ_2, and have exponential service times with mean μ_2^{-1}. Assume preemptive-repeat priority discipline (a new value of the service time is chosen from the exponential distribution each time a preempted customer enters the server). All customers wait as long as necessary for service.

a. Find the probability that a low-priority customer is preempted from the server n times.

b. Find the distribution function of the total length of time that a low-priority customer occupies the server.

c. Find the mean length of time from the instant a low-priority customer first enters service until he leaves the system, assuming that when a customer is preempted no other low-priority customer can enter service until the preempted customer completes his service.

Answer: $\dfrac{1}{\mu_2} + \left(\dfrac{\lambda_1}{\mu_2}\right)\left(\dfrac{1}{\mu_1 - \lambda_1}\right).$

d. Find the waiting time distribution function for high-priority customers, assuming service in order of arrival within priority classes.

e. What criteria must be met to ensure bounded delays for customers of each class?

f. Repeat parts **a–e** assuming preemptive-resume priority discipline (preempted customers resume service where they left off).

26. Fill in the algebraic details separating (10.6) and (10.12).

27. Verify equation (10.18) directly.

28. Show that for BCD systems with exponential service times and quasi-random input generated by n sources,

$$(n - j)\hat{a} = a\,\frac{\Pi_j[n]}{P_j[n]},$$

where $\hat{a}$ is the load offered per idle source and a is the total offered load.

29. Derive the Erlang loss, Erlang delay, and Poisson formulas directly from their quasirandom input counterparts.

30. Consider a single-server queueing system with quasirandom input and blocked customers delayed, and assume that the service completion process is a pure death process with rate $\mu_j = j\mu$ (thus the server speeds up as the queue size increases). Find $\Pi_j[n]$ ($j = 0, 1, \ldots, n - 1$).

31. a. For BCD systems with Poisson input and exponential service times, show that

$$E(Q') = \frac{a}{\mu^{-1}}\,E(W),$$

where W is the waiting time for service, a is the offered load, μ^{-1} is the mean service time, and Q' is the number of customers found waiting in the queue by an outside observer sampling at random.

b. Repeat part **a** for quasirandom input.

Multidimensional Birth-and-Death Queueing Models

4

In this chapter we shall discuss methods of analysis of queueing models for which the natural definition of a state requires more than one variable. Our approach will be through the use of examples that illustrate various techniques and often represent systems important in themselves.

4-1. Introduction

In Section 2–2 we studied the one-dimensional birth-and-death process, the essential characteristic of which is that the system occupies "states" E_0, E_1, ... and the rates at which changes of state occur depend only on the instantaneous state of the system and not on the past history of the process (the Markov property). In Section 2–3 we showed that, under appropriate conditions often assumed to hold in practice, the state probabilities $\{P_j\}$ are related to each other according to the equations

$$(\lambda_j + \mu_j)P_j = \lambda_{j-1}P_{j-1} + \mu_{j+1}P_{j+1} \qquad (\lambda_{-1} = \mu_0 = 0; j = 0, 1, \ldots),$$

$$(1.1)$$

104

where $\{\lambda_j\}$ and $\{\mu_j\}$ are the rates of transition upward and downward, respectively.

We noted that equations (1.1) have the following simple and important interpretation. For each state, the rate at which the system leaves the state equals the rate at which the system enters the state. In other words, these equations express a law of *conservation of flow*, that is, rate out = rate in. Equations (1.1) are easily solved by recurrence [the normalized solution is given by equations (3.9)–(3.11) of Chapter 2].

In this chapter we consider systems that have the Markov property, but whose states require more than one variable for definition. For example, consider the infinite-server queue with Poisson input at rate λ and two types of customers, where the service times of customers of type i $(i = 1, 2)$ are independent identically distributed exponential random variables with mean duration τ_i. If $\tau_1 = \tau_2 = \tau$, then the equilibrium probabilities P_j $(j = 0, 1, \ldots)$ that there are j customers in the system satisfy equations (1.1) with $\lambda_j = \lambda$ and $\mu_j = j\tau^{-1}$. However, if $\tau_1 \neq \tau_2$, one cannot specify the death rate μ_j without knowledge of the composition of the state E_j. But if we define the two-dimensional states $\{E_{j_1, j_2}\}$, where j_i is the number of customers of type i in the system, with corresponding equilibrium distribution $\{P(j_1, j_2)\}$, then clearly the Markov property still holds, and the death rate corresponding to the state E_{j_1, j_2} is

$$\mu(j_1, j_2) = j_1 \tau_1^{-1} + j_2 \tau_2^{-1}.$$

Note that the one-dimensional equations (1.1) are not incorrect in this case; they are simply inapplicable because the death rates cannot be specified.

In what follows, we consider systems that can be described by a multi-dimensional analogue of the simple birth-and-death equations (1.1). More precisely, we will *assume* that systems that have the Markov property when the states are properly defined, have equilibrium state distributions that satisfy rate out = rate in equations analogous to (1.1). Unlike the equation for the one-dimensional case, however, the analogous set of multidimensional difference equations cannot, in general, be solved by recurrence. We shall devote this chapter to a discussion of queueing models, many of practical importance, that can be formulated as multidimensional birth-and-death processes and to special techniques for solving the equations of conservation of flow that are assumed to describe these systems in equilibrium.

4–2. Product Solutions (Mixed Traffic, Queues in Tandem)

Infinite-server Group with Two Types of Customers

Consider an infinite-server group that receives two distinct types of Poisson traffic (such as ordinary telephone conversations and data) with arrival rates λ_1 and λ_2. Assume that customers of type 1 have exponentially distributed service times with mean μ_1^{-1}, that customers of type 2 have exponentially distributed service times with mean μ_2^{-1}, and that each value of a service time is obtained from its corresponding distribution independently of all others and the arrival process. Let $P(j_1, j_2)$ be the statistical equilibrium joint probability that at any instant there are j_1 customers of type 1 and j_2 customers of type 2 in service. Then, equating rate out to rate in for each state, the statistical equilibrium state equations are

$$(\lambda_1 + \lambda_2 + j_1\mu_1 + j_2\mu_2)P(j_1, j_2)$$
$$= \lambda_1 P(j_1 - 1, j_2) + \lambda_2 P(j_1, j_2 - 1) + (j_1 + 1)\mu_1 P(j_1 + 1, j_2)$$
$$+ (j_2 + 1)\mu_2 P(j_1, j_2 + 1)$$
$$[P(-1, j_2) = P(j_1, -1) = 0; j_1 = 0, 1, \ldots; j_2 = 0, 1, \ldots]. \quad (2.1)$$

In addition, of course, the probabilities must satisfy the normalization equation

$$\sum_{j_1=0}^{\infty} \sum_{j_2=0}^{\infty} P(j_1, j_2) = 1. \quad (2.2)$$

In this case, we already know the answer. Since the server group is infinite, the two types of customers do not affect one another. Thus the marginal distribution of the number of customers of each type is that which would be obtained by solving the corresponding one-dimensional problem, namely the Poisson distribution:

$$P_1(j) = \sum_{k=0}^{\infty} P(j, k) = \frac{(\lambda_1/\mu_1)^j}{j!} e^{-(\lambda_1/\mu_1)} \quad (2.3)$$

$$P_2(j) = \sum_{k=0}^{\infty} P(k, j) = \frac{(\lambda_2/\mu_2)^j}{j!} e^{-(\lambda_2/\mu_2)}. \quad (2.4)$$

Since the number of customers present of each type is independent of the number present of the other type, therefore

$$P(j_1, j_2) = \frac{(\lambda_1/\mu_1)^{j_1}}{j_1!} \frac{(\lambda_2/\mu_2)^{j_2}}{j_2!} e^{-[(\lambda_1/\mu_1)+(\lambda_2/\mu_2)]}. \tag{2.5}$$

Let us substitute the solution (2.5) into equations (2.1). We see immediately that, as far as (2.1) is concerned, the factor

$$\exp\left\{-\left[\frac{\lambda_1}{\mu_1} + \frac{\lambda_2}{\mu_2}\right]\right\}$$

is irrelevant since it divides out. More important, each factor on the left of (2.1) corresponds to a single factor on the right and vice versa. For example,

$$\lambda_1 \frac{(\lambda_1/\mu_1)^{j_1}}{j_1!} \frac{(\lambda_2/\mu_2)^{j_2}}{j_2!} = \mu_1 \frac{(\lambda_1/\mu_1)^{j_1+1}}{j_1!} \frac{(\lambda_2/\mu_2)^{j_2}}{j_2!}$$

$$= (j_1 + 1)\mu_1 \frac{(\lambda_1/\mu_1)^{j_1+1}}{(j_1 + 1)!} \frac{(\lambda_2/\mu_2)^{j_2}}{j_2!}. \tag{2.6}$$

Hence, if we had not known the solution in advance, we could have found it (disregarding questions of uniqueness) by assuming a solution of the form

$$P(j_1, j_2) = \frac{(\lambda_1/\mu_1)^{j_1}}{j_1!} \frac{(\lambda_2/\mu_2)^{j_2}}{j_2!} c, \tag{2.7}$$

verifying that it indeed satisfies (2.1), and determining the constant c from the normalization equation (2.2). (The extension to more than two variables should be clear.) Of course, guessing a solution of the form (2.7) without prior knowledge would be a pretty good trick and of little general interest. However, the next time we try a product solution, it will not be completely without prior knowledge. As it turns out, solutions of the form (2.7) do, in fact, satisfy state equations that describe other systems.

Finally, we remark that although we have assumed that the service times for each type of customer are exponentially distributed, we know from previous considerations that the marginal distributions are of the form (2.3) and (2.4) for any distribution of service times with means μ_1^{-1} and μ_2^{-1}. It is probably true that in any system in which customers of a certain type are cleared when blocked, the results are independent of the form of the service time distribution function for that type. (See Fortet and Grandjean [1964].)

Finite-server Group with Two Types of Customers and Blocked Customers Cleared

As in the previous example, we assume two types of customers, with customers of type *i* characterized by parameters λ_i and μ_i; but the number of servers is now $s < \infty$, and blocked customers are cleared. The system is again described by (2.1), which is valid now only for $j_1 + j_2 < s$. When $j_1 + j_2 = s$, then the states $(j_1 + 1, j_2)$ and $(j_1, j_2 + 1)$ cannot occur. Therefore, again equating the rate of flow out of state E_{j_1, j_2} to the rate of flow into E_{j_1, j_2}, we have

$$(j_1\mu_1 + j_2\mu_2)P(j_1, j_2) = \lambda_1 P(j_1 - 1, j_2) + \lambda_2 P(j_1, j_2 - 1)$$

$$(j_1 + j_2 = s). \qquad (2.8)$$

Observe that (2.8) can be obtained from (2.1) by deleting the first two terms on the left and the last two terms on the right. It follows that the product solution (2.7) also satisfies (2.8), since each term deleted (remaining) on the left corresponds to a term deleted (remaining) on the right.

Thus, in this case the boundary conditions do not change the form of the solution, which is again given by equation (2.7). The probability $P(j)$ that there are j customers in service is given by $P(j) = \sum_{j_1 + j_2 = j} P(j_1, j_2)$ which, with the help of the binomial theorem, reduces to

$$P(j) = \frac{1}{j!}\left(\frac{\lambda_1}{\mu_1} + \frac{\lambda_2}{\mu_2}\right)^j c. \qquad (2.9)$$

The normalization equation, $\sum_{k=0}^{s} P(k) = 1$, implies that

$$c = \left[\sum_{k=0}^{s} \frac{1}{k!}\left(\frac{\lambda_1}{\mu_1} + \frac{\lambda_2}{\mu_2}\right)^k\right]^{-1}.$$

We conclude that

$$P(j) = \frac{a^j/j!}{\sum\limits_{k=0}^{s} a^k/k!} \qquad (j = 0, 1, \ldots, s), \qquad (2.10)$$

where $a = (\lambda_1/\mu_1) + (\lambda_2/\mu_2)$. This result agrees, of course, with that obtained by different reasoning in Section 3–3: when two streams of

Poisson traffic of magnitudes a_1 erl and a_2 erl are simultaneously served by a group of s servers on a BCC basis, each stream sees the state distribution given by the Erlang loss (truncated Poisson) probabilities with parameter $a = a_1 + a_2$.

Queues in Tandem

Consider two sets of servers arranged in tandem, so that the output (customers completing service) from the first set of servers comprises the input to the second set. Assume that the arrival process at the first stage of this tandem queueing system is Poisson with rate λ, the service times in the first stage are exponential with mean μ_1^{-1}, and the queue discipline is blocked customers delayed. The customers completing service in the first stage enter the second stage, where the service times are assumed exponential with mean μ_2^{-1}. Customers leaving the first stage who find all servers occupied in the second stage wait in a queue in the second stage until they are served. The number of servers in stage i is s_i.

Let $P(j_1, j_2)$ be the statistical equilibrium probability that there are j_1 customers in stage 1 and j_2 customers in stage 2. To save rewriting the state equations for each set of boundary conditions, let

$$\mu_i(j) = \begin{cases} j\mu_i & (j = 0, 1, \ldots, s_i) \\ s_i\mu_i & (j = s_i + 1, s_i + 2, \ldots) \end{cases} \qquad (i = 1, 2). \qquad (2.11)$$

Then the statistical equilibrium state equations, obtained by equating the rate the system leaves each state to the rate it enters that state, are

$$[\lambda + \mu_1(j_1) + \mu_2(j_2)]P(j_1, j_2)$$
$$= \lambda P(j_1 - 1, j_2) + \mu_1(j_1 + 1)P(j_1 + 1, j_2 - 1)$$
$$+ \mu_2(j_2 + 1)P(j_1, j_2 + 1)$$
$$[P(-1, j_2) = P(j_1, -1) = 0; j_1 = 0, 1, \ldots; j_2 = 0, 1, \ldots].$$
$$(2.12)$$

The term $\mu_1(j_1 + 1)P(j_1 + 1, j_2 - 1)$ reflects the fact that a departure from stage 1 constitutes an arrival at stage 2.

In the previous two examples, it has turned out that the joint probability $P(j_1, j_2)$ could be written as the product of the marginal probabilities $P_1(j_1)$ and $P_2(j_2)$:

$$P(j_1, j_2) = P_1(j_1)P_2(j_2). \qquad (2.13)$$

In the example under consideration, we can evaluate without calculation the marginal distribution of the number of customers in the first stage. For the first stage of this tandem queueing system is precisely an Erlang delay system, so that the marginal distribution of the number of customers in stage 1 is given by the Erlang delay probabilities (4.3), (4.4), and (4.5) of Chapter 3.

Therefore, because of our previous success, and because it is certainly worth a try, let us assume a product solution of the form (2.13), with

$$
P_1(j_1) = \begin{cases} c_1 \dfrac{(\lambda/\mu_1)^{j_1}}{j_1!} & (j_1 = 0, 1, \ldots, s_1) \\[3mm] c_1 \dfrac{(\lambda/\mu_1)^{j_1}}{s_1!\, s_1^{j_1-s_1}} & (j_1 = s_1 + 1, s_1 + 2, \ldots). \end{cases}
\tag{2.14}
$$

We shall substitute the assumed product solution (2.13) and (2.14) into the equilibrium state equations (2.12), with the hope that we will be left with a one-dimensional set of equations that we can solve for the remaining factor $P_2(j_2)$ of our assumed product solution.

It is readily verified that substitution of the assumed product solution (2.13) and (2.14) into the state equations (2.12) yields, after cancellation,

$$
[\lambda + \mu_2(j_2)]P_2(j_2) = \lambda P_2(j_2 - 1) + \mu_2(j_2 + 1)P_2(j_2 + 1)
$$

$$
[P_2(-1) = 0; j_2 = 0, 1, \ldots].
\tag{2.15}
$$

Inspection of equations (2.15) shows that these are precisely the equilibrium state equations that, except for the normalization condition, define the Erlang delay probabilities. We conclude that $P_2(j_2)$ is given by

$$
P_2(j_2) = \begin{cases} c_2 \dfrac{(\lambda/\mu_2)^{j_2}}{j_2!} & (j_2 = 0, 1, \ldots, s_2) \\[3mm] c_2 \dfrac{(\lambda/\mu_2)^{j_2}}{s_2!\, s_2^{j_2-s_2}} & (j_2 = s_2 + 1, s_2 + 2, \ldots). \end{cases}
\tag{2.16}
$$

Since

$$
\sum_{j=0}^{\infty} P_i(j) = 1 \quad (i = 1, 2),
\tag{2.17}
$$

it follows that

$$
c_i = \left[\sum_{k=0}^{s_i-1} \frac{(\lambda/\mu_i)^k}{k!} + \frac{(\lambda/\mu_i)^{s_i}}{(s_i - 1)!\, [s_i - (\lambda/\mu_i)]} \right]^{-1} \quad (i = 1, 2).
\tag{2.18}
$$

Equation (2.18) implies, as expected, that a proper distribution exists only when $\lambda/\mu_1 < s_1$ and $\lambda/\mu_2 < s_2$.

Note that, as in the previous cases, each term on the left-hand side of equation (2.12) corresponds to a single term on the right-hand side of (2.12) and vice versa. Specifically, we have the correspondences

$$\lambda P(j_1, j_2) = \mu_2(j_2 + 1)P(j_1, j_2 + 1)$$

$$\mu_1(j_1)P(j_1, j_2) = \lambda P(j_1 - 1, j_2)$$

$$\mu_2(j_2)P(j_1, j_2) = \mu_1(j_1 + 1)P(j_1 + 1, j_2 - 1),$$

as can be easily verified by substitution. We have thus derived three conservation of flow equations that hold in this particular problem. However, there was no intuitive reason to predict that these conservation laws would hold individually, but only that they would hold jointly [which, of course, is the basis for equation (2.12)]. This must be viewed as an enlightening and unexpected result.

We have shown that the joint equilibrium probability $P(j_1, j_2)$ factors into a product of two Erlang delay probabilities, $P_1(j_1)$ and $P_2(j_2)$. We conclude that the number of customers in either stage of this tandem queue is independent of the number of customers simultaneously present in the other stage. These results were first obtained by Jackson [1954 and 1956].

We have also shown that the marginal distribution of the number of customers in the second stage is the Erlang delay distribution; that is, the distribution of the number of customers in the second stage is exactly that which would obtain if the first stage were not present, and the customers arrived according to a Poisson process directly at the second stage. This fact suggests that the output process from the first stage might, in fact, be the same as the input process to the first stage, that is, a Poisson process. This conjecture is true (Burke's theorem); Burke's proof is outlined in Exercise 2 of Chapter 5, and a different proof is outlined in Exercise 8 of this chapter. As one might guess, there are many other remarkable facts about tandem queueing systems to be uncovered. The interested reader should see Burke [1968] and Reich [1965].

4–3. Generating Functions (Overflow Traffic)

As with state equations in one variable, generating functions are often useful in solving multidimensional state equations. It is interesting that the generating function technique may be applicable even when some of the variables take on only finitely many distinct values.

As an example of the use of generating functions for solving such a problem, we consider the case of a queueing system composed of an s-server primary group and an infinite-server overflow group. In this so-called simple overflow model, it is assumed that customers request service first from the s-server primary group, and that all customers who find all servers busy in the primary group overflow to and are handled by the infinite-server overflow group.

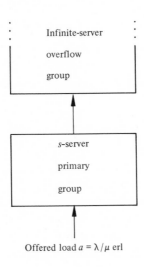

Figure 4–1.

The system to be studied is represented by Figure 4–1. Let $P\{M = j, N = k\} = P(j, k)$ be the statistical equilibrium probability that $M = j$ and $N = k$ customers are simultaneously in service on the primary and overflow groups, respectively. The input is Poisson with rate λ and the service times are exponential with mean μ^{-1}.

Following Kosten [1937], we shall obtain the generating function of the distribution $\{P(j, k)\}$, from which the following important formulas for the mean $E(N) = \alpha$ and variance $V(N) = v$ are easily found:

$$\alpha = aB(s, a) \tag{3.1}$$

and

$$v = \alpha \left(1 - \alpha + \frac{a}{s + 1 + \alpha - a}\right) \tag{3.2}$$

where $a = \lambda/\mu$ is the offered load in erlangs and $B(s, a)$ is the Erlang loss formula.

These results form the basis for an important approximation technique, called the *equivalent random method*, which we shall discuss in Section 7. The derivation given here is instructive, but it is not the most elegant route leading to formula (3.1) (which is intuitively obvious) and formula (3.2). (See Brockmeyer [1954], Riordan [1956 and 1962], Wallström [1966], and Descloux [1970]. The properties of overflow streams are discussed in Palm [1943] and Khintchine [1969]. Although (3.1) and (3.2) follow easily from Kosten's analysis, which we give here, according to Riordan they were first given explicitly in independent unpublished memoranda (1941) by H. Nyquist and E. C. Molina.) Also, despite the elementary nature of these calculations, they are involved. If the reader is willing to accept formulas (3.1) and (3.2), he can skip the calculations without loss of continuity.

The equations for the probabilities $\{P(j, k)\}$ when $j \leq s - 1$ are

$$(a + j + k)P(j, k) = aP(j - 1, k) + (j + 1)P(j + 1, k)$$
$$+ (k + 1)P(j, k + 1)$$
$$[P(-1, k) = 0; j = 0, 1, \ldots, s - 1; k = 0, 1 \ldots], \qquad (3.3)$$

where $a = \lambda/\mu$. When an arriving customer finds all s servers in the primary group busy, he takes a server in the overflow group. Thus, for $j = s$,

$$(a + s + k)P(s, k) = aP(s - 1, k) + aP(s, k - 1)$$
$$+ (k + 1)P(s, k + 1)$$
$$[P(s, -1) = 0; k = 0, 1, \ldots]. \qquad (3.4)$$

The system is completely described by equations (3.3), (3.4), and

$$\sum_{j=0}^{s} \sum_{k=0}^{\infty} P(j, k) = 1. \qquad (3.5)$$

To solve these equations using generating functions, consider the auxiliary system of equations obtained from (3.3) by ignoring the finiteness of s:

$$(a + j + k)\hat{P}(j, k) = a\hat{P}(j - 1, k) + (j + 1)\hat{P}(j + 1, k)$$
$$+ (k + 1)\hat{P}(j, k + 1)$$
$$[\hat{P}(-1, k) = 0; j = 0, 1, \ldots; k = 0, 1, \ldots]. \qquad (3.6)$$

We shall solve the set (3.6) in such a way that

$$\hat{P}(j, k) = P(j, k) \qquad (j = 0, 1, \ldots, s; k = 0, 1, \ldots). \tag{3.7}$$

The values $\{P(j, k)\}$ for $j > s$ yielded by equations (3.6) are of no consequence.

Define the two-dimensional probability generating function

$$\hat{\psi}(x, y) = \sum_{j=0}^{\infty} \sum_{k=0}^{\infty} \hat{P}(j, k)x^j y^k. \tag{3.8}$$

Substitution of equations (3.6) into (3.8) yields, after some straightforward manipulation, the partial differential equation

$$(1 - x) \frac{\partial}{\partial x} \hat{\psi}(x, y) + (1 - y) \frac{\partial}{\partial y} \hat{\psi}(x, y) = a(1 - x)\hat{\psi}(x, y), \tag{3.9}$$

whose solution is

$$\hat{\psi}(x, y) = e^{-a(1-x)} G\left(\frac{1 - y}{1 - x}\right), \tag{3.10}$$

where G is an arbitrary function. (For discussions of partial differential equations of the form (3.9) see, for example, Garabedian [1964].)

We now determine the function G such that the coefficients $\{\hat{P}(j, k)\}$ generated by $\hat{\psi}(x, y)$, which satisfy the state equations (3.3), also satisfy the boundary condition implied by equation (3.4). Then equation (3.7) will be satisfied. To this end, we first expand G in powers of $(1 - y)/(1 - x)$. Then, from (3.10),

$$\hat{\psi}(x, y) = e^{-a(1-x)} \sum_{v=0}^{\infty} c_v \left(\frac{1 - y}{1 - x}\right)^v, \tag{3.11}$$

where the coefficients $\{c_v\}$ remain to be determined.

Let us expand the term $e^{-a(1-x)}(1 - x)^{-v}$ in equation (3.11) into a power series in x:

$$e^{-a(1-x)}(1 - x)^{-v} = \sum_{j=0}^{\infty} \phi_v(j)x^j, \tag{3.12}$$

where, as is easily verified,

$$\phi_v(j) = \begin{cases} \dfrac{a^j}{j!} e^{-a} & (v = 0) \\ e^{-a} \displaystyle\sum_{i=0}^{j} \binom{v + i - 1}{i} \dfrac{a^{j-i}}{(j - i)!} & (v = 1, 2, \ldots). \end{cases} \tag{3.13}$$

Two useful identities are

$$\sum_{j=0}^{n} \phi_\nu(j) = \phi_{\nu+1}(n) \tag{3.14}$$

and

$$(j + 1)\phi_\nu(j + 1) = a\phi_\nu(j) + \nu\phi_{\nu+1}(j). \tag{3.15}$$

To obtain equation (3.14), we simply equate coefficients on both sides of the identity

$$e^{-a(1-x)}(1 - x)^{-\nu} = e^{-a(1-x)}(1 - x)^{-(\nu+1)} - e^{-a(1-x)}(1 - x)^{-(\nu+1)}x.$$

The result is

$$\phi_\nu(j) = \phi_{\nu+1}(j) - \phi_{\nu+1}(j - 1),$$

from which equation (3.14) follows directly. Similarly, equation (3.15) follows after we equate coefficients on both sides of the identity

$$\frac{d}{dx} e^{-a(1-x)}(1 - x)^{-\nu} = ae^{-a(1-x)}(1 - x)^{-\nu} + \nu e^{-a(1-x)}(1 - x)^{-(\nu+1)}.$$

Now consider equation (3.7). When $j = s$, comparison of equation (3.4) and (3.6) shows that, if (3.7) is true, then

$$a\hat{P}(s, k - 1) = (s + 1)\hat{P}(s + 1, k) \qquad (k = 1, 2, \ldots). \tag{3.16}$$

Let $\hat{\psi}_j(y)$ be the marginal generating function

$$\hat{\psi}_j(y) = \sum_{k=0}^{\infty} \hat{P}(j, k)y^k, \tag{3.17}$$

so that

$$\hat{\psi}(x, y) = \sum_{j=0}^{\infty} \hat{\psi}_j(y)x^j. \tag{3.18}$$

Then, introducing (3.16) into (3.17), we obtain

$$ay\hat{\psi}_s(y) = (s + 1)\hat{\psi}_{s+1}(y). \tag{3.19}$$

From equation (3.18) we see that

$$\hat{\psi}_j(y) = \frac{1}{j!} \frac{\partial^j}{\partial x^j} \hat{\psi}(x, y)\bigg|_{x=0}. \tag{3.20}$$

Using (3.12) in (3.11), we have

$$\hat{\psi}(x, y) = \sum_{v=0}^{\infty} c_v (1 - y)^v \sum_{j=0}^{\infty} \phi_v(j) x^j. \qquad (3.21)$$

It follows from equations (3.20) and (3.21) that

$$\hat{\psi}_j(y) = \sum_{v=0}^{\infty} c_v \phi_v(j)(1 - y)^v. \qquad (3.22)$$

In particular,

$$\hat{\psi}_s(y) = \sum_{v=0}^{\infty} c_v \phi_v(s)(1 - y)^v. \qquad (3.23)$$

If we use the identity

$$(1 - y)^v - (1 - y)^{v+1} = (1 - y)^v y$$

we can write

$$y \hat{\psi}_s(y) = \sum_{v=0}^{\infty} c_v \phi_v(s)(1 - y)^v - \sum_{v=0}^{\infty} c_v \phi_v(s)(1 - y)^{v+1}. \qquad (3.24)$$

Therefore, equating coefficients of $(1 - y)^v$ in equation (3.19) we have, by virtue of equations (3.23) and (3.24),

$$ac_v \phi_v(s) - ac_{v-1} \phi_{v-1}(s) = (s + 1)c_v \phi_v(s + 1). \qquad (3.25)$$

Comparison of equation (3.25) with (3.15) when $j = s$ shows that

$$c_v v \phi_{v+1}(s) = -ac_{v-1} \phi_{v-1}(s) \qquad (v = 1, 2, \ldots)$$

or, solving recursively,

$$c_v = (-1)^v \frac{a^v}{v!} \frac{\phi_1(s)\phi_0(s)}{\phi_{v+1}(s)\phi_v(s)} c_0 \qquad (v = 1, 2, \ldots). \qquad (3.26)$$

It remains to find c_0.

Applying the binomial theorem to the factor $(1 - y)^v$ in equation (3.21), we can write

$$\hat{\psi}(x, y) = \sum_{v=0}^{\infty} c_v \sum_{k=0}^{v} (-1)^k \binom{v}{k} y^k \sum_{j=0}^{\infty} \phi_v(j) x^j,$$

where we define $\begin{pmatrix} 0 \\ 0 \end{pmatrix} = 1$, and which, after interchanging the orders of summation over v and k, becomes

$$\hat{\psi}(x, y) = \sum_{k=0}^{\infty} \left[\sum_{v=k}^{\infty} (-1)^k \begin{pmatrix} v \\ k \end{pmatrix} c_v \right] y^k \sum_{j=0}^{\infty} \phi_v(j) x^j.$$

Finally, interchanging the orders of summation over v and j, we have

$$\hat{\psi}(x, y) = \sum_{k=0}^{\infty} \sum_{j=0}^{\infty} \left[(-1)^k \sum_{v=k}^{\infty} \begin{pmatrix} v \\ k \end{pmatrix} c_v \phi_v(j) \right] y^k x^j. \tag{3.27}$$

Comparison of equations (3.8) and (3.27) shows that

$$\hat{P}(j, k) = (-1)^k \sum_{v=k}^{\infty} \begin{pmatrix} v \\ k \end{pmatrix} c_v \phi_v(j),$$

which, in view of equation (3.26), can be written

$$\hat{P}(j, k) = (-1)^k \sum_{v=k}^{\infty} (-1)^v \begin{pmatrix} v \\ k \end{pmatrix} \frac{a^v}{v!} \frac{\phi_1(s)\phi_0(s)}{\phi_{v+1}(s)\phi_v(s)} \phi_v(j) c_0. \tag{3.28}$$

We now determine c_0 from equation (3.7) and the normalization equation (3.5). Summing first with respect to the index k, we have

$$\sum_{k=0}^{\infty} P(j, k) = \sum_{k=0}^{\infty} (-1)^k \sum_{v=k}^{\infty} (-1)^v \begin{pmatrix} v \\ k \end{pmatrix} \frac{a^v}{v!} \frac{\phi_1(s)\phi_0(s)}{\phi_{v+1}(s)\phi_v(s)} \phi_v(j) c_0,$$

which, after interchange of the order of summation, becomes

$$\sum_{k=0}^{\infty} P(j, k) = c_0 \sum_{v=0}^{\infty} (-1)^v \frac{a^v}{v!} \frac{\phi_1(s)\phi_0(s)}{\phi_{v+1}(s)\phi_v(s)} \phi_v(j) \sum_{k=0}^{v} (-1)^k \begin{pmatrix} v \\ k \end{pmatrix}. \tag{3.29}$$

The last summation on the right-hand side of (3.29) is the binomial expansion of $(1 - 1)^v$; therefore

$$\sum_{k=0}^{v} (-1)^k \begin{pmatrix} v \\ k \end{pmatrix} = 0 \qquad (v \geqq 1).$$

Since by definition $\begin{pmatrix} 0 \\ 0 \end{pmatrix} = 1$, equation (3.29) becomes

$$\sum_{k=0}^{\infty} P(j, k) = c_0 \phi_0(j). \tag{3.30}$$

Summing both sides of equation (3.30) with respect to j, we have

$$\sum_{j=0}^{s} \sum_{k=0}^{\infty} P(j, k) = c_0 \sum_{j=0}^{s} \phi_0(j). \qquad (3.31)$$

Using the normalization equation (3.5), it follows that

$$c_0 = \frac{1}{\sum_{j=0}^{s} \phi_0(j)}$$

and finally, using the identity (3.14), we conclude that

$$c_0 = \frac{1}{\phi_1(s)}. \qquad (3.32)$$

Thus, in view of equation (3.28), we have Kosten's explicit expression for the distribution $\{P(j, k)\}$:

$$P(j, k) = (-1)^k \phi_0(s) \sum_{v=k}^{\infty} (-1)^v \binom{v}{k} \frac{a^v}{v!} \frac{\phi_v(j)}{\phi_{v+1}(s)\phi_v(s)}$$

$$(j = 0, 1, \ldots, s; \, k = 0, 1, \ldots), \qquad (3.33)$$

where $\{\phi_v(j)\}$ is given by equation (3.13).

Note that, according to equations (3.30), (3.32), and (3.13), the marginal distribution of the number of busy servers in the primary group is, of course, the Erlang loss distribution

$$\sum_{k=0}^{\infty} P(j, k) = \frac{\phi_0(j)}{\phi_1(s)} = \frac{a^j/j!}{\sum_{i=0}^{s} a^i/i!} \qquad (j = 0, 1, \ldots, s). \qquad (3.34)$$

We are now prepared to derive the required formulas (3.1) and (3.2) for the mean $E(N) = \alpha$ and the variance $V(N) = v$ of the overflow distribution.

It follows from equation (3.17) that

$$\frac{d}{dy} \hat{\psi}_j(y) \bigg|_{y=1} = \sum_{k=1}^{\infty} k P(j, k) \qquad (j = 0, 1, \ldots, s)$$

and therefore

$$\alpha = \sum_{j=0}^{s} \frac{d}{dy} \hat{\psi}_j(y) \bigg|_{y=1}. \qquad (3.35)$$

From equation (3.22) we see that

$$\frac{d}{dy} \hat{\psi}_j(y)\bigg|_{y=1} = -c_1\phi_1(j),$$

which, in view of (3.26) and (3.32), becomes

$$\frac{d}{dy} \hat{\psi}_j(y)\bigg|_{y=1} = a \frac{\phi_0(s)}{\phi_2(s)\phi_1(s)} \phi_1(j). \tag{3.36}$$

Using (3.36) in (3.35) we have, in light of the identity (3.14),

$$\alpha = a \frac{\phi_0(s)}{\phi_1(s)}. \tag{3.37}$$

The required result (3.1), which of course could have been anticipated on other grounds, follows from (3.37).

To calculate $v = V(N)$, note that

$$\sum_{j=0}^{s} \frac{d^2}{dy^2} \hat{\psi}_j(y)\bigg|_{y=1} = E(N^2) - \alpha.$$

Since $V(N) = E(N^2) - E^2(N)$, we have

$$\sum_{j=0}^{s} \frac{d^2}{dy^2} \hat{\psi}_j(y)\bigg|_{y=1} = v + \alpha^2 - \alpha. \tag{3.38}$$

From equation (3.22), we see that

$$\frac{d^2}{dy^2} \hat{\psi}_j(y)\bigg|_{y=1} = 2c_2\phi_2(j) \qquad (j = 0, 1, \ldots, s). \tag{3.39}$$

Therefore

$$v + \alpha^2 - \alpha = 2c_2 \sum_{j=0}^{s} \phi_2(j). \tag{3.40}$$

Using the identity (3.14), we have

$$v + \alpha^2 - \alpha = 2c_2\phi_3(s). \tag{3.41}$$

Equation (3.2) now follows directly from (3.41).

The important concept to be digested here is in the use of probability generating functions to solve multidimensional state equations which, at first glance, do not seem amenable to these techniques because of the existence of certain boundary conditions. The key steps are the extension of the original state equations so that the generating function technique can be used, the expansion of the generating function in a power series, and the calculation of the unknown coefficients by forcing the generating function to agree with the previously ignored boundary conditions.

It is interesting to speculate whether the preceding results are valid independently of the form of the service time distribution function. In particular, is formula (3.2) for the variance $V(N) = v$ of the overflow distribution valid in general for systems with Poisson input? One might suspect so, since both the distribution of the number M of customers on the primary group and the distribution of the total number $M + N$ of customers in the system are known to be independent of the form of the service time distribution function. Nevertheless, as Burke [1971] has recently shown in a study of the simple overflow model with constant service times, this is not the case. Of course, formula (3.1) remains true, since it gives the mean number of customers per service time who find all primary servers busy.

Overflow models are of both theoretical and practical interest, and have received much attention throughout the last fifty years. Syski [1960] summarizes most of this work, including practical applications. Riordan [1962] and Khintchine [1969] also discuss and summarize various aspects of overflow problems. Important papers not discussed or summarized in these books include Burke [1971], Descloux [1963 and 1970], Neal [1971], and Wallström [1966]. (See also Section 7 and Exercise 10.)

4–4. Macrostates (Priority Reservation)

In all the examples so far, the naming of the states of the system has been quite natural in the context of the problem, and our attention has been directed toward methods of solution of the corresponding equilibrium state equations. In this section we will observe that it is sometimes possible and convenient to consider groupings of the "natural" states (*microstates*) into *macrostates*.

For example, consider a system in which a group of s servers handles two independent Poisson streams of traffic, where customers in stream 1 are designated high-priority customers, and those in stream 2 are designated low-priority customers. A high-priority customer will be cleared from the system if on arrival he finds no idle servers, whereas a low-priority customer will be cleared from the system if on arrival he finds less than $n + 1$ idle servers. Service times for both high- and low-priority customers are assumed to be exponentially distributed with the same mean. We wish to find the probability of blocking experienced by the customers of each priority class.

One approach to this problem is to describe the system by the two-dimensional states E_{j_1,j_2}, where j_1 and j_2 are, respectively, the numbers of high-priority and low-priority customers in service; and then write and solve the "rate out = rate in" state equations for the corresponding distribution $\{P(j_1, j_2)\}$. If we define

$$P_j = \sum_{j_1 + j_2 = j} P(j_1, j_2) \qquad (j = 0, 1, \ldots, s) \qquad (4.1)$$

then P_s is the probability of blocking seen by the high-priority customers, and $\sum_{j=s-n}^{s} P_j$ is the probability of blocking suffered by the low-priority customers. The indicated calculations are tedious and, as the following illustrates, unnecessary.

Consider now the grouping of all those two-dimensional microstates E_{j_1,j_2} with the property that $j_1 + j_2 = j$ into a single one-dimensional macrostate E_j. That is, we define the macrostate E_j as the set of all microstates E_{j_1,j_2} that correspond to a total of j customers in service. It should now be clear that the probability corresponding to the state E_j is P_j, and that the distribution $\{P_j\}$ is easily found from the one-dimensional "rate up = rate down" state equations (where a_1 and a_2 are the offered loads in erlangs):

$$(a_1 + a_2)P_{j-1} = jP_j \qquad (j = 1, 2, \ldots, s - n) \qquad (4.2)$$

$$a_1 P_{j-1} = jP_j \qquad (j = s - n + 1, s - n + 2, \ldots, s). \qquad (4.3)$$

The solution, found easily by recurrence, is

$$P_j = \begin{cases} \dfrac{(a_1 + a_2)^j}{j!} P_0 & (j = 1, 2, \ldots, s - n) \\[4mm] \dfrac{(a_1 + a_2)^{s-n} a_1^{j-(s-n)}}{j!} P_0 & (j = s - n + 1, s - n + 2, \ldots, s) \end{cases}$$

$$(4.4)$$

where, from the normalization requirement,

$$P_0 = \left(\sum_{k=0}^{s-n} \frac{(a_1 + a_2)^k}{k!} + (a_1 + a_2)^{s-n} \sum_{k=s-n+1}^{s} \frac{a_1^{k-(s-n)}}{k!} \right)^{-1}. \quad (4.5)$$

In this example, the fact that a macrostate approach is possible is almost obvious, and once the proposed macrostates are identified, the validity of the results is clear. This is not always the case. When a valid set of equilibrium macrostate equations exist, the macrostate equations can always be derived from the ordinary equilibrium microstate equations. In general, however, it is arguable whether it is easier to write down directly an appropriate set of macrostate equations, or to derive them (if indeed they exist) from the more detailed but sometimes conceptually simpler ordinary microstate equations. An example that illustrates these difficulties is provided by Exercise 11, which is an extension of the priority reservation model given here.

It is worth pointing out that the example considered here is identical to Exercise 19 of Chapter 3. A reader with no knowledge of multidimensional birth-and-death processes would not make the mistake of doing this problem the hard way. Of course, if the mean service times of the high-priority and low-priority customers were unequal, the one-dimensional macrostate approach would not apply, and the advantage would lie with the more advanced reader.

4–5. Indirect Solution of Equations (Load Carried by Each Server of an Ordered Group)

We have seen that in many cases of practical interest, the probability state equations are easy to specify but difficult to solve in closed form. Such problems usually call for simulation (which we will not discuss) or numerical methods, but occasionally a closed-form solution can be obtained by indirect means.

Consider a group of s servers with a fixed order of access; the servers are numbered $1, 2, \ldots, s$, and arriving customers take the lowest-numbered idle server. No server can be idle if any customers are waiting. We assume Poisson input with rate λ, exponential service times with mean μ^{-1}, and statistical equilibrium. We wish to calculate the load carried by the mth ordered server ($m = 1, 2, \ldots, s$), which is the same as the equilibrium probability that the mth ordered server is busy.

We first consider the case in which blocked customers are cleared. Subsequently, we will extend the model to allow for defections from the queue at any arbitrary rate.

To calculate the probability that the mth ordered server is busy, one could write and solve equilibrium state equations for the probability $P(i, j, k)$ that i customers are in service on the first ordered $m - 1$ servers, $j \, (= 0 \text{ or } 1)$ customers are in service on the mth ordered server, and k customers are in service on the last ordered $s - m$ servers. The load $a'_{\text{BCC}}(m)$ carried by the mth server in this Erlang loss system is then given by

$$a'_{\text{BCC}}(m) = \sum_{i=0}^{m-1} \sum_{k=0}^{s-m} P(i, 1, k).$$

Although it is easy to write the state equations that determine the distribution $\{P(i, j, k)\}$, it is quite difficult to solve them in closed form directly. Fortunately, these calculations are unnecessary, since $a'_{\text{BCC}}(m)$ can easily be obtained by another argument (see Exercise 3 of Chapter 3): the load carried by the mth server is the difference between the load $aB(m - 1, a)$ overflowing the $(m - 1)$th server and the load $aB(m, a)$ overflowing the mth server; that is,

$$a'_{\text{BCC}}(m) = a[B(m - 1, a) - B(m, a)], \tag{5.1}$$

where $B(m, a)$ is the Erlang loss formula, given by equation (3.6) of Chapter 3. This argument is valid for loss systems only. Note that the distribution $\{P(i, j, k)\}$ was never found.

We now consider the more general case in which a queue is allowed to form and customers defect from the system with arbitrary death rates $\mu_j \, (j > s)$. [The distribution $\{P_j\}$ of the number of customers in the system is given by equation (1.1) of Chapter 3. When $\mu_j = s\mu$ for all $j > s$ we have the Erlang delay model, and when $\mu_j = \infty$ for all $j > s$ we have the Erlang loss model.] Again, the equilibrium state equations are easy to obtain but difficult to solve. Therefore, we will attempt to extend the preceding indirect approach.

To calculate the probability that the mth ordered server is busy, we partition time into two mutually exclusive and exhaustive sets of intervals, those time intervals during which there is at least one customer waiting and those time intervals during which there are no customers waiting. Clearly, the mth ordered server is busy with probability 1 whenever there are any waiting customers. It remains to calculate the probability that the mth ordered server is busy, given that no customers are waiting for service.

Observe that this conditional probability is the same as the corresponding unconditional probability for the Erlang loss system. This is true because with a birth-and-death process, if it is known that exactly j customers are present at some instant, the future evolution of the system is independent of the particular path by which this state was reached or how long it had been in that state, but depends only on the value j. Thus the behavior of the system during the time intervals in which there is at least one waiting customer has no effect on the behavior of the system during the time intervals in which there are no waiting customers. (See, for example, Exercise 20 of Chapter 3.)

From the above argument we conclude that the load $a'(m)$ carried by the mth ordered server during those time intervals when no customers are waiting for service is the same as that for the corresponding Erlang loss system. Hence

$$a'(m) = p(s + 1, a) + [1 - p(s + 1, a)]a'_{BCC}(m) \qquad (m = 1, 2, \ldots, s),$$
$$(5.2)$$

where $a'_{BCC}(m)$ is the load carried by the mth ordered server in an Erlang loss system, given by equation (5.1), and

$$p(s + 1, a) = \sum_{j=s+1}^{\infty} P_j, \qquad (5.3)$$

where $\{P_j\}$ is the equilibrium distribution of the number of customers in the system, given by equation (1.1) of Chapter 3.

Thus an apparently difficult problem (with an important application—see Exercise 12) is solved by an astute observation. It is interesting that formula (5.2) was obtained (by direct calculation) for the special case of blocked customers held almost fifty years ago (G. W. Kendrick [1923, unpublished]). The observation that (5.2) remains valid for birth-and-death systems with arbitrary death rates $\mu_j(j > s)$ was made by P. J. Burke [1963, unpublished].

4–6. Numerical Solution of State Equations by Iteration (Gauss–Seidel and Overrelaxation Methods)

Thus far we have seen that queueing problems often lead to sets of multidimensional probability state equations. In each of the cases considered so far in this chapter, we have been able to solve these equations without recourse to numerical methods. In most cases of practical interest, however, product solutions, generating functions, or astute observations will not lead to neat solutions. Fortunately, equations of the type we are concerned with often yield easily to a simple numerical iteration scheme. Convergence criteria are known, but are often difficult to apply in practical cases. However, real queueing problems in which this iteration technique fails rarely, if ever, occur. Because of its simplicity, its particular suitability for digital computer application, its apparent reliability, and the lack of anything better, we shall briefly describe an iteration procedure and its generalization and illustrate their application to the solution of multidimensional probability state equations.

Numerical analysis is a subject in itself. The present discussion is intended to provide only a starting point for one who is interested in the theory of numerical solution of large systems of linear equations. Hopefully, the following necessarily terse discussion will enable the reader to "get numbers" from multidimensional probability state equations. It is worth mentioning that the iteration procedure we shall describe is much simpler to apply than might appear from the mathematical description. The numerical example that follows the theoretical description should make this clear.

Consider a general set of linear equations

$$\mathbf{Ax} = \mathbf{b}, \tag{6.1}$$

where $\mathbf{A}$ is a given square matrix, $\mathbf{b}$ is a given vector, and $\mathbf{x}$ is an unknown vector. [In the cases of interest here, the components of $\mathbf{x}$ are the equilibrium state probabilities that are to be found; (6.1) is the set of equilibrium state equations.] Equation (6.1) can be rewritten in the form

$$(\mathbf{I} - \mathbf{L} - \mathbf{U})\mathbf{x} = \mathbf{d}, \tag{6.2}$$

where $\mathbf{L}$ and $\mathbf{U}$ are, respectively, lower and upper triangular matrices with zeroes along the main diagonal, and $\mathbf{I}$ is the unit matrix, with ones along the main diagonal and zeros everywhere else. Equation (6.2) can be written

$$\mathbf{x} = \mathbf{Lx} + \mathbf{Ux} + \mathbf{d}, \tag{6.3}$$

which suggests the iteration scheme

$$\mathbf{x}^{(n+1)} = \mathbf{Lx}^{(n+1)} + \mathbf{Ux}^{(n)} + \mathbf{d}, \tag{6.4}$$

where the vector $\mathbf{x}^{(n)}$ is the nth iterate, $n = 0, 1, \ldots$, and $\mathbf{x}^{(0)}$ is an arbitrary vector. Equation (6.4) simply says calculate each component of the vector $x^{(n+1)}$ based on the latest calculated values available, which are all the components of the vector $x^{(n+1)}$ calculated thus far and the remaining components of the vector $x^{(n)}$ calculated at the last stage of iteration. The iteration procedure (6.4) has associated with it the names Seidel, Gauss, Liebmann, Nekrasov, and probably several others. The general technique of solving equations by iteration is also called successive approximation and *relaxation*. The most common name of the scheme (6.4) is *Gauss–Seidel iteration.*

It can be shown that a necessary and sufficient condition for the con-vergence of the iteration procedure (6.4) for arbitrary $x^{(0)}$ is that all the eigenvalues of the iteration matrix $M = (I - L)^{-1}U$ lie inside the unit circle; that is, the iteration procedure (6.4) converges independently of the initial vector $x^{(0)}$ if and only if the spectral radius of the iteration matrix is less than unity.

This convergence criterion is ordinarily of theoretical interest only, since finding the spectral radius of the iteration matrix is usually of the same order of difficulty as solving the original equations (6.1). It is desirable to be able to predict behavior of the iteration scheme directly from inspection of the original matrix A. This is possible in certain special cases. In particular, a sufficient condition for convergence of the iteration scheme is that the original matrix A exhibit strict diagonal dominance; that is, if a_{ij} is the element in row i and column j of the original matrix A, then convergence is assured if

$$|a_{ii}| > \sum_{\substack{j=1 \\ j \neq i}}^{k} |a_{ij}| \qquad (i = 1, 2, \ldots, k),$$

where k is the number of rows (columns) of the matrix A. This condition is not usually met by probability state equations, but it does suggest why this iteration scheme has proven useful in this context. The greater the concentration of "mass" of the matrix A along its main diagonal, the more likely (and faster) will the procedure converge. State equations of the type we are concerned with are characterized by a large number of zero elements off the main diagonal, making convergence likely, and simultaneously making computer programming particularly easy.

A generalization of the Gauss–Seidel method that has proven useful is the so-called method of successive *overrelaxation*, in which the over-relaxation values are obtained by weighting the most recent value by a factor $\omega \geq 1$:

$$x^{(n+1)} = \omega[Lx^{(n+1)} + Ux^{(n)} + d] + (1 - \omega)x^{(n)} \qquad (\omega \geq 1).$$

$$(6.5)$$

The Gauss–Seidel method is thus the special case of overrelaxation for $\omega = 1$. An intuitive feel for the reason overrelaxation sometimes speeds convergence can best be gained by running through a numerical example. Mathematically, the use of a weighting factor ω will speed convergence if the corresponding iteration matrix has a smaller spectral radius.

Experience indicates that overrelaxation with $\omega \approx 1.3$ is often faster than simple Gauss–Seidel iteration. Many fundamental questions about convergence and rates of convergence remain unanswered. The interested reader should see Varga [1962].

From a practical point of view, it appears that the Gauss–Seidel and overrelaxation methods are the most useful methods for numerical solution of large sets of equations of the type that arise from analysis of multidimensional birth-and-death processes. These methods are especially suitable for implementation on a digital computer. Even so, a point of utmost importance to those who would solve equations (6.1) by hand calculation is that iteration schemes that converge for any starting vector $\mathbf{x}^{(0)}$ are self-correcting; an error is "absorbed" by the method and results in only a larger number of iterations. Anyone who has tried to solve systems of equations on a desk calculator will surely appreciate this fact.

We now give a simple illustration of the use of the Gauss–Seidel and overrelaxation methods in the solution of multidimensional statistical equilibrium probability state equations.

Consider two server groups, each of which receives direct Poisson traffic and also overflow traffic from the other group (see Figure 4–2). Let the

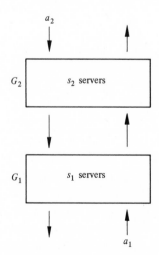

Figure 4–2.

server groups G_1 and G_2 be of sizes s_1 and s_2, with Poisson loads of magnitudes a_1 erl and a_2 erl, and exponential service times with mean μ^{-1}. Customers who find all $s_1 + s_2$ servers busy are cleared from the system. Let $P(j_1, j_2)$ be the statistical equilibrium probability that there are j_1 customers in service on G_1 and j_2 on G_2. Then, equating rates of flow out of and into each state, the statistical equilibrium probability state equations are

$$(a_1 + a_2 + j_1 + j_2)P(j_1, j_2)$$
$$= a_1 P(j_1 - 1, j_2) + a_2 P(j_1, j_2 - 1)$$
$$+ (j_1 + 1)P(j_1 + 1, j_2) + (j_2 + 1)P(j_1, j_2 + 1)$$
$$(j_1 < s_1, j_2 < s_2) \qquad (6.6)$$

$$(a_1 + a_2 + s_1 + j_2)P(s_1, j_2)$$
$$= a_1 P(s_1 - 1, j_2) + a_1 P(s_1, j_2 - 1)$$
$$+ a_2 P(s_1, j_2 - 1) + (j_2 + 1)P(s_1, j_2 + 1)$$
$$(j_1 = s_1, j_2 < s_2) \qquad (6.7)$$

$$(a_1 + a_2 + j_1 + s_2)P(j_1, s_2)$$
$$= a_1 P(j_1 - 1, s_2) + a_2 P(j_1, s_2 - 1)$$
$$+ a_2 P(j_1 - 1, s_2) + (j_1 + 1)P(j_1 + 1, s_2)$$
$$(j_1 < s_1, j_2 = s_2) \qquad (6.8)$$

$$(s_1 + s_2)P(s_1, s_2) = (a_1 + a_2)P(s_1 - 1, s_2) + (a_1 + a_2)P(s_1, s_2 - 1)$$
$$(j_1 = s_1, j_2 = s_2). \qquad (6.9)$$

The normalization equation is

$$\sum_{j_1=0}^{s_1} \sum_{j_2=0}^{s_2} P(j_1, j_2) = 1. \qquad (6.10)$$

We shall solve these equations for the particular case $s_1 = 4$, $a_1 = 5$, $s_2 = 2$, $a_2 = 1$. The total number of states is $(s_1 + 1)(s_2 + 1) = 15$. Consider the balance equations (6.6)–(6.9). For reasons that will be explained presently, we reorder these equations so that their matrix of coefficients is as shown in Table 4–1. All the entries on the main diagonal

Table 4-1.

	(0,0)	(0,1)	(0,2)	(1,0)	(1,1)	(1,2)	(2,0)	(2,1)	(2,2)	(3,0)	(3,1)	(3,2)	(4,0)	(4,1)	(4,2)
(4,2)	0	0	0	0	0	0	0	0	0	0	0	-6	0	-6	6
(4,1)	0	0	0	0	0	0	0	0	0	0	-5	0	-6	11	-2
(4,0)	0	0	0	0	0	0	0	0	0	-5	0	0	10	-1	0
(3,2)	0	0	0	0	0	0	0	0	-6	0	-1	11	0	0	-4
(3,1)	0	0	0	0	0	0	0	-5	0	-1	10	-2	0	-4	0
(3,0)	0	0	0	0	0	0	-5	0	0	9	-1	0	-4	0	0
(2,2)	0	0	0	0	0	-6	0	-1	10	0	0	-3	0	0	0
(2,1)	0	0	0	0	-5	0	-1	9	-2	0	-3	0	0	0	0
(2,0)	0	0	0	-5	0	0	8	-1	0	-3	0	0	0	0	0
(1,2)	0	0	-6	0	-1	9	0	0	-2	0	0	0	0	0	0
(1,1)	0	-5	0	-1	8	-2	0	-2	0	0	0	0	0	0	0
(1,0)	-5	0	0	7	-1	0	-2	0	0	0	0	0	0	0	0
(0,2)	0	-1	8	0	0	-1	0	0	0	0	0	0	0	0	0
(0,1)	-1	7	-2	0	-1	0	0	0	0	0	0	0	0	0	0
(0,0)	6	-1	0	-1	0	0	0	0	0	0	0	0	0	0	0

are positive, and all those off the main diagonal are negative or zero. Note how the nonzero elements cluster along the main diagonal.

Observe that this 15×15 matrix is of rank 14; that is, each column sums to zero and any one of the rows can be derived from the other 14.

In other words, one of the equations is redundant, and the other 14 equations determine the solution only up to a constant factor. This factor is supplied by the normalization condition (6.10).

Although one of the equations is redundant, it appears that the convergence of the iteration procedure sometimes is accelerated by using all the balance equations, as we shall do in this example. The normalization equation may be used after each complete round of iteration, as we do in this example, or it may be used only after the last stage of iteration. When all the balance equations are used, normalization is accomplished by summing the unnormalized values and dividing each by their sum. Normalizing only after the last stage of iteration is more efficient as long as computer overflows and/or underflows do not occur, since the relative values are unaffected by normalization. (We normalize after each round in this example because we want to display the values at each step.)

We now apply the method of successive overrelaxation (6.5) to our matrix of coefficients, using $\omega = 1.0$ (the ordinary Gauss–Seidel iteration), 1.1, 1.2, 1.3, and 1.4. As first step, we must specify the initial values $P^{(0)}(j_1, j_2)$.

Let us first consider ordinary Gauss–Seidel iteration ($\omega = 1.0$) with the initial values all equal. Then $P^{(0)}(j_1, j_2) = \frac{1}{15} = 0.06667$. Following the order indicated by the matrix, we first calculate $P^{(1)}(4, 2)$ according to

$$6P^{(1)}(4, 2) = 6P^{(0)}(4, 1) + 6P^{(0)}(3, 2).$$

We next calculate $P^{(1)}(4, 1)$ according to

$$11P^{(1)}(4, 1) = 2P^{(1)}(4, 2) + 6P^{(0)}(4, 0) + 5P^{(0)}(3, 1).$$

We continue in this manner, calculating $P^{(1)}(4, 0)$, $P^{(1)}(3, 2), \ldots,$ $P^{(1)}(0, 0)$. We may then normalize these values (divide each one by their sum) and start the second round of iteration, or we may start the next round of iteration immediately and normalize at completion of the iteration procedure. For this example, the normalized probabilities after $k = 0, 1, 2, 5, 12,$ and 13 stages of iteration are ($\omega = 1.0$), as shown in Table 4–2.

Observe that the probabilities change only slightly from the twelfth iteration to the thirteenth. Somehow it must be decided when to stop iterating, that is, when the procedure has converged (or shown that convergence is not occurring). In the present example the convergence

Table 4–2.

	$k = 0$	$k = 1$	$k = 2$	$k = 5$	$k = 11$	$k = 12$	$k = 13$
$P^{(k)}(4, 2)$	0.0667	0.12500	0.16304	0.23077	0.26404	0.26444	0.26466
$P^{(k)}(4, 1)$	0.0667	0.08523	0.08893	0.12338	0.12464	0.12455	0.12449
$P^{(k)}(4, 0)$	0.0667	0.03977	0.03866	0.04774	0.03978	0.03960	0.03949
$P^{(k)}(3, 2)$	0.0667	0.08523	0.10316	0.12751	0.13995	0.14019	0.14033
$P^{(k)}(3, 1)$	0.0667	0.08864	0.10358	0.12392	0.12059	0.12056	0.12054
$P^{(k)}(3, 0)$	0.0667	0.06225	0.06761	0.06623	0.05431	0.05410	0.05399
$P^{(k)}(2, 2)$	0.0667	0.06932	0.07597	0.05920	0.06067	0.06076	0.06082
$P^{(k)}(2, 1)$	0.0667	0.08662	0.10412	0.08036	0.07458	0.07455	0.07454
$P^{(k)}(2, 0)$	0.0667	0.07323	0.08478	0.05100	0.04162	0.04149	0.04141
$P^{(k)}(1, 2)$	0.0667	0.06402	0.03595	0.01954	0.01876	0.01878	0.01880
$P^{(k)}(1, 1)$	0.0667	0.08543	0.05956	0.03260	0.02925	0.02923	0.02922
$P^{(k)}(1, 0)$	0.0667	0.07764	0.04448	0.02312	0.01901	0.01896	0.01893
$P^{(k)}(0, 2)$	0.0667	0.01581	0.00755	0.00332	0.00305	0.00305	0.00305
$P^{(k)}(0, 1)$	0.0667	0.02552	0.01301	0.00639	0.00564	0.00563	0.00563
$P^{(k)}(0, 0)$	0.0667	0.01719	0.00958	0.00492	0.00411	0.00410	0.00409

criterion was taken to be

$$\sum_{j_1=0}^{4} \sum_{j_2=0}^{2} |P^{(k)}(j_1, j_2) - P^{(k-1)}(j_1, j_2)| < 0.001.$$

That is, we assume that the process has converged when the sum of the absolute changes of the probabilities from one iteration to the next is less than 0.001. This criterion, which is completely arbitrary, is satisfied in our example at $k = 13$.

If we had used an ω different from the Gauss–Seidel value of unity, we might have speeded up the convergence; that is, we might have satisfied our arbitrary convergence criterion after less iterations. For this example use of an overrelaxation factor $\omega = 1.3$ will produce convergence (as defined above) for the same initial values after $k = 9$ iterations, a saving in computation time of about $\frac{4}{13} \approx 31$ percent.

Another way to speed convergence is to start out with a set of initial values closer to the solution. That is, use some intelligence in specifying the initial values, instead of choosing them in a completely arbitrary fashion. In the present example, we know that a product solution of the form

$$P(j_1, j_2) = \frac{a_1^{j_1} a_2^{j_2}}{j_1! j_2!} c$$

will satisfy the equilibrium state equations everywhere except on the boundary. Therefore it seems reasonable that the true solution should not differ numerically as much from the product solution values as from the arbitrary value $\frac{1}{15}$.

For the example under consideration, using the product

$$P^{(0)}(j_1, j_2) = \frac{a_1^{j_1} a_2^{j_2}}{j_1! \, j_2!} \, c,$$

where c is the normalization factor, leads to convergence (with respect to our criterion) in 10 iterations when $\omega = 1.0$, and in 6 iterations when $\omega = 1.3$ [as opposed to 13 and 9 when the initial values are $P^{(0)}(j_1, j_2) = \frac{1}{15}$]. Speeds of convergence (numbers of iterations required) for this example for various values of the overrelaxation factor ω and different initial values are summarized in Table 4–3.

Table 4–3.

$P^{(0)}(j_1, j_2)$ $\quad\omega$	1.0	1.1	1.2	1.3	1.4
$\dfrac{a_1^{j_1} a_2^{j_2}}{j_1! \, j_2!} \, c$	10	8	6	6	8
$\dfrac{1}{15}$	13	11	9	9	11

The reason for ordering the equations as we have done, starting with the boundary states, should now be apparent. If, when using the product $(a_1^{j_1}/j_1!)(a_2^{j_2}/j_2!)c$ as the initial vector, we had started the iteration procedure at interior states, then no change in the calculated values would have occurred until a boundary equation (where the product solution does not hold) was reached. Thus the computation time of the first round of iteration would have been largely wasted.

These tricks may seem hardly worth the effort for the simple example considered here. But for the solution of large sets of equations of the kind likely to arise in practical problems, the computer needs all the help it can get.

Finally, it should be mentioned that when mathematical or numerical solution is impractical, simulation is often a useful tool for analysis.

Simulation can be used to study processes that are much more complicated than those that can be studied by mathematical and numerical analysis. However, if an appropriate mathematical or numerical solution can be obtained, it is often more useful than simulation data.

4–7. The Equivalent Random Method

Consider the following important queueing system. Customers arrive in n independent Poisson streams, each stream directed at one of n different primary groups of servers. All customers who find all servers busy in their primary group are directed toward a single overflow group. The overflow group thus provides a common backup for the n primary groups. The service times on all groups are assumed to be independently and identically distributed negative exponential random variables. Customers who are blocked on the overflow group are cleared from the system. The operations researcher might be interested in determining the numbers of servers and the particular server arrangements that ensure that a prespecified probability of loss (overflow from both primary and overflow servers) is not exceeded.

We will describe a technique, called the equivalent random method, for the approximate analysis of such a system. The theoretical basis of the equivalent random method has already been discussed in Section 4–3. We begin with a discussion of the simplest overflow system, which consists of a single primary group with one server and an overflow group with one server, as illustrated in Figure 4–3.

Let P_1 be the proportion of time that the overflow server is busy. The load carried on the overflow server is the difference between the load $aB(1, a)$ that overflows the primary server and the load $aB(2, a)$ that overflows both the primary server and the overflow server. Since the load carried on a single server equals the proportion of time that server is busy,

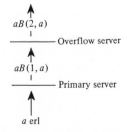

Figure 4–3.

it follows that

$$P_1 = a[B(1, a) - B(2, a)] \tag{7.1}$$

where $B(s, a)$ is the Erlang loss formula.

Now consider the probability Π_1 that a customer who overflows the primary server finds the overflow server busy. Since the customers arrive at the two-server (primary and overflow) system in a Poisson stream, they see the same distribution of states on the two-server system as would an outside observer. It follows that Π_1 is the conditional probability that the overflow server is busy, given that the primary server is busy. Applying the definition of conditional probability, we have

$$\Pi_1 = \frac{B(2, a)}{B(1, a)}, \tag{7.2}$$

which can be written

$$\Pi_1 = \frac{aB(2, a)}{aB(1, a)}. \tag{7.3}$$

We can conclude from equation (7.3) that the proportion of overflow customers who find the overflow server occupied, and thus are cleared from the system, is the ratio of the load overflowing the second server to the load overflowing the first server. Hence, viewing the overflow server as a system by itself, whose input stream is the overflow stream from the first server, the proportion of customers who find the overflow server busy is the ratio of the load not carried (that is, overflowing the second server) to the load offered (that is, overflowing the first server).

Comparison of equations (7.1) and (7.2) shows that

$$P_1 \neq \Pi_1, \tag{7.4}$$

from which we conclude that the overflow stream from the first server is not a Poisson stream. This should also be apparent from the fact that the probability that a customer will request service from the second server in any interval $(t, t + h)$ is $\lambda h + o(h)$ as $h \to 0$ if the first server is busy at time t, and zero if the first server is idle at time t. If the overflow stream were Poisson, then this probability would be $\lambda h + o(h)$ as $h \to 0$, independent of any other considerations.

It should now be clear that the following analogous properties are true for overflow systems composed of a single s-server primary group and a single c-server overflow group:

1. The overflow stream is not Poisson.

2. Of those customers who overflow the primary group, the proportion Π_c who are also blocked on the overflow group is the ratio

$$\Pi_c = \frac{aB(s + c, a)}{aB(s, a)}. \tag{7.5}$$

The situation can be represented by Figure 4–4. Property 1 implies that overflow systems cannot, in general, be studied by the elementary methods developed thus far in this text (except through the use of multidimensional state equations, which is not usually practical). Property 2 is used in the equivalent random method, which was developed independently by Bretschneider [1956] and Wilkinson [1956] to facilitate the approximate analysis of more complicated overflow systems, and to which we now direct our attention.

Consider the system on the left-hand side of Figure 4–5. In this system, a group of c servers acts as the common overflow group for all traffic overflowing the n primary groups. The ith primary group is assumed to consist of s_i servers, and to receive a direct Poisson load of a_i erl. The service times on all groups are assumed to be independently and identically exponentially distributed.

We shall analyze this system by means of an approximation technique widely known in teletraffic engineering as the *equivalent random method*:

For the purposes of our approximate analysis, we represent the load that overflows the ith primary group by two parameters, the mean α_i

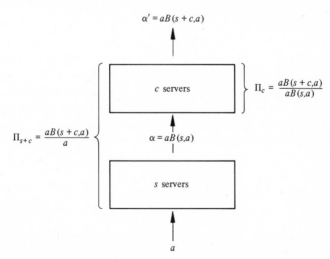

Figure 4–4.

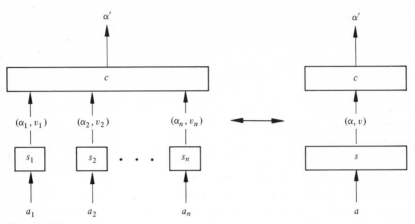

Figure 4–5.

and variance v_i, which are calculated according to equations (3.1) and (3.2):

$$\alpha_i = a_i B(s_i, a_i) \, (i = 1, 2, \ldots, n) \tag{7.6}$$

$$v_i = \alpha_i \left(1 - \alpha_i + \frac{a_i}{s_i + 1 + \alpha_i - a_i} \right) \quad (i = 1, 2, \ldots, n). \tag{7.7}$$

That is, the load overflowing a primary group is characterized by the mean and variance of the equilibrium overflow distribution that would result if the overflowing customers were handled by an infinite-server overflow group. We denote by α' the mean value of the load that overflows the c-server overflow group.

We wish to calculate the proportion of customers who overflow the c-server overflow group, given that they overflow a primary group. That is, we wish to calculate the probability that a customer who finds all s_i servers busy in his primary group will also find all c servers busy in the overflow group. Although in reality the value of this probability will, in general, be different for different values of the index i, it seems reasonable that the value of the ratio

$$\frac{\alpha'}{\alpha_1 + \alpha_2 + \cdots + \alpha_n}$$

should provide a meaningful approximation to this probability. It remains to calculate α'.

To this end, we replace the n primary groups and their respective Poisson loads with a single "equivalent random" primary group and a single "equivalent random" load, as indicated on the right-hand side of Figure 4–5. The number s of servers in the equivalent random group and the size a (in erlangs) of the equivalent random load are chosen such that the mean α and variance v of the total overflow load offered to the overflow group remain constant. Thus, since the primary groups are independent of each other, we have

$$\alpha = \alpha_1 + \cdots + \alpha_n \qquad (7.8)$$

$$v = v_1 + \cdots + v_n. \qquad (7.9)$$

Now the values of the equivalent random load a and the equivalent random group size s are chosen to satisfy the following equations for the (known) moments α and v:

$$\alpha = aB(s, a) \qquad (7.10)$$

$$v = \alpha \left(1 - \alpha + \frac{a}{s + 1 + \alpha - a} \right). \qquad (7.11)$$

Then it follows that

$$\alpha' = aB(s + c, a). \qquad (7.12)$$

In summary, the equivalent random method is to replace the system on the left-hand side of Figure 4–5 with the system on the right-hand side, where the values a and s are chosen such that the resulting overflow moments α and v remain constant. Then, in this new "equivalent random" system, of those customers who overflow the s-server primary group, the proportion who also find all c servers busy on the overflow group is, according to equation (7.5),

$$\Pi_c = \frac{aB(s + c, a)}{aB(s, a)} = \frac{\alpha'}{\alpha}. \qquad (7.13)$$

We take the value Π_c, calculated according to equation (7.13), as the probability of blocking on the overflow group suffered by overflow traffic from the primary groups. Likewise, the proportion Π of all customers who are blocked on both the primary and overflow groups is approximated by

$$\Pi = \frac{aB(s + c, a)}{a_1 + a_2 + \cdots + a_n}. \qquad (7.14)$$

It remains only to discuss how to solve equations (7.10) and (7.11) numerically for the values a and s that correspond to a given pair α and v.

Curves that effect this solution are given in Wilkinson [1956]. A useful set of tables and curves, with accompanying text and examples, is given in Wilkinson [1970].

An easy and fairly accurate approximate solution to equations (7.10) and (7.11), given by Rapp [1964], is (where $z = v/\alpha$ is the *peakedness factor*)

$$a = v + 3 z (z - 1) \qquad (7.15)$$

and, solving equation (7.11) for s,

$$s = \frac{a(\alpha + z)}{\alpha + z - 1} - \alpha - 1. \qquad (7.16)$$

(Note that $z > 1$. See Exercise 9.) These estimates of a and s are generally on the high side of the exact values. By rounding s down to its integral part $[s]$, the corresponding value of a that produces the desired peakedness factor z is then found by solving equation (7.16) for a:

$$a = \frac{([s] + \alpha + 1)(\alpha + z - 1)}{\alpha + z}. \qquad (7.17)$$

For a numerical example, see Exercise 14.

Suppose now that an overflow system is composed of a single primary group to which two independent Poisson loads a_1 and a_2 are offered, and an overflow group that receives only the overflow from a_1. To determine the proportion of overflow customers (from a_1) who are blocked on the overflow group, one would calculate the overflow mean and variance associated with only the load a_1. These values α_1 and v_1, which can be calculated according to formulas given in Exercise 10, would then determine the equivalent random values (a, s). For a numerical example, see Exercises 15. An extension of the equivalent random method to the case where the overflow streams are correlated is given by Neal [1971].

The equivalent random method has proved to be very useful in teletraffic engineering, and doubtless will prove useful in other applications.

Exercises

1. **a.** Three cities, A, B, and C, are interconnected by two trunk groups, group 1 consisting of s_1 trunks connecting A and B, and group 2 consisting of s_2 trunks between B and C (Figure 4–6). A call

Figure 4–6.

between A and C simultaneously holds a trunk in each group. Blocked calls are cleared. Write and solve the equilibrium state equations for this network.

b. Consider the network of part **a** augmented by the addition of group of s trunks directly connecting A and C. In the augmented network, all calls between A and C are carried on the new group if a trunk is available. Calls between A and C that find all s trunks in the new group busy are alternate-routed via groups 1 and 2 if there is an idle trunk in each group, and are cleared otherwise. Whenever a direct trunk between A and C becomes available and there is at least one overflow call in progress, an overflow call will be switched down from the alternate route to the direct route, thus using one less trunk to complete the call. Write and solve the equilibrium state equations for this network.

c. Consider the same network as in part **b**, but without the capability of switching alternate-routed calls down to the direct route. Is this system easier or harder to analyze than that of part **b**? Why?

d. Suppose now that calls offered to any of the three direct groups can be alternate-routed via the other two, and that any alternate-routed call can be switched back to its direct route. Write and solve the equilibrium state equations for this network.

2. A group of s trunks serves two types of Poisson traffic on a BCC basis. Type 1 is ordinary telephone traffic, with arrival rate λ_1 and exponential holding times with mean μ_1^{-1}. Type 2 is "wideband" data traffic, with arrival rate λ_2 and exponential holding times with mean μ_2^{-1}. Each wideband call requires the simultaneous use of k trunks for transmission. If a wideband call finds less than k idle trunks, it is cleared from the system. Find the proportion of ordinary calls and the proportion of wideband calls that are lost.

3. A group of s servers handles n types of customers. A customer of type i is cleared from the system if on arrival he finds all servers busy or $k_i \leq s$ other customers of his own type in service $(i = 1, 2, \ldots, n)$. Customers of type i arrive in an independent Poisson stream at rate

λ_i, and have exponential service times with mean μ_i^{-1}. Find the probability of blocking seen by customers of each type.

4. A group of s servers handles two types of customers on a BCC basis. Type 1 is Poisson traffic with arrival rate λ. Type 2 is quasirandom traffic generated by n sources, each bidding with rate γ when idle. Service times are exponential with means μ_1^{-1} and μ_2^{-1}, respectively. Find the probability of blocking for customers of each type.

5. Customers arrive according to a Poisson process with rate λ at a group of s servers, and blocked customers are cleared. The service time T of a customer is composed of n independent phases, $T = T_1 + \cdots + T_n$, where the duration T_i of the ith phase has the exponential distribution, $P\{T_i > x\} = e^{-\mu_i x}$ $(x \geqq 0; i = 1, 2, \ldots, n)$. Let P_j be the equilibrium probability that j servers are busy $(j = 0, 1, \ldots, s)$. Show that $\{P_j\}$ is the Erlang loss distribution

$$P_j = \frac{a^j/j!}{\sum_{k=0}^{s} a^k/k!} \qquad (j = 0, 1, \ldots, s),$$

where $a = \lambda\tau$ with $\tau = 1/\mu_1 + \cdots + 1/\mu_n$. (This proves a restricted version of the theorem of Chapter 3 that the equilibrium state distribution for any BCC system with Poisson input and arbitrary service time distribution function with finite mean is the Erlang loss distribution.)

6. The following model can be used to study talking and dialing equipment interactions in a modern private branch exchange telephone switching system. Calls arrive at random to two groups of servers, G_1 (time slots for talking) and G_2 (digit trunks for dialing). If an arrival finds all servers in G_1 busy, the call is cleared from the system. If an arrival finds at least one idle server in each of G_1 and G_2, the call holds one server in each group simultaneously for an exponentially distributed time interval with mean μ_1^{-1} (dialing time); it then releases the server in G_2 but retains the server in G_1 for an additional exponentially distributed time with mean μ_2^{-1} (conversation length). If an arrival finds all servers in G_2 busy and at least one idle server in G_1, the call holds a server (waits) in G_1 until it gains access to an idle server in G_2; it then proceeds in the same manner as a call that initially finds an idle server in both G_1 and G_2. Write and solve an appropriate set of equilibrium state equations for this system.

7. Calls arrive according to a Poisson process with rate λ at a call distributor that routes each call to one of two trunk groups, composed

of s_1 and s_2 trunks, respectively. Let $n_1 \geq s_1$ and $n_2 \geq s_2$ be integers. If an arrival occurs when j_i calls are in progress on group i ($i = 1, 2$) then with probability $(n_i - j_i)/(n_1 + n_2 - j_1 - j_2)$ the new arrival is routed to group i. A call routed to group i that finds all s_i trunks busy is cleared from the system. Call holding times are exponential with mean μ^{-1}, and $\lambda/\mu = a$. If $P(j_1, j_2)$ is the equilibrium probability that there are j_1 calls on group 1 and j_2 calls on group 2, show that (see Appendix D of Buchner and Neal [1971])

$$P(j_1, j_2) = c \, \frac{\dbinom{n_1}{j_1} \dbinom{n_2}{j_2}}{\dbinom{n_1 + n_2}{j_1 + j_2}} \, \frac{a^{j_1 + j_2}}{(j_1 + j_2)!}.$$

How might one surmise a solution of this form?

8. *Burke's theorem.* The output of an equilibrium BCD s-server queue with exponential service times and Poisson input with rate λ is again a Poisson process with rate λ. That is, if equilibrium exists at time zero, then the probability $P_j(t)$ that exactly j customers will complete service in an interval $(0, t)$ is given by

$$P_j(t) = \frac{(\lambda t)^j}{j!} e^{-\lambda t} \qquad (j = 0, 1, \ldots).$$

a. Consider the time intervals $(0, h)$ and $(h, t + h)$. Let $N(a, b)$ be the number of service completions in (a, b), and let $M(x)$ be the number of customers waiting or in service at time x. Show that

$$
\begin{aligned}
P\{N(0, t + h) &= j \mid M(0) = k\} \\
&= \lambda h P\{N(h, t + h) = j \mid M(h) = k + 1\} \\
&\quad + \mu(k) h P\{N(h, t + h) = j - 1 \mid M(h) = k - 1\} \\
&\quad + [1 - \lambda h - \mu(k)h] P\{N(h, t + h) = j \mid M(h) = k\} + o(h) \\
&\qquad\qquad\qquad\qquad\qquad\qquad\qquad\qquad\qquad\qquad (h \to 0)
\end{aligned}
$$

where $\mu(k) = k\mu$ for $k = 0, 1, \ldots, s$, and $\mu(k) = s\mu$ for $k = s, s + 1, \ldots$; and μ^{-1} is the mean service time.

b. Let $P_j(t \mid k) = P\{N(0, t) = j \mid M(0) = k\}$, and show that

$$
\begin{aligned}
\frac{d}{dt} P_j(t \mid k) &= \lambda P_j(t \mid k + 1) + \mu(k) P_{j-1}(t \mid k - 1) \\
&\quad - [\lambda + \mu(k)] P_j(t \mid k).
\end{aligned}
$$

c. Let $P_j(t; k) = P\{N(0, t) = j, M(0) = k\}$, and show that

$$\frac{d}{dt} P_j(t; k) = \mu(k + 1)P_j(t; k + 1) + \lambda P_{j-1}(t; k - 1)$$
$$- [\mu(k) + \lambda]P_j(t; k).$$

d. Let $P_j(t) = \sum_{k=0}^{\infty} P_j(t; k)$, and show that

$$\frac{d}{dt} P_j(t) = \lambda P_{j-1}(t) - \lambda P_j(t).$$

e. Conclude that Burke's theorem is true.
Proofs of this theorem were given by Burke [1956] and Reich [1957]. The proof outlined here was given by Galliher [1959]. An outline of Burke's proof is given in Exercise 2 of Chapter 5.

9. Show that, if $a > 0$, then

$$v = \alpha \qquad \text{when } s = 0$$

$$v > \alpha \qquad \text{when } s \geq 1,$$

where α and v are defined by equations (3.1) and (3.2).

10. *Apportioning the moments of the overflow distribution.* Suppose that customers arrive in n independent Poisson streams with rates $\lambda_1, \ldots, \lambda_n$ at a single primary group of servers and, if all servers in the primary group are busy, are served on a single infinite-server overflow group. Let μ^{-1} be the mean service time, and set $a_i = \lambda_i/\mu$ $(i = 1, 2, \ldots, n)$. Let N_i be the number of customers from the ith Poisson stream present on the overflow group at an arbitrary instant in equilibrium. Then, with $a = a_1 + \cdots + a_n$ and $N = N_1 + \cdots + N_n$,

$$E(N_i) = \frac{a_i}{a} E(N) \tag{10.1}$$

$$V(N_i) = \left(\frac{a_i}{a}\right)^2 V(N) + \frac{a_i}{a}\left(1 - \frac{a_i}{a}\right) E(N) \tag{10.2}$$

$$\text{Cov}(N_i, N_j) = \left(\frac{a_i}{a}\right)\left(\frac{a_j}{a}\right)[V(N) - E(N)]. \tag{10.3}$$

For simplicity, we shall prove the results (10.1)–(10.3) for the case $n = 2$ only.

a. Assume exponential service times. Let M be the number of customers in service on the primary group, and define $h(j, k_1, k_2) = P\{M = j, N_1 = k_1, N_2 = k_2\}$. Write the equilibrium state equations for the distribution $\{h(j, k_1, k_2)\}$ and show that the solution is

$$h(j, k_1, k_2) = P(j, k) \binom{k}{k_i} \left(\frac{a_1}{a}\right)^{k_1} \left(\frac{a_2}{a}\right)^{k_2},$$

where $P(j, k)$ is given by equation (3.33). [*Hint:* Substitute the above expression for $h(j, k_1, k_2)$ into the state equations, and show that equations (3.3) and (3.4) result.]

b. Show that

$$P\{N_1 = k_1, N_2 = k_2 \mid N = k\} = \binom{k}{k_i} \left(\frac{a_1}{a}\right)^{k_1} \left(\frac{a_2}{a}\right)^{k_2}.$$

$$(10.4)$$

c. Show that

$$E(N_i \mid N = k) = k \frac{a_i}{a} \tag{10.5}$$

$$E(N_i^2 \mid N = k) = k(k-1)\left(\frac{a_i}{a}\right)^2 + k\frac{a_i}{a}. \tag{10.6}$$

d. Show that (10.5) implies (10.1).

e. Show that (10.6) implies

$$E(N_i^2) = \left(\frac{a_i}{a}\right)^2 E(N^2) + \left(\frac{a_i}{a}\right)\left(1 - \frac{a_i}{a}\right)E(N). \tag{10.7}$$

f. Show that (10.7) implies (10.2). Define the *peakedness factor* for any stream as its overflow distribution variance-to-mean ratio, and show that equation (10.2) can be written

$$z_i - 1 = p_i(z - 1), \tag{10.8}$$

where p_i is the proportion of customers in stream i, and z_i and z are the relevant peakedness factors.

g. Continue the argument of parts **b–f** to prove (10.3).

h. Conclude that, for exponential service times, the moments of the overflow distribution corresponding to the ith Poisson stream (at least for $n = 2$) are given by equations (10.1), (10.2), and (10.3) with $E(N) = \alpha$ given by (3.1) and $V(N) = v$ given by (3.2). These results, which are useful in the application of the equivalent random method, were originally obtained by A. Descloux [1962, unpublished] and Lotze [1964]. The following argument shows that the assumption of exponential service times is not necessary for the validity of equation (10.4), and therefore the results (10.1)–(10.3) are valid for arbitrary service time distribution function: Because the original streams of traffic are Poisson, each sees the same probability of blocking on the primary group. Hence, given that a customer is blocked, the probability that this customer is from stream i is the ratio a_i/a. Further, this probability is independent of the composition of the other customers in service on the overflow group. Therefore, given the number of simultaneous customers in service on the overflow group, the distribution of the number of customers of type i is the binomial with proportion a_i/a, given by equation (10.4). It is interesting that the formulas (10.1)–(10.3) are valid for arbitrary service time distribution function, whereas the moment $V(N)$ [but not $E(N)$] depends on the distribution of service times. [If the service times are exponentially distributed, then $V(N) = v$ is given by equation (3.2).]

11. (A. Descloux [1969, unpublished].) Consider a priority reservation system with s identical exponential servers, where customers arrive in s independent Poisson streams, $S_1, S_2, \ldots, S_s$. Customers in stream S_i may start service only when $i - 1$ or fewer servers are busy. All customers wait as long as necessary to obtain service. (If we denote by a_i the magnitude of the load offered by the customers in stream S_i, then this model reduces to the s-server Erlang delay model when $a_1 = a_2 = \cdots = a_{s-1} = 0$.)

   a. Let $P(k; n_1, n_2, \ldots, n_k)$ be the equilibrium probability of the following event: k servers are busy and n_i customers from stream S_i are waiting, $i = 1, 2, \ldots, k, k = 1, 2, \ldots$. Verify that the corresponding equilibrium state equations are (where $a = a_1 + \cdots + a_s$):

$$aP(0) = P(1; 0) \qquad (k = 0) \qquad (11.1)$$

$$(a + 1)P(1; 0) = 2P(2; 0, 0) + P(1; 1) + aP(0)$$
$$(k = 1, n_1 = 0) \qquad (11.2)$$

$$(a + 1)P(1; n_1) = 2P(2; n_1, 0)$$
$$+ P(1; n_1 + 1) + a_1 P(1; n_1 - 1)$$
$$(k = 1, n_1 > 0) \qquad (11.3)$$

$$(a + k)P(k; n_1, n_2, \ldots, n_{k-1}, 0)$$

$$= (k + 1)P(k + 1; n_1, n_2, \ldots, n_{k-1}, 0, 0)$$

$$+ kP(k; n_1, n_2, \ldots, n_{k-1}, 1)$$

$$+ \sum_{i=1}^{k-1} a_i P(k; n_1, \ldots, n_{i-1}, n_i - 1, n_{i+1}, \ldots, n_{k-1}, 0)$$

$$+ (a_k + a_{k+1} + \cdots + a_s)P(k - 1; n_1, \ldots, n_{k-1})$$

$$(1 < k < s, n_k = 0) \qquad (11.4)$$

$$(a + k)P(k; n_1, \ldots, n_k)$$

$$= (k + 1)P(k + 1; n_1, \ldots, n_k, 0)$$

$$+ kP(k; n_1, \ldots, n_k + 1)$$

$$+ \sum_{i=1}^{k} a_i P(k; n_1, \ldots, n_i - 1, \ldots, n_k)$$

$$(1 < k < s, n_k > 0) \qquad (11.5)$$

$$(a + s)P(s; n_1, n_2, \ldots, n_{s-1}, 0)$$

$$= sP(s; n_1, n_2, \ldots, n_{s-1}, 1)$$

$$+ \sum_{i=1}^{s-1} a_i P(s; n_1, \ldots, n_i - 1, \ldots, n_{s-1}, 0)$$

$$+ a_s P(s - 1; n_1, \ldots, n_{s-1})$$

$$(k = s, n_s = 0) \qquad (11.6)$$

$$(a + s)P(s; n_1, \ldots, n_s)$$

$$= sP(s; n_1, n_2, \ldots, n_s + 1)$$

$$+ \sum_{i=1}^{s} a_i P(s; n_1, \ldots, n_i - 1, \ldots, n_s)$$

$$(k = s, n_s > 0). \qquad (11.7)$$

b. Define the generating functions

$$G(k; x_1, x_2, \ldots, x_k) = \sum_n P(k; n_1, n_2, \ldots, n_k)x_1^{n_1}x_2^{n_2} \cdots x_k^{n_k}$$

$$(11.8)$$

and

$$F(k; x_1, x_2, \ldots, x_{k-1})$$

$$= \sum_n P(k; n_1, \ldots, n_{k-1}, 0)x_1^{n_1}x_2^{n_2} \cdots x_{k-1}^{n_{k-1}} \qquad (11.9)$$

where $\sum_n$ indicates a summation over all nonnegative values of

$n_1, n_2, \ldots$. Show that these generating functions satisfy the following equations:

$$aG(0) - F(1) = 0 \qquad (k = 0) \qquad (11.10)$$

$$\left[(a + k)x_k - k - x_k \sum_{i=1}^{k} a_i x_i \right] G(k; x_1, \ldots, x_k)$$

$$+ kF(k; x_1, \ldots, x_{k-1})$$

$$- x_k(a_k + \cdots + a_s)G(k - 1; x_1, \ldots, x_{k-1})$$

$$- x_k(k + 1)F(k + 1; x_1, \ldots, x_k) = 0$$

$$(0 < k < s) \qquad (11.11)$$

$$\left[(a + s)x_s - s - x_s \sum_{i=1}^{s} a_i x_i \right] G(s; x_1, \ldots, x_s)$$

$$+ sF(s; x_1, \ldots, x_{s-1})$$

$$- x_s a_s G(s - 1; x_1, \ldots, x_{s-1}) = 0$$

$$(k = s). \qquad (11.12)$$

c. In what follows, we make the convention that a sum whose lower limit exceeds its upper limit is to be set equal to zero. To avoid minor qualifications, it will also be convenient to introduce two dummy variables x_0 and x_{-1}, the latter being used only to avoid an empty product in (11.13).

Show that, if we multiply equation (11.10) by $x_{-1}x_0$ and the kth equation in (11.11)–(11.12) by $x_{-1}x_0x_1 \ldots x_{k-1}$, then addition of the resulting expressions yields

$$\sum_{k=0}^{s} x_{-1}x_0x_1 \cdots x_{k-1}$$

$$\times \left[x_k(a + k) - k - x_k \sum_{i=1}^{k} a_i x_i - x_k x_{k+1} \sum_{i=k+1}^{s} a_i \right]$$

$$\times G(k; x_1, \ldots, x_k) = 0. \qquad (11.13)$$

d. Observe that the expressions within the square brackets in (11.13) vanish for $x_i = 1, i = 0, 1, \ldots, s$. Differentiate (11.13) with respect

to $x_j, j = 1, 2, \ldots, s$, set all the x's equal to unity, and conclude
that

$$P(j - 1) \sum_{i=j}^{s} a_i + a_j \sum_{k=j}^{s} P(k) = jP(j) \qquad (j = 1, 2, \ldots, s)$$

$$(11.14)$$

where $P(k) = G(k; 1, 1, \ldots, 1)$ is the equilibrium probability
that k servers are busy. Note that $P(k)$ is also the probability of
blocking for customers in stream S_k.

Equation (11.14) and the normalization equation

$$\sum_{k=0}^{s} P(k) = 1$$

permit successive calculation of the distribution $\{P(k)\}$ whenever
the offered loads $a_1, \ldots, a_s$ are such that statistical equilibrium
obtains (an assumption made tacitly in the preceding derivation).
Interestingly, the equilibrium conditions can be shown (through
rather complicated analysis) to be polynomial functions of the
offered loads, this nonlinearity being a reflection of the interaction
among the different streams of traffic. For instance, when $s = 3$
the equilibrium condition for stream S_1 is

$$6a_1 + 3a_2 + 2a_3 + a_1 a_3 - 6 < 0.$$

e. Give a "conservation of flow" argument for equation (11.14).
f. Show that when $a_1 = a_2 = \cdots = a_{s-1} = 0$ and $a_s = a$, then
equation (11.14) yields

$$P(s) = C(s, a)$$

where $C(s, a)$ is the Erlang delay formula.
12. *Economic engineering of flat-rate and measured-rate trunks* (P. J.
Burke [1963, unpublished]). Suppose two classes of trunks are
available, the first of which is paid for by a flat monthly rental per
trunk, and the second of which is charged for according to usage.
It is ascertained that a total of n trunks are needed to meet a given
service criterion, and it is desired to divide these into two groups, c
flat-rate trunks and s measured-rate trunks, in such a manner as to
minimize overall cost. The trunks are arranged so that a call hunts
first over the flat-rate trunks and then, if there are no idle flat-rate

trunks, over the measured-rate trunks. If the call fails to find an idle measured-rate trunk, the call is handled by an operator, who puts it into a queue. The queued calls seize the first available trunks of either type. All calls are assumed to wait as long as necessary for service. To compare costs of various divisions of the total group of n trunks, it is necessary to calculate the load carried on the c flat-rate trunks and the s measured-rate trunks for different values of c and s $(c + s = n)$ for a given offered load a. Show that the load $L(s)$ carried on the s measured-rate trunks is

$$L(s) = s \frac{a}{s + c} C(s + c, a) + a \left(1 - \frac{a}{s + c} C(s + c, a)\right)$$

$$\times [B(c, a) - B(s + c, a)].$$

What is the load carried on the flat-rate trunks?

13. Consider a group of s servers with a fixed order of access. No server can be idle if any customers are waiting. The arrival process is Poisson, service times are exponential, and the magnitude of the offered load is a erl. Customers who find all s servers occupied may wait or defect from the queue in any arbitrary manner. Let $p(s + 1, a)$ be the equilibrium probability that at least one customer is waiting for service.

   a. Show that equation (5.2) of the text remains valid with this new definition of $p(s + 1, a)$.

   b. Show that the probability p_m that a customer is not blocked and is served by the mth server is given by

$$p_m = [1 - p(s + 1, a)][B(m - 1, a) - B(m, a)]$$

$$(m = 1, 2, \ldots, s). \qquad (13.1)$$

Note: If the queueing model is a birth-and-death process, then $p(s + 1, a) = \sum_{j=s+1}^{\infty} P_j$, where the distribution $\{P_j\}$ is given by equation (1.1) of Chapter 3. An example of a queueing model that is not a birth-and-death process, but for which equations (5.2) of the text and (13.1) in this exercise are valid, is one where any customer whose service does not commence within a fixed time t after his arrival will defect from the queue. To evaluate these formulas, of course, one must be able to evaluate $p(s + 1, a)$.

14. $a_1 = 10$ erl of Poisson traffic is offered to a group of 10 servers, and

$a_2 = 5$ erl of Poisson traffic is offered to a group of 5 servers. An overflow group of c servers handles the overflow from the two primary groups on a BCC basis. Service times are independent, identically distributed exponential variables.

a. Find the value of c that gives a loss of 10 percent on the overflow group.

b. Find the loss for the system as a whole.

c. Find the loss on the overflow group and the loss for the system as a whole if a_1 and a_2 are each increased by 50 percent.

15. Ten erl of Poisson traffic is offered to a group of 10 servers. This stream of Poisson traffic is evenly divided between two types of customers, called high- and low-priority customers. Both substreams of traffic are Poisson, and service times have a common exponential distribution. The high-priority customers who overflow the 10-server group are routed to an overflow group of c servers (where they are handled on a BCC basis). The low-priority customers who overflow the 10-server group are cleared from the system. Determine the smallest value of c such that the proportion of high-priority customers who do not receive service is no greater than 0.01. [*Hint:* Use formulas (10.1) and (10.2) of the exercises.]

16. *Finite-source systems with nonidentical sources.* We proved in Section 3–8 that in any equilibrium n-source (one-dimensional) birth-and-death queueing system with quasirandom input (identical sources), the state distribution seen by a source when placing a request is the same as would be seen by an outside observer of the corresponding $(n - 1)$-source system. This suggests that for (multi-dimensional) birth-and-death systems with nonidentical sources, the state distribution seen by a particular source when placing a request is the same as that particular source would see if he placed no requests, but instead acted as an outside observer of the system. A. Descloux [1967] has observed that this generalization cannot always be made, and has given the necessary and sufficient conditions for its validity. The following simple example was provided by P. J. Burke.

   Consider a single-server system with two sources. Assume that source i generates requests at constant rate γ_i when idle and rate 0 otherwise, and has exponential service times with mean μ_i^{-1}. Let $S_i = 0$ if source i is idle, $S_i = 1$ if source i is being served, and, when applicable, $S_i = 2$ if source i is waiting for service. Let $P\{S_1 = j, S_2 = k\} = p(j, k)$ $(j, k = 0, 1, 2)$ be the equilibrium state distribution.

a. Show that the probability b_2 that source 2 is blocked (finds the server occupied when placing a request for service) is given by

$$b_2 = \frac{p(1, 0)}{p(0, 0) + p(1, 0)}.$$

b. Show that if source 2 makes no requests for service but instead acts the part of an outside observer, then the probability b_2' that source 2 sees the server occupied is given by

$$b_2' = \frac{\gamma_1/\mu_1}{1 + (\gamma_1/\mu_1)}.$$

c. Assume that blocked customers are cleared. Find the distribution $\{p(j, k)\}$ and show that $b_2 = b_2'$.

d. Assume that blocked customers are delayed. Find the distribution $\{p(j, k)\}$ and show that

$$b_2 = \frac{(\gamma_1/\mu_2)(\mu_2 + \gamma_1 + \gamma_2)}{\mu_1 + (\mu_1/\mu_2)\gamma_1 + \gamma_2 + (\gamma_1/\mu_2)(\mu_2 + \gamma_1 + \gamma_2)}.$$

Conclude that, in general, $b_2 \neq b_2'$. Note, however, that if $\mu_1 = \mu_2$, then indeed $b_2 = b_2'$.

Imbedded Markov Chain Queueing Models

5

5–1. Introduction

In this chapter we shall investigate some important queueing models that cannot be studied in the framework of the birth-and-death process.

Recall that a queue is characterized by the input process, the service mechanism, and the queue discipline. In the preceding chapters we concentrated mainly on queues with Poisson or quasirandom input and exponential service times. These assumptions imply that the future evolution of the system from some time t depends only on the state of the system at time t, and is independent of the history of the system prior to time t. In these models, the "state" of the system could always be specified in terms of the number of customers present. (In the multidimensional case, the state was specified in terms of the numbers of customers of each type present at time t.)

Suppose that we are interested in a queue for which knowledge of the number of customers present at any time t is not sufficient information to permit complete analysis of the model. For example, consider the case in which the service times are assumed exponential, but the customers' arrival epochs are separated by a constant time interval. Then the future evolution of the system from some time t would depend not only on the number of customers present at time t, but also on the elapsed time since the last customer arrival epoch (because the arrival epoch of the next customer is strictly determined by the arrival epoch of the last customer).

Clearly, a new method of analysis is required. A powerful method for the analysis of certain queueing models, such as the model in the above example, is that of the *imbedded Markov chain*, introduced by Kendall [1951, 1953]. As with the birth-and-death process, there is a vast theory of Markov chains. More generally, both are subsumed under the heading Markov processes. As is our policy, we shall aim at as direct an approach to the analysis of our queueing models as possible, without extended excursions into the surrounding theoretical structure. Thus we shall introduce the main ideas behind the theory of the imbedded Markov chain, and show how these ideas facilitate the analysis of certain important queueing models.

That is, we shall study in this chapter queueing models in which the input process and service time distribution function are such that the imbedded Markov chain analysis is applicable. We shall restrict our attention mainly to equilibrium queues in which blocked customers wait until served and in which service is in order of arrival.

Consider the following input process. Customers arrive at epochs T_1, $T_2, \ldots, T_k, \ldots$. The interarrival times $T_{k+1} - T_k$ $(k = 0, 1, \ldots; T_0 = 0)$ are identically distributed, mutually independent, positive random variables with distribution function

$$G(x) = P\{T_{k+1} - T_k \leq x\}$$

independent of the index k. The input process is then said to be *recurrent*. Queues with recurrent input can sometimes be studied by the imbedded Markov chain analysis.

An example of a recurrent input process is the previously mentioned case of constant interrarrival times $[G(x) = 0$ when $x <$ constant and $G(x) = 1$ when $x \geq$ constant]. Another example is Poisson input $[G(x) = 1 - e^{-\lambda x}]$. Quasirandom input is not recurrent (why?).

Let us calculate, for a recurrent input process with arrival epochs $T_1, T_2, \ldots$ and interarrival time distribution function $G(x) = P\{T_{k+1} - T_k \leq x\}$ $(k = 0, 1, \ldots; T_0 = 0)$, the probability $P_j(t)$ that j arrivals occur in an interval $(T_k, T_k + t]$. Note that the point T_k is either an arrival epoch $(k \geq 1)$ or the starting point of the process $(k = 0)$, and that T_k is not included in the interval. Denote by $G^{*j}(t)$ the j-fold convolution of G with itself. Then

$$G^{*j}(t) = P\{T_{k+j} - T_k \leq t\} \qquad (j = 2, 3, \ldots; k = 0, 1, \ldots). \qquad (1.1)$$

If we define $G^{*0}(t) = 1$ and $G^{*1}(t) = G(t)$, then it follows that

$$P_j(t) = G^{*j}(t) - G^{*(j+1)}(t) \qquad (j = 0, 1, \ldots). \qquad (1.2)$$

For example, if the interarrival times are exponentially distributed, $G(t) = 1 - e^{-\lambda t}$, then $G^{*j}(t)$ is the j-phase Erlangian distribution function:

$$G^{*j}(t) = 1 - \sum_{i=0}^{j-1} \frac{(\lambda t)^i}{i!} e^{-\lambda t}.$$

[See equation (5.31) of Chapter 2.] It follows from equation (1.2) that, as expected, $\{P_j(t)\}$ is the Poisson distribution

$$P_j(t) = \frac{(\lambda t)^j}{j!} e^{-\lambda t} \qquad (j = 0, 1, \ldots).$$

The shorthand notation $a/b/c$ is often used to describe the recurrent input BCD queue, where a specifies the interarrival time distribution function, b the service time distribution function, and c the number of servers. For example,

$GI/M/s$— arbitrary recurrent (General Independent) input, exponential (Markov) service times, s servers.

$M/G/1$— Poisson (Markov) input, arbitrary (General) service time distribution function, 1 server.

$M/D/s$— Poisson input, constant (Deterministic) service times, s servers.

$E_k/M/s$— k-phase Erlangian interarrival time distribution function, exponential service times, s servers.

From a theoretical point of view, it suffices to solve the $GI/G/s$ queue; the models listed above are merely special cases. But, of course, the more general the analysis, the less specific (and useful) is the derived information. We shall analyze some of the above models separately, in each case using special properties of the component distributions to obtain detailed quantitative information, and, hopefully, providing insight as a fringe benefit.

In preparation for the analyses of these queueing models, we start with a discussion of some important related results.

5–2. Equality of State Distributions at Arrival and Departure Epochs

Often, queueing models are analyzed by writing equations that relate state probabilities to one another at certain well-defined points in time (epochs). The choice of the particular set of points with respect to which the equations are written is governed by the mathematical properties of the model under consideration, not by unfettered choice. For example, the $M/G/1$ model is easily analyzed by relating the system states to each other at the instants at which customers finish service and leave the system. That is, we define the state of the system to be the number of customers left behind by a departing customer, and the corresponding *departing customer's distribution* $\{\Pi_j^*\}$ describes the system at this special set of points. However, the quantities of interest are the state probabilities at a different set of points, namely the arrival epochs. That is, from the point of view of an arriving customer, the number of customers that he finds in the system, not the number he leaves behind, is the quantity of interest. Fortunately, for a wide range of processes that includes the important ones, the state distributions at these two sets of points are identical.

We have already encountered some similar situations. In the $M/M/s$ (Erlang delay) model, the birth-and-death formulation led directly to the outside observer's distribution $\{P_j(t)\}$. But it was shown in Chapter 3 that the arriving customer's distribution $\{\Pi_j(t)\}$ is identical to the outside observer's distribution $\{P_j(t)\}$ whenever the input is Poisson. Thus the more relevant arriving customer's distribution had been found indirectly. Likewise, the birth-and-death formulation for the case of quasirandom input in Chapter 3 yielded the outside observer's distribution, which, though not directly equal to, was easily translated into the arriving customer's distribution.

We have the following important theorem relating the equilibrium distribution $\{\Pi_j\}$ of the number of customers found by an arrival (the arriving customer's distribution) and the equilibrium distribution $\{\Pi_j^*\}$ of the number of customers left behind by a departure (the departing customer's distribution):

In any queueing system for which the realizations of the state process are step functions with only unit jumps (positive and negative) the equilibrium state distribution just prior to arrival epochs is the same as that just following departure epochs: $\{\Pi_j\} = \{\Pi_j^*\}$. (And in addition, when the input is Poisson: $\{P_j\} = \{\Pi_j\} = \{\Pi_j^*\}$.)

Note that in this theorem, the term "queueing system" is not used in a restricted sense. The theorem applies even to systems with no servers; the queue alone may be considered the "system." The essential characteristic is simply that the number of customers present can increase and decrease by at most one customer at a time. Thus the theorem holds for all systems in statistical equilibrium considered so far in this text.

This theorem becomes intuitively obvious when one observes that during any time interval the number of upward transitions $E_j \rightarrow E_{j+1}$ cannot differ by more than one from the number of downward transitions $E_{j+1} \rightarrow E_j$. Since, in any time interval in equilibrium, the average number of upward transitions must equal the average number of downward transitions, the proportion of customers finding the system in state E_j approaches the same limit as the proportion of customers leaving the system in state E_j.

Because of this theorem's importance (which will become obvious) and because (strangely) it does not appear to be well known even among experts, we now give a formal statement and proof. The theorem and proof are taken from an adaptation by P. J. Burke [1968, unpublished] of a corresponding result by L. Takács for the $M/G/1$ queue.

Theorem. Let $\chi(t)$ be a stochastic process whose sample functions are (almost all) step functions with unit jumps. Let the points of increase after some time $t = 0$ be labeled consecutively t_α, and the points of decrease t'_α, $\alpha = 1, 2, \ldots$. Let $\chi(t_\alpha-)$ be denoted ξ_α and $\chi(t'_\alpha+)$, ζ_α. Then if either $\lim_{n \to \infty} P\{\xi_n \leq k\}$ or $\lim_{n \to \infty} P\{\zeta_n \leq k\}$ exists, then so does the other and these are equal. [Thus $\chi(t)$ has the same limiting distribution at its points of increase as it does at its points of decrease if this limiting distribution exists.]

Proof. (In the following "with probability one" may be inserted where appropriate.) Let $\chi(0) = i$. We show first that $\zeta_{n+i} \leq k \Rightarrow \xi_{n+k+1} \leq k$. Suppose $\zeta_{n+i} = j \leq k$. Then there are $n + j$ of the t_α preceding t'_{n+1}. Thus $\xi_{n+j+1} \leq j$, and, since $k - j$ arrivals later than t_{n+j+1} the state can be at most $k - j$ greater, $\xi_{n+k+1} \leq k$. Conversely, suppose $\xi_{n+k+1} = j \leq k$. Then there are $n + i + k - j$ of the t'_α preceding t_{n+k+1}, i.e., $t'_{n+i+k-j}$ is the last t'_α preceding t_{n+k+1}. Hence $\zeta_{n+i+k-j} \leq j$ and $\zeta_{n+i} \leq k$.

Therefore $P\{\zeta_{n+i} \leq k\} = P\{\xi_{n+k+1} \leq k\}$ and both sides must have the same limit. Thus, for any k,

$$\lim_{n \to \infty} P\{\zeta_{n+i} \leq k\} = \lim_{n \to \infty} P\{\xi_{n+k+1} \leq k\}$$

or

$$\lim_{n \to \infty} P\{\zeta_n \leq k\} = \lim_{n \to \infty} P\{\xi_n \leq k\}.$$

In summary, $\{P_j(t)\} = \{\Pi_j(t)\}$ when the input is Poisson, and $\{\Pi_j\} = \{\Pi_j^*\}$ when the state changes occur one at a time and statistical equilibrium prevails.

5–3. The Equation $L = \lambda W$

In an equilibrium queueing process, let $1/\lambda$ be the mean time between the arrivals of two consecutive customers, L be the mean number of customers in the system, and W be the mean time spent by a customer in the system. If the three means are finite, and certain very general conditions are met, then

$$L = \lambda W. \tag{3.1}$$

The well-known equation (3.1), which was first stated in a rigorous manner by Little [1961] (see also Jewell [1967]), is one of the most remarkable results in queueing theory. Even the definition of *system* is left flexible. For example, one may denote by L the mean queue length and W the mean waiting time for service, or by L the mean number of customers in the system (on queue and in service) and W the mean time spent in the system. It is easy to verify (3.1) for the $M/M/s$ queue for each of these interpretations. (See Exercise 8 of Chapter 3.) The result (or theorem) given by (3.1) is often referred to simply as "the equation $L = \lambda W$."

Consider for example the s-server Erlang loss system with Poisson input with rate λ and mean service time μ^{-1} ($\lambda/\mu = a$). The mean number of customers in the system during equilibrium is by definition the carried load a', given by equation (3.8) of Chapter 3:

$$L = a' = a[1 - B(s, a)].$$

The mean time spent in the system is zero for a blocked customer and μ^{-1} for a carried customer. The proportion of customers that are carried is $1 - B(s, a)$, so that the average time spent in the system by an arbitrary customer is

$$W = B(s, a) \cdot 0 + [1 - B(s, a)]\mu^{-1}.$$

Hence, $L = \lambda W$ for the Erlang loss system.

Another example of the use of the equation $L = \lambda W$ is provided by equation (10.10) of Chapter 3:

$$\sum_{j=1}^{n} jP_j[n] = a\left(1 + \frac{E(W)}{\mu^{-1}}\right) = a\mu\left(\frac{1}{\mu} + E(W)\right).$$

Direct verification of this equation, which is rather tedious, is left to Exercise 26 of Chapter 3. But it follows easily from equation (3.1); the quantity on the left-hand side is the mean number of busy sources, $a\mu$ is the mean number of customers requesting service per unit time, and $1/\mu + E(W)$ is the mean length of time from the instant a source places a request until it is again idle and available to place another request.

We can use equation (3.1) to prove easily an important assertion made several times previously in this text: In any nonscheduled system, the mean wait for service suffered by an arbitrary customer is independent of the order of service. (Recall that a nonscheduled system is one in which customers are selected for service from among those waiting without regard to the service times of the waiting customers; that is, the next customer chosen for service has the same service time distribution function as an arbitrary customer.)

To prove this fact, note that according to the equation $L = \lambda W$, the mean wait for service is proportional to the mean queue length. But the state equations from which one calculates the distribution of the number of customers in the queue are derived without regard to the order of service; the number of customers in the system does not depend on the identity of the particular customer chosen for service at any instant. Therefore, the mean queue length is also independent of the order of service, and hence, by equation (3.1), so is the mean wait for service.

This is a particularly useful fact, since the waiting time distribution function does depend on the order of service. This will be discussed in detail in Chapter 6.

As mentioned, rigorous statements and proofs of the theorem $L = \lambda W$ are given by Little [1961] and Jewell [1967]. In addition, heuristic proofs have been proposed by several authors. The following heuristic proof was suggested by P. J. Burke.

Assume that the mean values L and W exist, and consider a long time interval $(0, t)$ throughout which statistical equilibrium prevails. The mean number of customers who enter the system during this interval is λt. Imagine that each arriving customer has associated with him a waiting time. If the average waiting time is W, then the average amount of waiting time brought into the system during $(0, t)$ is $\lambda t W$. On the other hand, each customer present in the system uses up his waiting time linearly with time. If L is the average number of customers present throughout $(0, t)$, then Lt is the average amount of waiting time used up in $(0, t)$. If the system is in statistical equilibrium, then as $t \to \infty$ the accumulation of waiting time must equal the amount of waiting time used up. Hence

$$\lim_{t \to \infty} \lambda t W = \lim_{t \to \infty} Lt, \tag{3.2}$$

from which (3.1) follows.

5–4. A Result from Renewal Theory

During the discussion of the Poisson distribution in Section 2–5, the following phenomenon was noted: If the mean time between successive Poisson customer arrival epochs is λ^{-1}, then an outside observer who samples (observes) at a random instant will see that the elapsed time between his sampling epoch and the arrival epoch of the next customer also has mean λ^{-1}, instead of $\frac{1}{2}\lambda^{-1}$ as one might naively expect. The fact that this mean value exceeds $\frac{1}{2}\lambda^{-1}$ was explained (or, more precisely, verbalized) by noting that the observer would tend to sample during an interarrival interval longer than the average. In the particular case of a Poisson process, the value of this mean was obtained directly from consideration of the Markov property. In the more general case of an arbitrary recurrent process, again an observer would tend to sample during a long interarrival interval, but the length of his wait for the next customer arrival cannot be calculated by this simple device. We now discuss this phenomenon in detail for the general case of an arbitrary recurrent process.

Suppose that events occur at epochs $T_1, T_2, \ldots$, with interevent times $X_{v+1} = T_{v+1} - T_v$ $(v = 0, 1, \ldots; T_0 = 0)$ mutually independent, positive random variables with distribution function $G(x) = P\{X_v \leq x\}$ and mean interevent time β. (For example, the epochs $T_1, T_2, \ldots$ might be arrival instants of customers following a recurrent input process.) We consider an arbitrary instant t, and ask for the distribution function of the length of time R_t separating the instant t and the first event occurring after t. The time interval R_t is known as the *recurrence time* or the *residual lifetime*.

Denote by $F_t(x)$ this distribution function; that is, $F_t(x) = P\{R_t \leq x\}$ is the probability that the recurrence time R_t from an arbitrary point t to the occurrence of the next event will not exceed the value x.

The recurrence time R_t will not exceed the value x if and only if at least one event occurs between t and $t + x$. Let j be the value of the index of the last event to occur prior to epoch $t + x$. Then $R_t \leq x$ if and only if for some index j we have $t < T_j \leq t + x$; and since T_j is the last event epoch prior to $t + x$, then it follows that $t + x < T_{j+1}$. That is, as Figure 5–1 illustrates, $R_t \leq x$ if and only if the point $t + x$ is bracketed

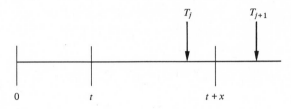

Figure 5–1.

by two successive events, the first of which lies between t and $t + x$: $t < T_j \leq t + x < T_{j+1}$. Therefore

$$F_t(x) = \sum_{j=1}^{\infty} \int_t^{t+x} [1 - G(t + x - y)]\, dP\{T_j \leq y\}$$

$$= \int_t^{t+x} [1 - G(t + x - y)]\, d\left(\sum_{j=1}^{\infty} P\{T_j \leq y\}\right). \qquad (4.1)$$

Since T_j is the time of occurrence of the jth event, $T_j \leq y$ if and only if the number $N(y)$ of events occurring in $(0, y)$ is at least j:

$$P\{T_j \leq y\} = P\{N(y) \geq j\}. \qquad (4.2)$$

Therefore

$$\sum_{j=1}^{\infty} P\{T_j \leq y\} = \sum_{j=1}^{\infty} P\{N(y) \geq j\}$$

$$= \sum_{j=1}^{\infty} \sum_{k=j}^{\infty} P\{N(y) = k\} \qquad (4.3)$$

and rearrangement of the terms on the right-hand side of equation (4.3) yields

$$\sum_{j=1}^{\infty} P\{T_j \leq y\} = \sum_{j=1}^{\infty} j P\{N(y) = j\}. \qquad (4.4)$$

That is, $\sum_{j=1}^{\infty} P\{T_j \leq y\}$ is the mean number of events occurring in the time interval $(0, y)$. For large values of y, this mean is asymptotic to

y/β, where β is the mean time between successive events. Thus

$$F_t(x) \to \frac{1}{\beta} \int_t^{t+x} [1 - G(t + x - y)] \, dy. \qquad (4.5)$$

Define $F(x) = \lim_{t \to \infty} F_t(x)$ and $R = \lim_{t \to \infty} R_t$ so that $F(x) = P\{R \leq x\}$. Then it follows from (4.5), after a change of variable, that the statistical equilibrium distribution function $F(x)$ of the recurrence time R from an arbitrary instant to the occurrence of the next event is given by

$$P\{R \leq x\} = F(x) = \frac{1}{\beta} \int_0^x [1 - G(\xi)] \, d\xi. \qquad (4.6)$$

(For a more rigorous discussion see Cox [1962] or Chapter XI of Feller [1971].)

The corresponding mean value is

$$E(R) = \int_0^\infty x \, dF(x) = \frac{1}{\beta} \int_0^\infty x[1 - G(x)] \, dx, \qquad (4.7)$$

which yields (see Exercise 3)

$$E(R) = \frac{\beta}{2} + \frac{\sigma^2}{2\beta}, \qquad (4.8)$$

where σ^2 is the variance of the interevent times.

For example, consider the special case of Poisson input with mean time λ^{-1} between successive customer arrival epochs. Then $\beta = \lambda^{-1}$, $\sigma^2 = \lambda^{-2}$, and equation (4.8) gives $E(R) = \lambda^{-1}$, the result previously obtained through consideration of the Markov property of the exponential distribution.

Following Takács, let us consider this question from a more intuitive viewpoint. If $G(x)$ is the distribution function of the length of the interval separating an arbitrary pair of successive events, let $\hat{G}(x)$ be the distribution function of the length of the particular interval that contains the observer's sampling point t. We have already argued that an observer sampling without regard to the underlying process is more likely to sample during a long interevent interval than a short one. Roughly speaking, the frequency with which an interval of length x occurs in the general population of interevent intervals is $dG(x)$. If the frequency $d\hat{G}(x)$ with which an observer selects a sampling interval of length x is proportional to both its frequency $dG(x)$ of occurrence in the population as a whole and its length x, then

$$d\hat{G}(x) = kx\, dG(x),$$

where k is the normalization constant such that $\int_0^\infty d\hat{G}(x) = 1$. Thus

$$d\hat{G}(x) = \frac{1}{\beta} x\, dG(x). \qquad (4.9)$$

The distribution function (4.6) of the length of the partial interval (from the sampling point to the next event) can be derived from the distribution function (4.9) of the length of the whole sampling interval, with the additional assumption that the location of the sampling point is uniformly distributed throughout the sampling interval. (See Exercise 4.)

In particular, for an interevent interval of given fixed length x, the mean elapsed time from a randomly chosen sampling point to the end of the interval is $x/2$; hence

$$E(R) = \int_0^\infty \frac{x}{2}\, d\hat{G}(x) = \frac{\beta}{2} + \frac{\sigma^2}{2\beta}, \qquad (4.10)$$

in agreement with equation (4.8).

The result (4.8) shows that only when the time between successive events has the constant value β is the mean recurrence time from an arbitrary point to the next event equal to $\frac{1}{2}\beta$. That is, when $\sigma^2 > 0$, then $E(R) > \beta/2$. If the time between successive events has infinite variance, then the mean wait from an arbitrary instant for the occurrence of the next event is infinite, even if the mean time between successive events is finite.

Finally, with regard to (4.6), we note for future reference the fact that if $G(\xi)$ is a distribution function defined for $0 \leq \xi < \infty$ with mean β, then the function $F(x)$ defined by

$$F(x) = \frac{1}{\beta} \int_0^x [1 - G(\xi)]\, d\xi$$

is also a distribution function, whose Laplace–Stieltjes transform $\phi(s)$ is given by

$$\phi(s) = \frac{1}{\beta} \frac{1 - \gamma(s)}{s}, \qquad (4.11)$$

where $\gamma(s)$ is the Laplace–Stieltjes transform of the distribution function $G(\xi)$. (See Exercise 5.)

5–5. The $M/G/1$ Queue

We now turn our attention to the $M/G/1$ queue in equilibrium. Customers arrive at a single server according to a Poisson process with rate λ. Customers who find the server idle seize it immediately and hold it for the service time interval. Customers who find the server busy wait until served, however long that may be. The service times are identically distributed random variables, independent of each other and the arrival epochs, with arbitrary distribution function $H(x)$ and mean length τ. Unless specifically stated otherwise, no assumption is made about the order of service of waiting customers.

We shall obtain, using several different techniques, the distribution of queue size, mean queue size, probability of delay, and mean delay (mean waiting time); and for the special case of service in order of arrival, we shall obtain the Laplace–Stieltjes transform of the waiting time distribution function.

Mean Queue Length and Mean Waiting Time: Direct Approach

Let the random variable W denote the delay or wait for service in the queue experienced by an arbitrary customer. Similarly, denote by Q the queue length (number of customers waiting for service in the queue) found by an arbitrary arrival. Using equation (3.1) and noting the equality of the outside observer's distribution and the arriving customer's distribution for systems with Poisson input we have, in the present notation,

$$E(Q) = \lambda E(W). \tag{5.1}$$

We now derive another equation relating the mean values of queue length Q and waiting time W that, together with (5.1), will give us explicit expressions for both $E(Q)$ and $E(W)$.

By definition, the carried load a' is the mean number of busy servers in statistical equilibrium. For a single-server queue then, by definition $a' = \sum_{j=1}^{\infty} P_j$; that is, for the single-server queue in equilibrium, the carried load equals the proportion of time the server is occupied. Thus, for equilibrium single-server queues with Poisson input, the carried load a' is the same as the probability that an arbitrary arrival will find the server busy: $a' = P\{W > 0\}$.

Recall from Section 3–3 that we defined the utilization factor ρ as the carried load per server, $\rho = a'/s$. Also, it was argued in Section 3–4 that in any BCD system in equilibrium, the offered load a ($= \lambda\tau$, where λ is the arrival rate and τ is the mean service time) and the carried load a' are equal (because all arriving customers are served). Hence, in every equilibrium single-server BCD system, the offered load $a = \lambda\tau$ and the utilization factor ρ are equal; $\rho = \lambda\tau$. It follows that for single-server BCD queues with Poisson input the equilibrium probability $P\{W > 0\}$ that a customer must wait for service is given by

$$P\{W > 0\} = \lambda\tau = \rho. \tag{5.2}$$

We are now ready to write an equation for the mean wait for service from the point of view of an arbitrary arriving customer. The delay suffered by an arrival who finds the server busy is the sum of the service times of the customers waiting in the queue ahead of him, plus the remaining service time R of the customer in service at the new customer's arrival epoch. Hence

$$E(W) = P\{W > 0\}[E(Q \mid W > 0)\tau + E(R)] + P\{W = 0\} \cdot 0. \tag{5.3}$$

Note that in writing (5.3) we have tacitly assumed service in order of arrival but, as we proved in Section 5–3, the mean wait is independent of the order of service.

We must now evaluate the quantities on the right-hand side of equation (5.3). By equation (5.2), $P\{W > 0\} = \rho$. Using the relation

$$E(Q) = E(Q \mid W = 0)P\{W = 0\} + E(Q \mid W > 0)P\{W > 0\},$$

it follows, since $E(Q \mid W = 0) = 0$, that

$$E(Q \mid W > 0) = \frac{E(Q)}{P\{W > 0\}}.$$

Therefore

$$E(Q \mid W > 0) = \frac{E(Q)}{\rho}. \tag{5.4}$$

To find $E(R)$, we note that the analysis of Section 5–4 is applicable. We observe the system with a timer, keeping the timer off during periods when the server is idle. Then the epochs $T_1, T_2, \ldots$ are instants of seizure of the server, and equation (4.8) applies:

$$E(R) = \frac{\tau}{2} + \frac{\sigma^2}{2\tau}, \tag{5.5}$$

where τ is the mean service time (the mean interevent time) and σ^2 is the variance of the service time distribution function. Substitution of (5.4) and (5.5) into (5.3) yields

$$E(W) = E(Q)\tau + \rho \left(\frac{\tau}{2} + \frac{\sigma^2}{2\tau} \right). \tag{5.6}$$

Combination of equations (5.6) and (5.1) gives

$$E(W) = \frac{\rho\tau[1 + (\sigma^2/\tau^2)]}{2(1 - \rho)} \quad (\rho < 1) \tag{5.7}$$

and

$$E(Q) = \frac{\rho^2[1 + (\sigma^2/\tau^2)]}{2(1 - \rho)} \quad (\rho < 1). \tag{5.8}$$

Note that equations (5.7) and (5.8) are meaningless unless $\rho < 1$, and that $E(W)$ and $E(Q) \rightarrow \infty$ hyperbolically as $\rho \rightarrow 1$.

As a check, note that when the service times are exponential, then $\sigma^2 = \tau^2$ and $E(W) = \rho\tau/(1 - \rho)$, in agreement with equation (5.10) of Chapter 3 with $s = 1$.

When the service times are constant, then $\sigma^2 = 0$ and $E(W) = \rho\tau/2(1 - \rho)$. Hence, for the same arrival rate and same mean service time, the mean delay (and mean queue length) for the $M/M/1$ queue is twice that for the $M/D/1$ queue, even though the probability of delay ($= \rho$) is the same in both systems. This vividly illustrates the effect of the form of the service time distribution function on the queue length and the waiting times.

Mean Queue Length and Mean Waiting Time: Kendall's Method

We shall now derive the result (5.8) by a different method (Kendall [1951]) with some interesting concepts. Instead of viewing the process through the eyes of an arriving customer, as done in equation (5.3), we formulate the equations completely from the viewpoint of a departing customer. The results, of course, are the same because of the equality of the arrival and departure state distributions. Further, we shall not need the renewal theory result (5.5); indeed, we could deduce it by combining the two methods of analysis and solving for $E(R)$.

Let N_k^* be the number of customers in the system (including any customer in service) just after the service completion epoch of the kth customer, and let X_k be the number of customers that arrive during the service time of the kth customer. Clearly the random variables $X_1, X_2, \ldots$ are mutually independent and identically distributed, and X_k is independent of $N_1^*, N_2^*, \ldots, N_{k-1}^*$.

If the kth departing customer does not leave the system empty, then the $(k + 1)$th departure will leave behind those same customers in the queue left by the kth departure except for himself, plus all those customers who arrived during the service time of the $(k + 1)$th customer. Thus

$$N_{k+1}^* = N_k^* - 1 + X_{k+1} \qquad (N_k^* > 0). \tag{5.9}$$

On the other hand, if the kth customer leaves the system empty, then the $(k + 1)$th customer will leave behind just those customers who arrived during his service time. Thus

$$N_{k+1}^* = X_{k+1} \qquad (N_k^* = 0). \tag{5.10}$$

Equations (5.9) and (5.10) can be combined into a single equation

$$N_{k+1}^* = N_k^* - \delta(N_k^*) + X_{k+1}, \tag{5.11}$$

where the random variable $\delta(N_k^*)$ is defined as

$$\delta(N_k^*) = \begin{cases} 0 & \text{if } N_k^* = 0 \\ 1 & \text{if } N_k^* > 0. \end{cases} \tag{5.12}$$

We now square both sides of (5.11):

$$N_{k+1}^{*2} = N_k^{*2} + \delta^2(N_k^*) + X_{k+1}^2 + 2N_k^* X_{k+1}$$
$$- 2X_{k+1}\,\delta(N_k^*) - 2N_k^*\,\delta(N_k^*). \tag{5.13}$$

It follows from the definition (5.12) that

$$\delta^2(N_k^*) = \delta(N_k^*) \tag{5.14}$$

and

$$N_k^*\,\delta(N_k^*) = N_k^*, \tag{5.15}$$

so that equation (5.13) can be written

$$N_{k+1}^{*2} = N_k^{*2} + \delta(N_k^*) + X_{k+1}^2 + 2N_k^* X_{k+1}$$
$$- 2X_{k+1}\,\delta(N_k^*) - 2N_k^*. \tag{5.16}$$

We now take expected values through (5.16). Since N_k^* and X_{k+1} are independent, we have

$$E(N_{k+1}^{*2}) = E(N_k^{*2}) + E\,(\delta(N_k^*)) + E(X_{k+1}^2)$$
$$+ 2E(N_k^*)E(X_{k+1}) - 2E(X_{k+1})E\,(\delta(N_k^*))$$
$$- 2E(N_k^*). \tag{5.17}$$

Now let $k \to \infty$ in (5.17). Assuming that a statistical equilibrium distribution exists, then in equilibrium the distribution of the number of customers left behind by each customer is the same. Therefore $\lim_{k \to \infty} E(N_{k+1}^{*2}) = \lim_{k \to \infty} E(N_k^{*2}) = E(N^{*2})$ and (5.17) becomes

$$E(N^*) = \frac{E\,(\delta(N^*))[1 - 2E(X)] + E(X^2)}{2[1 - E(X)]}. \tag{5.18}$$

Similarly, taking expectations and limits through (5.11), we have

$$E(\delta(N^*)) = E(X). \tag{5.19}$$

It remains to calculate $E(X)$ and $E(X^2)$. $E(X)$ is simply the mean number of arrivals occurring during an arbitrary service time, that is, the offered load:

$$E(X) = \lambda\tau = \rho. \tag{5.20}$$

Direct calculation of $E(X^2)$ gives

$$E(X^2) = \lambda^2(\sigma^2 + \tau^2) + \rho. \tag{5.21}$$

(See Exercise 7.) Substitution of equations (5.19), (5.20), and (5.21) into (5.18) yields

$$E(N^*) = \rho + \frac{\rho^2[1 + (\sigma^2/\tau^2)]}{2(1 - \rho)}. \tag{5.22}$$

Q is the number of customers waiting in the queue just prior to an arrival epoch, and N^* is the number of customers in the system just after a departure epoch. Since the arrival and departure distributions are equal, we can equate the mean number $E(N^*)$ of customers left by an arbitrary departure to the mean number of customers found by an arbitrary arrival. The latter quantity is the sum of the mean number ρ in service and the mean number $E(Q)$ waiting for service. Thus

$$E(N^*) = \rho + E(Q). \tag{5.23}$$

Finally, comparison of (5.22) and (5.23) shows that (5.22) is equivalent to (5.8).

Notice that in this derivation the variance term arises from evaluation of the term $E(X^2)$, the second moment of the distribution of the number of customers who arrive during an arbitrary service time; whereas in the first derivation it arose from evaluation of the term $E(R)$, the first moment of the distribution of the remainder of a service time during which a customer was postulated to have arrived. Also, the term $E(X^2)$ arose from squaring both sides of the basic relation (5.11), whereas the term $E(R)$ arose directly from physical considerations.

Thus Kendall's method uses neither renewal theory nor the equation $L = \lambda W$, but simply the elementary relations (5.9) and (5.10).

The Imbedded Markov Chain

We shall now analyze the $M/G/1$ queue in more depth, using a technique, introduced also by Kendall [1951, 1953], of great importance throughout queueing theory.

In Chapter 2 we saw that an important characteristic of a birth-and-death process is that if at any instant t the system state E_j is known, then in principle the state probabilities for all $t + x$ ($x \geqq 0$) are also known, independent of whatever route the system may have followed in reaching state E_j at time t. When this is true, we may write equations relating the state probabilities at any time t to those at any other time $t + x$. We showed that a necessary and sufficient condition for a system to have this property, called the Markov property, is that the time between successive changes of state be exponentially distributed (but not necessarily identically distributed). A process that has this characteristic Markov property is called (naturally) a *Markov process*. An example is the number of customers in the $M/M/s$ (Erlang delay) system, which was discussed in Chapter 3.

Let us consider the birth-and-death process again, and see why the $M/G/1$ queue, unlike the $M/M/s$ queue, cannot be modeled as a birth-

and-death process. Let $N(t)$ be the number of customers in the system at time t. Then, by the law of total probability,

$$P\{N(t + x) = j\} = \sum_{i=0}^{\infty} P\{N(t + x) = j \mid N(t) = i\}P\{N(t) = i\}$$

$$(t \geq 0, x \geq 0; i = 0, 1, \ldots). \qquad (5.24)$$

Note that equation (5.24) is valid for any queueing model. All that is required is to evaluate the conditional probabilities $P\{N(t + x) = j \mid N(t) = i\}$, called the *transition probabilities*, and solve the equations (5.24) for the state probabilities $P\{N(\xi) = k\}(\xi \geq 0; k = 0, 1, \ldots)$.

In the analysis of those queueing models that are birth-and-death processes, we wisely chose x small and let $x \to 0$. Since all the transition probabilities except those representing a transition of step size 0 or ± 1 are o(x) as $x \to 0$, we were saved from laboriously calculating the transition probabilities, only to see most of them become irrelevant as $x \to 0$. But the fact remains that in principle we could have calculated the transition probabilities first, simply because the birth-and-death process is a Markov process; that is, the time separating successive transitions is exponentially distributed, obviating the need to consider how long the system had been in state E_i at time t, or by what path state E_i at time t evolved.

In the $M/G/1$ queue this is not true; since the service time distribution function is not assumed to be exponential, in order to specify the transition probabilities one must know not only what state the system is in at time t, but also how long it has been there. Equation (5.24) is not incorrect; it is just inapplicable to the analysis of the $M/G/1$ queue.

A *renewal point* is a time epoch at which the Markov property holds; that is, if t is a renewal point for a given process, then the future evolution of the process depends only on the state at time t. In a Markov process, every point t is a renewal point. A *Markov chain* is the discrete analogue of a Markov process, in which the Markov property holds only at discrete values of the parameter t, that is, at a discrete set of renewal points.

With regard to the $M/G/1$ queue, the service completion points, which are those epochs at which customers complete service and leave the system, are renewal points. For whenever a customer leaves the system, either the system becomes empty or a previously waiting customer starts service; in either case the transition probabilities (and therefore the future evolution of the system) depend only on the number of customers in the system at the service completion point. The system states at this discrete set of renewal points is termed an *imbedded* (in the continuum of all nonnegative points)

Markov chain. We now proceed to study the *M/G/1* queue using the concept of the imbedded Markov chain. (The theory of Markov chains has been studied extensively, but deep knowledge of this theory is not required for an understanding of the imbedded Markov chain technique in queueing theory. For an introductory treatment see, for example, Feller [1968].)

Let N_k^* be the number of customers in the system (including any in service, but excluding the departing customer) at the instant the kth customer completes service. That is, if $T_1, T_2, \ldots$ are the successive service completion points, then N_k^* is the state of the system at $T_k + 0$. Then by the law of total probability [compare with (5.24)]

$$P\{N_{k+1}^* = j\} = \sum_{i=0}^{\infty} P\{N_{k+1}^* = j \mid N_k^* = i\}P\{N_k^* = i\}$$

$$(j = 0, 1, \ldots; k = 1, 2, \ldots). \qquad (5.25)$$

Consider first the transition probability $P\{N_{k+1}^* = j \mid N_k^* = 0\}$. If the kth customer leaves the system empty, then the $(k + 1)$th customer necessarily finds the server idle. Hence the number of customers left behind by this customer will be all those who will have arrived during his service time. Since with probability $e^{-\lambda\xi}(\lambda\xi)^j/j!$ exactly j customers will arrive during any interval of length ξ, we have

$$P\{N_{k+1}^* = j \mid N_k^* = 0\} = \int_0^{\infty} \frac{(\lambda\xi)^j}{j!} e^{-\lambda\xi} \, dH(\xi) \qquad (j \geq 0),$$

where $H(\xi)$ is the service time distribution function. Similarly when $N_k^* = i > 0$, the $(k + 1)$th customer will leave behind those same customers left behind by the kth customer except for himself, plus all those customers who will have arrived during the service time of the $(k + 1)$th customer. Therefore

$$P\{N_{k+1}^* = j \mid N_k^* = i\} = \int_0^{\infty} \frac{(\lambda\xi)^{j-i+1}}{(j - i + 1)!} e^{-\lambda\xi} \, dH(\xi)$$

$$(i > 0, j \geq i - 1)$$

and, of course,

$$P\{N_{k+1}^* = j \mid N_k^* = i\} = 0 \qquad (i > 0, j < i - 1).$$

Let us define

$$p_j = \int_0^{\infty} \frac{(\lambda\xi)^j}{j!} e^{-\lambda\xi} \, dH(\xi) \qquad (j = 0, 1, \ldots). \qquad (5.26)$$

Then the transition probabilities are

$$P\{N^*_{k+1} = j \mid N^*_k = i\} = \begin{cases} p_j & \text{if } i = 0 \\ p_{j-i+1} & \text{if } i > 0 \text{ and } j \geq i - 1 \\ 0 & \text{if } i > 0 \text{ and } j < i - 1. \end{cases} \quad (5.27)$$

Note that the transition probabilities are independent of the value of the index k, that is, are the same for every pair of successive customers.

With the transition probabilities thus specified, we turn our attention to equation (5.25), which relates the distribution of the number of customers left behind by the $(k + 1)$th departing customer to the distribution of the number left behind by the kth departure, for each $k = 1, 2, \ldots$. From a practical point of view, we are rarely interested in this distribution for any particular value of k; rather we wish to know the distribution of the number of customers left behind by an *arbitrary* departing customer. Clearly the distribution is different for each k, but it seems reasonable that the dependency on k should diminish as $k \to \infty$. Intuitively, one would expect that $\lim_{k \to \infty} P\{N^*_k = j\} = \Pi^*_j$ should exist under the appropriate conditions for the imbedded Markov chain, just as does $\lim_{t \to \infty} P\{N(t) = j\} = P_j$ for the Markov (birth-and-death) process studied in Chapter 2. The distribution $\{\Pi^*_j\}$ is thus a statistical equilibrium distribution; Π^*_j is the probability that an arbitrary departing customer leaves behind j other customers in a system that has been operating for a sufficiently long period of time.

From a mathematical point of view, it can be shown using the theory of Markov chains that a unique proper stationary distribution

$$\Pi^*_j = \lim_{k \to \infty} P\{N^*_k = j\} \qquad (j = 0, 1, \ldots), \qquad (5.28)$$

independent of the initial conditions, exists if and only if $\rho < 1$. (If $\rho \geq 1$, then $\Pi^*_j = 0$ for all finite j.) The proof of this statement is the only place where the formal theory of Markov chains is relevant. Since both the existence of the limiting distribution (5.28) and the requisite condition $\rho < 1$ are obvious in the queueing theory context, we shall accept this intuitively plausible statement without proof. Equation (5.25) becomes

$$\Pi^*_j = p_j \Pi^*_0 + \sum_{i=1}^{j+1} p_{j-i+1} \Pi^*_i \qquad (j = 0, 1, \ldots). \qquad (5.29)$$

(This is the derivation promised in part **b** of Exercise 17 of Chapter 2.)

The normalization equation is

$$\sum_{j=0}^{\infty} \Pi_j^* = 1. \tag{5.30}$$

We proceed to solve equations (5.29) and (5.30) for the departing customer's distribution $\{\Pi_j^*\}$.

Define the probability generating function

$$g(z) = \sum_{j=0}^{\infty} \Pi_j^* z^j. \tag{5.31}$$

Substituting (5.29) into (5.31) we have

$$g(z) = \sum_{j=0}^{\infty} \left(p_j \Pi_0^* + \sum_{i=1}^{j+1} p_{j-i+1} \Pi_i^* \right) z^j. \tag{5.32}$$

If we also define

$$h(z) = \sum_{j=0}^{\infty} p_j z^j, \tag{5.33}$$

we obtain, after some manipulation of (5.32),

$$g(z) = \frac{h(z)(z-1)}{z - h(z)} \Pi_0^*. \tag{5.34}$$

The generating function $h(z)$, of course, can be calculated for any particular service time distribution function. Referring to (5.26) we see that $h(z)$ is the probability generating function of the number of Poisson arrivals during an arbitrary service time. Hence, if the service time distribution function $H(\xi)$ has Laplace–Stieltjes transform

$$\eta(s) = \int_0^{\infty} e^{-s\xi} \, dH(\xi), \tag{5.35}$$

then substitution of (5.26) into (5.33) yields

$$h(z) = \eta(\lambda - \lambda z). \tag{5.36}$$

[See equation (6.6) of Chapter 2.] Thus (5.34) gives the generating function $g(z)$ of the unknown distribution $\{\Pi_j^*\}$ in terms of the Laplace–Stieltjes transform of the (arbitrary) service time distribution function and the single probability Π_0^*. We know from previous arguments that $\Pi_0^* = 1 - \rho$. [See equation (5.2), and remember that the arriving customer's distribution and the departing customer's distribution are equal.] To obtain this result directly, simply use the normalization equation (5.30); that is, set $g(1) = 1$ in equation (5.34). We have the final result for the generating function of the distribution $\{\Pi_j^*\}$ $(= \{\Pi_j\} = \{P_j\})$:

$$g(z) = \frac{(z-1)\eta(\lambda - \lambda z)}{z - \eta(\lambda - \lambda z)}(1 - \rho) \qquad (\rho < 1, |z| \le 1). \qquad (5.37)$$

The moments of the distribution $\{\Pi_j^*\}$ can now be obtained from (5.37) by differentiation. In particular $E(N^*) = g'(1)$, which gives the previously obtained result (5.22). (See Exercise 8.)

We turn now to the waiting time distribution function $W(t) = P\{W \le t\}$ for the $M/G/1$ queue with service in order of arrival. Let $W(t)$ have Laplace–Stieltjes transform $\omega(s)$,

$$\omega(s) = \int_0^\infty e^{-st}\, dW(t), \qquad (5.38)$$

and denote by $\phi(s)$ the Laplace–Stieltjes transform of the distribution function of the sojourn time (the sum of the waiting time and the service time) of an arbitrary customer (the test customer). Since the waiting time and service time of a customer are independent random variables, the Laplace–Stieltjes transform of the distribution function of their sum is the product of the Laplace–Stieltjes transforms of the component distribution functions:

$$\phi(s) = \omega(s)\eta(s). \qquad (5.39)$$

$\phi(s)$ is the Laplace–Stieltjes transform of the distribution function of the total length of time (sojourn time) the test customer spends in the system. The distribution of the number of customers left behind by the test customer has probability generating function $g(z)$ given by (5.37). Since service is in arrival order, the customers left behind by the test customer must all have arrived during his sojourn time. And since the arrivals follow a Poisson process with rate λ, the generating function of the distribution of the number of arrivals during this sojourn time is related to the Laplace–Stieltjes transform of the distribution function of the length of the sojourn time as follows (see again Section 2–6):

$$g(z) = \phi(\lambda - \lambda z). \qquad (5.40)$$

Using equations (5.40) and (5.37) in (5.39), we have

$$\omega(s) = \frac{s(1 - \rho)}{s - \lambda[1 - \eta(s)]}. \tag{5.41}$$

The result (5.41), widely known as the *Pollaczek–Khintchine formula*, gives the Laplace–Stieltjes transform $\omega(s)$ of the equilibrium waiting time distribution function for the order-of-arrival $M/G/1$ queue directly in terms of the Laplace–Stieltjes transform $\eta(s)$ of the service time distribution function. (The derivation given here is by Kendall [1951].)

Notice that in the derivation of (5.41) no appeal was made to arguments equating the distributions $\{\Pi_j\}$ and $\{\Pi_j^*\}$. Further, no direct consideration of the problem of remaining service time at arrival points was necessary.

Interestingly, the Pollaczek–Khintchine formula (5.41) can easily be inverted with the help of equation (4.11). Rewriting (5.41) we have $\omega(s) = (1 - \rho)/\left[1 - \rho\left(\dfrac{1}{\tau}\dfrac{1 - \eta(s)}{s}\right)\right]$, which expands to

$$\omega(s) = (1 - \rho) \sum_{j=0}^{\infty} \rho^j \left(\frac{1}{\tau}\frac{1 - \eta(s)}{s}\right)^j.$$

According to equation (4.11), the factor $(1/\tau)[1 - \eta(s)]/s$ is the Laplace–Stieltjes transform $\tilde{\eta}(s)$ of a distribution function $\tilde{H}(x)$ defined by

$$\tilde{H}(x) = \frac{1}{\tau} \int_0^x [1 - H(\xi)]\, d\xi. \tag{5.42}$$

Therefore, equation (5.41) can be written

$$\omega(s) = (1 - \rho) \sum_{j=0}^{\infty} \rho^j [\tilde{\eta}(s)]^j, \tag{5.43}$$

where

$$\tilde{\eta}(s) = \int_0^{\infty} e^{-st}\, d\tilde{H}(t).$$

Term-by-term inversion of (5.43) yields the remarkable formula, found by Beneš [1957],

$$W(t) = (1 - \rho) \sum_{j=0}^{\infty} \rho^j \tilde{H}^{*j}(t), \tag{5.44}$$

where $\tilde{H}^{*j}(t)$ is the j-fold convolution with itself of the distribution function $\tilde{H}(t)$ defined by (5.42), and $\tilde{H}^{*0}(t) = 1$.

Although not introduced into the analysis directly, we see from equation (5.42) that the distribution function of remaining service time at arrival points appears, but in a rather mysterious way. Despite its simple form, equation (5.44) does not seem to yield to an intuitive term-by-term interpretation except in the special case of exponential service times. Equation (5.44) provides a dramatic counterexample to the oft-stated (and oft-true) sentiment that simple results have simple explanations.

The Busy Period

A notion that will prove useful and instructive is that of the *busy period*, defined as the length of time from the instant a customer enters a previously empty system until the next instant at which the system is completely empty.

A typical realization of a busy period is illustrated in Figure 5–2. The height of the graph at any time x is the duration of time from x until all those customers present in the system at time x are finished with service. Arrivals are represented by arrows pointing up and departures by arrows pointing down. At each arrival epoch the graph jumps up by an amount equal to the service time of the customer who just arrived. The graph decreases linearly with time until either another customer arrives or the graph decreases to zero, signifying the end of the busy period. The realization pictured in Figure 5–2 is a busy period composed of six service times.

We shall now derive an expression for the distribution function $B(t)$ of the busy period for the $M/G/1$ queue. Consider first the system in which the server does not start to serve any customers until there are $j \geq 1$ customers in the system, and then serves these j customers one at a time, and all subsequent arrivals, until for the first time the system becomes

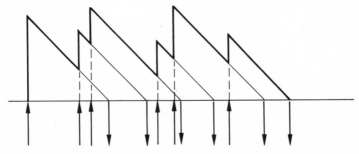

Figure 5–2.

empty. Call this length of time a *j-busy period*. Hence a *j*-busy period is the length of continuous busy time of a server that starts serving when *j* customers are in the system.

Let $B(t)$ be the distribution function of the busy period, and $B_j(t)$ be the distribution function of the *j*-busy period, where $B_1(t) = B(t)$. Following Takács [1962a], we now show that the distribution function $B_j(t)$ of the *j*-busy period is the *j*-fold convolution with itself of the distribution function $B(t)$ of the ordinary 1-busy period,

$$B_j(t) = B^{*j}(t) \qquad (j = 0, 1, 2, \ldots ; B^{*0}(t) = 1) \qquad (5.45)$$

(where the case $j = 0$ is included to simplify forthcoming calculations).

A little thought should convince the reader that the length of a *j*-busy period is independent of the order in which the waiting customers are served. This being so, we choose to consider the following particular order of service. Suppose the server is about to begin service on one of $j \geq 1$ waiting customers. When it finishes serving the first of these *j* customers, it then serves all those customers, if any, who arrived during the service time of the first customer, and then those customers, if any, who arrived during these service periods, and so on. That is, it serves first all those customers who arrive during the 1-busy period generated by the first of the original *j* customers. When the 1-busy period generated by the first of the original *j* customers terminates, the server starts on the next of the original *j* customers, and serves all those customers who arrive during the 1-busy period generated by him. The server continues in this manner, so that the length of time during which it is continuously busy is the sum of *j* 1-busy periods. These *j* 1-busy periods are clearly mutually independent and identically distributed. Hence equation (5.45) is true.

We shall now use (5.45) to obtain the Laplace–Stieltjes transform $\beta(s)$,

$$\beta(s) = \int_0^\infty e^{-st} \, dB(t), \qquad (5.46)$$

of the 1-busy period distribution function $B(t)$. Note that a 1-busy period will not exceed a value *t* if and only if the first service time lasts a length $\xi \leq t$ and the $j \geq 0$ customers who arrive during the first service time generate a *j*-busy period that does not exceed $t - \xi$. Thus we may write

$$B(t) = \sum_{j=0}^\infty \int_0^t \frac{(\lambda\xi)^j}{j!} e^{-\lambda\xi} B_j(t - \xi) \, dH(\xi), \qquad (5.47)$$

where $H(\xi)$ is the service time distribution function.

Taking Laplace–Stieltjes transforms on both sides of (5.47), and noting that (5.45) implies that the Laplace–Stieltjes transform $\beta_j(s)$ of the j-busy period distribution function $B_j(t)$ is

$$\beta_j(s) = [\beta(s)]^j \qquad (j = 0, 1, \ldots), \tag{5.48}$$

we obtain

$$\beta(s) = \sum_{j=0}^{\infty} \int_0^{\infty} \frac{(\lambda\xi)^j}{j!} e^{-\lambda\xi} e^{-s\xi} [\beta(s)]^j \, dH(\xi). \tag{5.49}$$

Equation (5.49) reduces to

$$\beta(s) = \sum_{j=0}^{\infty} \int_0^{\infty} \frac{[\lambda\xi\beta(s)]^j}{j!} e^{-(\lambda+s)\xi} \, dH(\xi)$$

$$= \int_0^{\infty} e^{-[s+\lambda-\lambda\beta(s)]\xi} \, dH(\xi). \tag{5.50}$$

The integral on the right-hand side of (5.50) is the Laplace–Stieltjes transform $\eta(x)$ of the service time distribution function, with argument $x = s + \lambda - \lambda\beta(s)$. Thus we have the functional equation

$$\beta(s) = \eta[s + \lambda - \lambda\beta(s)]. \tag{5.51}$$

We can obtain the mean b of the busy period by differentiating equation (5.51) and using the fact that $-\beta'(0) = b$ and $-\eta'(0) = \tau$, where τ is the mean service time:

$$\beta'(s) = [1 - \lambda\beta'(s)]\eta'[s + \lambda - \lambda\beta(s)] \tag{5.52}$$

and therefore

$$-b = -(1 + \lambda b)\tau$$

or

$$b = \frac{\tau}{1 - \lambda\tau}. \tag{5.53}$$

[Compare equation (5.53) with (4.9) of Chapter 3.]

It is interesting to consider directly the special case of the $M/D/1$ queue. Let N_j be the number of customers served during a j-busy period, and set

$$f_n^{(j)} = P\{N_j = n\}.$$

Then we have the following recurrence:

$$f_n^{(j)} = \begin{cases} e^{-\lambda \tau j} & (n = j) \\ \sum_{k=1}^{n-j} \dfrac{(\lambda \tau j)^k}{k!} e^{-\lambda \tau j} f_{n-j}^{(k)}, & (n \geq j + 1), \end{cases} \qquad (5.54)$$

where τ is the (constant) service time. It is easy to show (Prabhu [1965]) that equations (5.54) have solution (see Exercise 16)

$$f_n^{(j)} = \frac{j}{n} \left[\frac{(\lambda \tau n)^{n-j}}{(n-j)!} e^{-\lambda \tau n} \right] \qquad (n \geq j). \qquad (5.55)$$

Note that the expression in brackets on the right-hand side of equation (5.55) is the probability that during a time interval of length $n\tau$ (which is the time required to serve the n customers whose service times comprise this j-busy period) exactly $n - j$ customers arrive. Evidently, the factor j/n equals the probability that these $n - j$ arrivals occur in such a way as to make this a busy period.

In an exposition of the use of combinatorial methods and ballot theorems in the theory of queues and related subjects, Takács [1967] showed that the above interpretation of the factor j/n is valid in the general case of the $M/G/1$ queue. It follows for the $M/G/1$ queue that, if $B_j(n, t)$ is the joint probability that the number of customers served during a j-busy period is n and the length of the j-busy period does not exceed t, then

$$B_j(n, t) = \frac{j}{n} \int_0^t \frac{(\lambda \xi)^{n-j}}{(n-j)!} e^{-\lambda \xi} \, dH^{*n}(\xi) \qquad (n \geq j) \qquad (5.56)$$

where $H^{*n}(\xi)$ is the n-fold convolution with itself of the service time distribution function. Since

$$B_j(t) = \sum_{n=j}^{\infty} B_j(n, t)$$

it follows that

$$B_j(t) = \sum_{n=j}^{\infty} \frac{j}{n} \int_0^t \frac{(\lambda \xi)^{n-j}}{(n-j)!} e^{-\lambda \xi} \, dH^{*n}(\xi). \qquad (5.57)$$

In particular, equation (5.57) with $j = 1$ provides us with the inversion of the Laplace–Stieltjes transform $\beta(s)$ defined by the functional equation (5.51). Thus,

$$B(t) = \sum_{n=1}^{\infty} \frac{1}{n} \int_0^t \frac{(\lambda\xi)^{n-1}}{(n-1)!} e^{-\lambda\xi} \, dH^{*n}(\xi). \tag{5.58}$$

Prior to his derivation of equation (5.58) by combinatorial methods, Takács [1962a] obtained (5.58) by inversion directly from the functional equation (5.51).

We have observed that the transform $\beta(s)$ can be inverted to obtain an infinite series representation for the distribution function $B(t)$, as given by equation (5.58). With regard to numerical inversion of the transform $\beta(s)$, it can be shown by using the monotonicity of the Laplace–Stieltjes transform that the iteration scheme

$$x_{i+1}(s) = \eta[s + \lambda - \lambda x_i(s)] \qquad [i = 0, 1, \ldots; 0 \leq x_0(s) \leq 1] \tag{5.59}$$

converges to $\beta(s)$, $x_i(s) \to \beta(s)$, for $s \geq 0$ whenever $\lambda\tau < 1$. This is illustrated in Figure 5–3. Therefore one may calculate, for each $s \geq 0$, the value of the Laplace–Stieltjes transform $\beta(s)$, and, at least in theory,

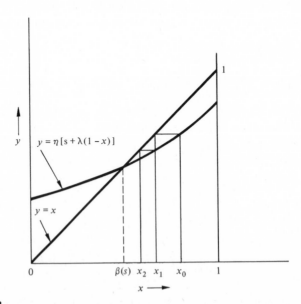

Figure 5–3.

invert numerically. In practice, as we shall see, the quantity of interest may well be the Laplace–Stieltjes transform $\beta(s)$ itself, not the original distribution function $B(t)$.

The interesting point here is not so much the mathematics of solving functional equations (although this is important if one wants to get an answer), but the characteristic combination of mathematical and heuristic reasoning that leads to the functional equation (5.51) and the explicit solution (5.58).

5–6. The *M/G/1* Queue with Finite Waiting Room

In this section we shall discuss the single-server queue with Poisson input, general service times, and a finite number n of waiting positions. [Hence there are $n + 2$ states $E_j (j = 0, 1, \ldots, n, n + 1)$, where the value of the index j is the number of customers in the system.] In the analysis of this important model we overcome a difficulty that has not appeared in any previous model.

Let N_k^* be the number of customers in the system (including any in service) just after the kth departing customer leaves the system. When the number of waiting positions is finite, a customer will depart from the system either after he has completed service, or, if he arrives when all waiting positions are occupied, immediately upon arriving. Note that no customer departing after having been served can leave behind him a completely full system; at least one waiting position must be empty.

We consider first those states $E_0, E_1, \ldots, E_n$ in which a customer who has just completed service can leave the system. Let $\Pi_j^* (j = 0, 1, \ldots, n)$ be the probability that a departing customer (after completing service) leaves behind j other customers. Then, following the previous analysis for the infinite-waiting room model, we obtain again equation (5.29), this time valid only for $j = 0, 1, \ldots, n - 1$, which can be written

$$\Pi_{j+1}^* = p_0^{-1} \left(\Pi_j^* - p_j \Pi_0^* - \sum_{i=1}^{j} p_{j-i+1} \Pi_i^* \right) \qquad (j = 0, 1, \ldots, n - 1).$$

$$(6.1)$$

Equation (6.1) can be solved numerically by recurrence; one can successively determine $\Pi_1^*, \Pi_2^*, \ldots, \Pi_n^*$ in terms of Π_0^*.

If we are interested only in the distribution of the number of customers left behind by a customer who gets served, then Π_0^* is determined from the normalization equation

$$\Pi_0^* + \Pi_1^* + \cdots + \Pi_n^* = 1. \tag{6.2}$$

Observe that since this distribution $\{\Pi_0^*, \Pi_1^*, \ldots, \Pi_n^*\}$ satisfies the same equations (6.1) as does that of the infinite-waiting room model, the finite-waiting room probabilities $\Pi_0^*, \Pi_1^*, \ldots, \Pi_n^*$ are proportional to the corresponding infinite-waiting room probabilities. We assume in what follows that the probabilities $\Pi_0^*, \Pi_1^*, \ldots, \Pi_n^*$ are now known.

We wish to find the distribution $\{\Pi_0, \Pi_1, \ldots, \Pi_n, \Pi_{n+1}\}$ of the number of customers found by an arbitrary arrival (not just those arrivals that are served). That is, we wish to find the arriving customer's distribution $\{\Pi_0, \Pi_1, \ldots, \Pi_n, \Pi_{n+1}\}$, as seen by all arriving customers. We have found the distribution $\{\Pi_0^*, \Pi_1^*, \ldots, \Pi_n^*\}$ of the number of customers left in the system by a departing customer who is completing service. By the theorem of Section 2, $\{\Pi_0^*, \Pi_1^*, \ldots, \Pi_n^*\}$ is also the conditional arriving customer's distribution as seen by those customers who do not find the system in state E_{n+1}. (Π_j^* is the conditional probability that an arrival finds the system in state E_j, given that $j < n + 1$.) Therefore, the probabilities $\{\Pi_j\}$ and $\{\Pi_j^*\}$ both satisfy the same equation (6.1) when $j < n + 1$, and it follows that they are proportional when $j < n + 1$:

$$\Pi_j = c\Pi_j^* \qquad (j = 0, 1, \ldots, n). \tag{6.3}$$

It remains to find a new equation that permits calculation of the probability Π_{n+1} that an arriving customer finds all n waiting positions occupied. The constant of proportionality c is then calculated from the normalization equation

$$\Pi_0 + \Pi_1 + \cdots + \Pi_n + \Pi_{n+1} = 1. \tag{6.4}$$

Observe that Π_{n+1} is the proportion of customers who are not served. If one wished to design a system with sufficient number of waiting positions so that only a given proportion of the arriving customers are turned away (cleared), then he could determine the number n of waiting positions required from a plot of Π_{n+1} versus n.

We return to consideration of the new equation required to calculate Π_{n+1}. The load carried a' (the mean number of busy servers) is

$$a' = P_1 + \cdots + P_{n+1} = 1 - P_0, \tag{6.5}$$

and, by virtue of the equality of the outside observer's distribution $\{P_0, P_1, \ldots, P_n, P_{n+1}\}$ and the arriving customer's distribution $\{\Pi_0, \Pi_1, \ldots, \Pi_n, \Pi_{n+1}\}$ for systems with Poisson input, it follows that the carried load a' is given by

$$a' = 1 - \Pi_0. \tag{6.6}$$

The probability that an arbitrary customer is served is $1 - \Pi_{n+1}$; therefore, since the carried load a' is that portion of the offered load a that is carried (served), we have

$$a' = a(1 - \Pi_{n+1}). \tag{6.7}$$

Combination of (6.6) and (6.7) yields the required equation:

$$\Pi_{n+1} = \frac{a - (1 - \Pi_0)}{a}. \tag{6.8}$$

(See Exercise 22 of Chapter 3.) It follows from equations (6.3), (6.4), and (6.8) that

$$c = \frac{1}{\Pi_0^* + a \sum\limits_{j=0}^{n} \Pi_j^*}. \tag{6.9}$$

If the probabilities $\{\Pi_0^*, \Pi_1^*, \ldots, \Pi_n^*\}$ have been normalized according to (6.2), then we have from (6.3) and (6.9)

$$\Pi_j = \frac{\Pi_j^*}{\Pi_0^* + a} \qquad (j = 0, 1, \ldots, n). \tag{6.10}$$

Finally, it follows from equations (6.8) and (6.10) that the remaining probability Π_{n+1} is given by

$$\Pi_{n+1} = \frac{\Pi_0^* + a - 1}{\Pi_0^* + a}. \tag{6.11}$$

Thus we see that although the finiteness of the waiting room precludes the writing of an equation for the probability Π_{n+1}^* from the point of view of a customer completing service, we can obtain the necessary equation (6.8) independently from consideration of the carried load.

Another approach to the analysis of single-server queueing systems with finite waiting space is through the use of the mean busy period. Consider again the $M/G/1$ queue with n waiting positions. It follows from equation (6.7) that in order to evaluate the probability Π_{n+1} that an arriving customer finds all n waiting positions occupied, it is sufficient to calculate the carried load a'.

In any single-server system, the carried load a' equals the proportion of time that the server is busy. Let b be the mean busy period. Then the proportion of time that the server is busy, in terms of the mean busy period b, is given by $b/(\lambda^{-1} + b)$. Therefore it follows that

$$a' = \frac{b}{\lambda^{-1} + b}. \tag{6.12}$$

Thus, in order to calculate the loss probability Π_{n+1}, it is sufficient to calculate the mean busy period b.

Let b_k be the mean length of a k-busy period, with $b_1 = b$. With probability p_0, no customers will arrive during the initial service time, and the mean busy period will be τ; with probability p_1, one customer will arrive during the initial service time, and the mean busy period will be $\tau + b_1$; and so on [where $\{p_j\}$ is given by (5.26)]. Thus

$$b_1 = p_0\tau + p_1(\tau + b_1) + p_2(\tau + b_2) + \cdots + p_{n-1}(\tau + b_{n-1})$$

$$+ (\tau + b_n) \sum_{j=n}^{\infty} p_j$$

and this can be rewritten

$$b_1 = \tau + p_1 b_1 + p_2 b_2 + \cdots + p_{n-1} b_{n-1} + b_n \sum_{j=n}^{\infty} p_j. \tag{6.13}$$

Similarly, for $k = 2, 3, \ldots, n$ we have

$$b_k = \tau + \sum_{j=0}^{n-k} p_j b_{k+j-1} + b_n \sum_{j=n-k+1}^{\infty} p_j \quad (k = 2, 3, \ldots, n). \tag{6.14}$$

Equations (6.13) and (6.14) can now be solved recurrently, starting with $k = n$ and working backward to obtain $b_1 = b$; the probability Π_{n+1} of loss is then obtained from equations (6.7) and (6.12).

In the example given here, the $M/G/1$ queue with finite waiting room, the first approach is probably easier. However, the busy period method is conceptually easier, and might be easier in practice if the number of waiting positions is small and the queueing structure is not standard. An example is provided by Exercise 19.

5–7. The *GI/M/s* Queue

In Section 5–5 we studied the $M/G/1$ queue by writing equations relating the state probabilities to each other at successive renewal points, where, by definition, a renewal point is an epoch at which the future evolution of the system depends on the present state only, and not on the path by which that state was reached. We showed that in the $M/G/1$ queue the service completion epochs, which are the instants at which customers leave the server, constitute a set of renewal points. We then wrote an equation relating the state probabilities to each other at a pair of successive renewal points, namely the service completion points of the kth and $(k + 1)$th departing customers [equation (5.25)]. Using a statistical equilibrium argument, we obtained an equation [equation (5.29)] defining the statistical equilibrium distribution $\{\Pi_j^*\}$ of the number of customers left behind by an arbitrary departing customer, from which blocking and waiting time information was subsequently obtained.

We shall analyze the $GI/M/s$ queue by the same technique: identify a set of renewal points, relate the state probabilities at successive renewal points to each other, assume the existence of a limiting stationary distribution, and solve the resulting system of equations.

Suppose that customers arrive at epochs $T_1, T_2, \ldots$, and assume that the interarrival times $T_{k+1} - T_k$ ($k = 0, 1, \ldots; T_0 = 0$) are mutually independent, identically distributed random variables, with common distribution function $G(x) = P\{T_{k+1} - T_k \leq x\}$ ($k = 0, 1, \ldots$), and mean interarrival time λ^{-1}. All customers wait as long as necessary for service. Let N_k be the number of customers in the system just prior to the arrival of the kth customer; N_k is the number of customers present at $T_k - 0$. Since the input is recurrent, and since the service times are by assumption identically distributed exponential variables (with mean μ^{-1}), independent of the arrival epochs and each other, the arrival epochs $T_1, T_2, \ldots$ are renewal points. Hence, by the law of total probability

$$P\{N_{k+1} = j\} = \sum_{i=0}^{\infty} P\{N_{k+1} = j \mid N_k = i\}P\{N_k = i\}$$

$$(j = 0, 1, \ldots; k = 1, 2, \ldots). \qquad (7.1)$$

As with the $M/G/1$ queue, the transition probabilities $P\{N_{k+1} = j \mid N_k = i\}$ depend on the indices i and j, but not on the index k. Let

$$p_{ij} = P\{N_{k+1} = j \mid N_k = i\}.$$

In analogy with equation (5.28) for the $M/G/1$ queue, it can be shown using the theory of Markov chains that a unique stationary distribution

$$\Pi_j = \lim_{k \to \infty} P\{N_k = j\} \qquad (j = 0, 1, \ldots) \tag{7.2}$$

exists if and only if $\rho = \lambda/s\mu < 1$.

Therefore, after taking limits on both sides of equation (7.1), it follows that the equilibrium state equations for the arriving customer's distribution $\{\Pi_j\}$ are

$$\Pi_j = \sum_{i=0}^{\infty} p_{ij}\Pi_i \qquad (j = 0, 1, \ldots). \tag{7.3}$$

In order that $\{\Pi_j\}$ be a proper distribution, equation (7.3) is supplemented by the normalization equation

$$\sum_{j=0}^{\infty} \Pi_j = 1. \tag{7.4}$$

We now proceed to evaluate the transition probabilities $\{p_{ij}\}$ and solve the state equations (7.3) and (7.4) that determine the distribution $\{\Pi_j\}$.

Note first that since any arrival can find at most one more customer in the system than was found by the preceding arrival, we have

$$p_{ij} = 0 \qquad (j > i + 1). \tag{7.5}$$

Now consider the case where both the kth and the $(k + 1)$th customers find all s servers busy. In this case, all s servers will be continuously busy throughout this interval of length $T_{k+1} - T_k$. Suppose that $T_{k+1} - T_k = x$. Since the service times are exponential with mean $\tau = \mu^{-1}$, and since by hypothesis all s servers are continuously busy throughout the interval of length x, it follows that

$$P\{N_{k+1} = j \mid N_k = i \quad \text{and} \quad T_{k+1} - T_k = x\} = \frac{(s\mu x)^{i+1-j}}{(i + 1 - j)!} e^{-s\mu x}$$

$$(i \geqq s, j \geqq s, i + 1 - j \geqq 0)$$

and, since $T_{k+1} - T_k$ has distribution function $G(x)$, therefore

$$p_{ij} = P\{N_{k+1} = j \mid N_k = i\} = \int_0^\infty \frac{(s\mu x)^{i+1-j}}{(i+1-j)!} e^{-s\mu x} \, dG(x)$$

$$(i \geq s, j \geq s, i + 1 - j \geq 0). \qquad (7.6)$$

To solve equations (7.3) completely, we must specify the transition probabilities for all possible values of i and j, not just the particular values $i \geq s$ and $j \geq s$. (See Exercise 21.) However, inspection of (7.3) shows that consideration of the particular cases $i \geq s$, $j \geq s$ will yield the state probabilities (up to a constant factor) for the blocking states $\Pi_s, \Pi_{s+1}, \ldots$. Let us first determine these probabilities.

Substitution of the transition probabilities (7.5) and (7.6) into equation (7.3) yields

$$\Pi_j = \sum_{i=j-1}^\infty \Pi_i \int_0^\infty \frac{(s\mu x)^{i+1-j}}{(i+1-j)!} e^{-s\mu x} \, dG(x) \qquad (j = s, s+1, \ldots),$$

which, with a change of variable, becomes

$$\Pi_j = \sum_{i=0}^\infty \Pi_{i+j-1} \int_0^\infty \frac{(s\mu x)^i}{i!} e^{-s\mu x} \, dG(x) \qquad (j = s, s+1, \ldots). \qquad (7.7)$$

At this point we assume a geometric solution of the form

$$\Pi_j = A\omega^{j-s} \qquad (j \geq s-1), \qquad (7.8)$$

which, upon substitution into (7.7), gives

$$A\omega^{j-s} = \sum_{i=0}^\infty A\omega^i \omega^{j-1-s} \int_0^\infty \frac{(s\mu x)^i}{i!} e^{-s\mu x} \, dG(x)$$

$$= A\omega^{j-1-s} \int_0^\infty e^{-(1-\omega)s\mu x} \, dG(x) \qquad (j \geq s). \qquad (7.9)$$

Cancellation of the term $A\omega^{j-s}$ on both sides of (7.9) yields

$$\omega = \int_0^\infty e^{-(1-\omega)s\mu x} \, dG(x). \qquad (7.10)$$

The right-hand side of (7.10) is the Laplace–Stieltjes transform $\gamma(z)$ of the interarrival time distribution function $G(x)$, evaluated at $z = (1 - \omega)s\mu$. Hence equation (7.10) can be written

$$\omega = \gamma[(1 - \omega)s\mu]. \tag{7.11}$$

It can be shown (see, for example, Takács [1962a]) that (7.11) has a unique root in $(0, 1)$ whenever $\rho = \lambda/s\mu < 1$, and in this case the numerical solution can be found using the iteration procedure

$$\omega_{i+1} = \gamma[(1 - \omega_i)s\mu] \qquad (i = 0, 1, \ldots ; 0 \leq \omega_0 < 1). \tag{7.12}$$

Note that for Poisson input, the root ω of equation (7.11) equals the server occupancy; $\omega = \lambda/s\mu = \rho$. For this reason, ω is sometimes referred to as the *generalized occupancy*, although the true occupancy, defined to be the carried load per server in erlangs, is still $\rho = \lambda/s\mu$ and, in general, $\omega \neq \rho$.

We conclude that our guess (7.8) is indeed correct. It remains to calculate the constant A and the remaining state probabilities $\Pi_{s-1}, \Pi_{s-2}, \ldots, \Pi_0$. The determination of these probabilities, described now by a finite number of equations, requires much labor. (See, for example, Takács [1962a].) Since these probabilities are not required explicitly for most applications, we content ourselves here with the statement of a formula for the calculation of the constant A:

$$A = \left\{ \frac{1}{1 - \omega} + \sum_{j=1}^{s} \frac{\binom{s}{j}}{C_j(1 - \gamma_j)} \left(\frac{s(1 - \gamma_j) - j}{s(1 - \omega) - j} \right) \right\}^{-1}, \tag{7.13}$$

where

$$\gamma_j = \gamma(j\mu) \qquad\qquad (j = 0, 1, \ldots, s) \tag{7.14}$$

and

$$C_j = \prod_{i=1}^{j} \left(\frac{\gamma_i}{1 - \gamma_i} \right) \qquad (j = 1, 2, \ldots, s). \tag{7.15}$$

Let the random variable W be the length of time an arbitrary customer spends waiting in the queue for service to commence. An arbitrary customer will not receive immediate service if on arrival he finds at least s other customers in the system, and this event occurs with probability $\sum_{j=s}^{\infty} \Pi_j$. Hence

$$P\{W > 0\} = \frac{A}{1 - \omega}. \tag{7.16}$$

For the particular case of Poisson input, the right-hand side of (7.16) is identical with the Erlang delay formula, given by equation (4.7) of Chapter 3. (See Exercise 22.) This provides another illustration of the equality of the outside observer's distribution $\{P_j\}$ and the arriving customer's distribution $\{\Pi_j\}$ for systems with Poisson input.

It is instructive to calculate the order-of-arrival waiting time distribution function for the $GI/M/s$ queue, while simultaneously comparing it with the corresponding analysis of the $M/M/s$ ordered queue carried out in Chapter 3.

First note that the relation

$$P\{W > t\} = P\{W > 0\}P\{W > t \mid W > 0\} \tag{7.17}$$

is valid for any order of service. Since the probability $P\{W > 0\} = A/(1 - \omega)$ does not depend on the order of service, it suffices (and indeed is most convenient) to study the conditional complementary delay distribution function $P\{W > t \mid W > 0\}$ directly.

Also true for any order of service is the relation

$$P\{W > t\} = \sum_{j=0}^{\infty} P\{W > t \mid N = j + s\}P\{N = j + s\}, \tag{7.18}$$

which is simply the law of total probability. From equation (7.8) we have

$$P\{N = j + s\} = A\omega^j. \tag{7.19}$$

It now follows from equations (7.16)–(7.19) that, for any order of service,

$$P\{W > t \mid W > 0\} = (1 - \omega) \sum_{j=0}^{\infty} \omega^j P\{W > t \mid N = j + s\}. \tag{7.20}$$

The reader should compare equation (7.20) and equation (5.5) of Chapter 3.

It remains to calculate $P\{W > t \mid N = j + s\}$. A (test) customer who on arrival finds all s servers busy and j other customers ahead of him in the queue will wait a length of time equal to the sum of the times, measured from the test customer's arrival instant, that each of these j customers spends at the head of the queue, plus the time that the test customer himself spends at the head of the queue. Since the customer service times are independent exponential variables with common mean μ^{-1}, we have

$$P\{W > t \mid N = j + s\} = e^{-s\mu t} \sum_{k=0}^{j} \frac{(s\mu t)^k}{k!}. \tag{7.21}$$

The derivation of (7.21) depends only on the assumptions of exponential service times and order-of-arrival service, not on the input process. Indeed, the derivation (and hence the result) is identical with that of (5.6) of Chapter 3.

As in Chapter 3, insertion of (7.21) into (7.20) yields

$$P\{W > t \mid W > 0\} = e^{-(1-\omega)s\mu t} \qquad (t \geq 0), \qquad (7.22)$$

the analogue of (5.7) of Chapter 3, with ρ replaced by the generalized occupancy ω.

Finally, the conditional mean waiting time (for any order of service) is

$$E(W \mid W > 0) = \frac{1}{(1 - \omega)s\mu} \qquad (7.23)$$

and the overall mean waiting time is

$$E(W) = \frac{A}{(1 - \omega)^2 s\mu}. \qquad (7.24)$$

5–8. Queues Served in Cyclic Order: An Example

So far in this chapter we have discussed some fundamental concepts and applied them to the analyses of two standard models, the $M/G/1$ queue and the $GI/M/s$ queue. Our purpose was to expose fruitful methods of attack rather than to compile results for specific models. The reader interested in other models not covered here, such as the $M/D/s$ queue, should consult reference works such as Syski [1960]; hopefully, the preceding discussions will make the literature more accessible than it might otherwise be. Quite often, however, applications require models that do not fit into the standard molds and are not available in the literature in packaged form. Then the reader must develop his own model if possible. We give here an example of a model suggested by a practical problem that has received some attention in the literature, but is not one that would usually be called standard. The point is that even though this model cannot be equated directly to a "standard" queueing model, it can be analyzed by the same techniques.

We shall first state the general problem, and then solve it for a particular special case. In so doing we hope to illustrate the underlying concepts while simultaneously avoiding inessential detail. The success of the method in the special case then suggests its own generalization. It is interesting to observe that in the literature, for reasons of economy and mathematical "elegance," such problems are usually presented in the most general form that the authors can handle. Such presentation often obscures the process by which the solution was reached, leaving the reader with only the answers and undue respect for the intelligence of the author.

We consider a system of queues served in cyclic order by a single server. The ith queue is characterized by general service time distribution function $H_i(x)$ and Poisson input with parameter λ_i. The process begins with the arrival of a customer at some queue, say A, when the system is otherwise empty. The server starts on this customer immediately, and continues to serve queue A until for the first time the server becomes idle and there are no customers waiting in queue A. The server then looks at the next queue in the cyclic order, queue $A + 1$, and serves those customers, if any, that have accumulated during the serving period of queue A. The server continues to serve $A + 1$ until for the first time the server becomes idle and there are no customers waiting in queue $A + 1$. The process continues in this manner, with the queues being served in cyclic order, until for the first time the system becomes completely empty. The process is then reinitiated by the arrival of the next customer. No time is required to switch from one queue to the next.

It should be pointed out that this description is quite precise, and, in fact, itself constitutes a large chunk of the solution. The original question is simply, how does one analyze a system in which queues are served in cyclic order?

Systems in which a single server is shared among several queues are common. For example, in a time-shared computer system the users have access through teletypewriters to a central computer that is shared among them. Similarly, in some electronic telephone switching systems, the central control spends much of its time polling various hoppers and performing work requests that it finds in these hoppers. Another possible application of this model is in the design of a dynamically controlled traffic light at an intersection.

These systems, of course, do not fit our model exactly. In particular, the assumptions (or lack of assumptions) made with regard to the various distributions, and the exact way in which the server moves among the queues, are the result of a tradeoff between the model's closeness of fit to reality and its mathematical tractability.

It is worth mentioning that this problem has been studied independently by authors motivated by particular applications, with apparent unawareness of related work by others motivated by different applications. A summary of work and a list of references for this problem are given in Stidham [1969]. Recent papers not mentioned by Stidham are Cooper and Murray [1969], Cooper [1970], Eisenberg [1970], and Sykes [1970].

We shall solve the problem posed above for the very special case of two queues, each characterized by the same general service time distribution function $H(x)$ and Poisson input with the same parameter λ. We start by writing probability state equations for the Markov chain imbedded at the instants at which the server finishes serving a queue. We call these time instants *switch points*. At a switch point, all the customers in the system are waiting in the queue other than that on which the server has just been working (because the server switches from a queue at the first instant the queue becomes empty). Since the two queues are identical, the "state" of the system at a switch point can be defined as the number of waiting customers, without regard for the identity of the queue in which they are waiting.

Note that we have chosen to study this system at a particular set of renewal points, the switch points, which is a "smaller" set than that of the usual choice of renewal points, the set of all service completion points. It is not clear, a priori, that this choice will yield as much information as would a solution based on the set of all service completion points. (It turns out that it does.) But if one were to imbed the chain at the latter set of points, the definition of state would require two variables—one for the number of customers in each queue at a service completion point.

Let $P(k)$ be the probability that at an arbitrary switch point the number of waiting customers is k ($k = 0, 1, \ldots$). This event can occur through the following exhaustive and mutually exclusive contingencies:

1. The server leaves a queue and finds $j \geq 1$ customers waiting for service in the other queue, and during the time that the server spends at the latter queue, exactly k customers arrive at the first queue. This length of time is precisely a j-busy period, with distribution function $B_j(t) = B^{*j}(t)$ and corresponding Laplace–Stieltjes transform $[\beta(s)]^j$. (See Section 5–5.)

2. The server leaves a queue and finds no customers waiting in the other queue. When the next arrival occurs (at either queue) the server spends a 1-busy period there, and during that time k customers arrive at the other queue.

These considerations lead directly to the imbedded Markov chain equilibrium probability state equations:

$$P(k) = \sum_{j=1}^{\infty} P(j) \int_0^{\infty} \frac{(\lambda t)^k}{k!} e^{-\lambda t} \, dB^{*j}(t)$$

$$+ P(0) \int_0^{\infty} \frac{(\lambda t)^k}{k!} e^{-\lambda t} \, dB(t) \qquad (k = 0, 1, \ldots). \qquad (8.1)$$

We now solve equations (8.1) by the use of a probability generating function $g(x)$:

$$g(x) = \sum_{k=0}^{\infty} P(k)x^k. \qquad (8.2)$$

Substitution of (8.1) into (8.2) yields

$$g(x) = \sum_{k=0}^{\infty} \left\{ \sum_{j=1}^{\infty} P(j) \int_0^{\infty} \frac{(\lambda t)^k}{k!} e^{-\lambda t} \, dB^{*j}(t) \right.$$

$$\left. + P(0) \int_0^{\infty} \frac{(\lambda t)^k}{k!} e^{-\lambda t} \, dB(t) \right\} x^k$$

$$= \sum_{j=1}^{\infty} P(j) \int_0^{\infty} \sum_{k=0}^{\infty} \frac{(\lambda t x)^k}{k!} e^{-\lambda t} \, dB^{*j}(t)$$

$$+ P(0) \int_0^{\infty} \sum_{k=0}^{\infty} \frac{(\lambda t x)^k}{k!} e^{-\lambda t} \, dB(t),$$

which becomes, after summing over k,

$$g(x) = \sum_{j=1}^{\infty} P(j) \int_0^{\infty} e^{-\lambda(1-x)t} \, dB^{*j}(t) + P(0) \int_0^{\infty} e^{-\lambda(1-x)t} \, dB(t).$$

$$(8.3)$$

The second integral on the right-hand side of (8.3) is simply the Laplace–Stieltjes transform $\beta(s)$ of the busy period distribution function, with argument $s = \lambda(1 - x)$; similarly, the first integral on the right of (8.3) is the Laplace–Stieltjes transform with argument $s = \lambda(1 - x)$ of the j-fold convolution with itself of the busy period distribution function. Since the transform of a j-fold self-convolution is the original transform raised to the jth power, equation (8.3) becomes

$$g(x) = \sum_{j=1}^{\infty} P(j)[\beta(\lambda - \lambda x)]^j + P(0)\beta(\lambda - \lambda x). \qquad (8.4)$$

But, with the addition of the term $P(0)$, the sum in (8.4) is simply the generating function $g(z)$ with argument $z = \beta(\lambda - \lambda x)$. Hence equation (8.4) may be written

$$g[\beta(\lambda - \lambda x)] - g(x) = P(0)[1 - \beta(\lambda - \lambda x)]. \tag{8.5}$$

Equation (8.5) is a functional equation for the probability generating function (8.2). It remains to solve equation (8.5) and find $P(0)$.

Let us now define the iteration procedure

$$z_{\nu+1} = \beta(\lambda - \lambda z_\nu) \qquad (\nu = 0, 1, \ldots ; z_0 = x). \tag{8.6}$$

[Notice that since $z_0 = x$, the νth iterate z_ν is a function of x; that is, $z_\nu = z_\nu(x)$]. Successive use of (8.6) in (8.5) gives

$$g(z_1) - g(x) = P(0)(1 - z_1)$$

$$g(z_2) - g(z_1) = P(0)(1 - z_2)$$

$$\vdots$$

$$g(z_{\nu-1}) - g(z_{\nu-2}) = P(0)(1 - z_{\nu-1})$$

$$g(z_\nu) - g(z_{\nu-1}) = P(0)(1 - z_\nu),$$

which, when added together, give

$$g(z_\nu) - g(x) = P(0) \sum_{j=1}^{\nu} (1 - z_j). \tag{8.7}$$

We shall now show that

$$\lim_{\nu \to \infty} z_\nu(x) = 1 \qquad (x \leqq 1). \tag{8.8}$$

From the definition (8.6) of z_ν as a Laplace–Stieltjes transform, we see that for any $z_0 = x \leqq 1$, the numbers $z_1, z_2, \ldots$ all lie in $(0, 1]$ and thus are bounded (by 1). Since $g(x)$ is a probability generating function, the sequence $g(z_1), g(z_2), \ldots$ is also bounded (by 1). Since $z_1, z_2, \ldots$ all lie in $(0, 1]$, the sum on the right-hand side of (8.7) increases monotonically with ν. Therefore the left-hand side of (8.7), and in particular the sequence $g(z_1), g(z_2), \ldots$, increases monotonically with ν. Thus the sequence $g(z_1), g(z_2), \ldots$ is both bounded and monotonically increasing, and therefore has a finite limit. Hence, the left-hand side of (8.7) has a limit, which implies that the series of nonnegative terms on the right-hand side of (8.7) converges. But a necessary condition for the convergence of a series of nonnegative terms is that the vth term must go to zero as $v \to \infty$. Hence $\lim_{v \to \infty} (1 - z_v) = 0$; that is, we have proved the assertion (8.8).

Returning from our digression, we see that taking limits as $v \to \infty$ in equation (8.7) gives, by virtue of (8.8),

$$g(1) - g(x) = P(0) \sum_{j=1}^{\infty} (1 - z_j). \tag{8.9}$$

Using the normalization requirement $g(1) = 1$ in equation (8.9), we have

$$g(x) = 1 - P(0) \sum_{j=1}^{\infty} [1 - z_j(x)]. \tag{8.10}$$

Setting $x = 0$ in equation (8.10) and noting that $g(0) = P(0)$, we obtain

$$P(0) = \left\{ 1 + \sum_{j=1}^{\infty} [1 - z_j(0)] \right\}^{-1}. \tag{8.11}$$

The functional equation (8.5) has now been solved in the sense that $g(x)$ can be evaluated [using equations (8.10) and (8.11)] for any $x \leq 1$. We can now use this fact to obtain some important characteristics of our queueing system.

To obtain the mean number $\bar{n} = g'(1)$ of customers in the system at a switch point, we differentiate through the functional equation (8.5):

$$-\lambda \beta'(\lambda - \lambda x) g'[\beta(\lambda - \lambda x)] - g'(x) = \lambda P(0) \beta'(\lambda - \lambda x). \tag{8.12}$$

Setting $x = 1$ in equation (8.12) gives

$$-\lambda \beta'(0)\bar{n} - \bar{n} = \lambda P(0) \beta'(0). \tag{8.13}$$

Recall that $\beta(s)$ is the Laplace–Stieltjes transform of the $M/G/1$ busy period distribution function, which has mean $\tau/(1 - \lambda \tau)$. Hence, $-\beta'(0) = \tau/(1 - \lambda \tau)$ and equation (8.13) yields

$$\bar{n} = P(0) \frac{\lambda \tau}{1 - 2\lambda \tau}. \tag{8.14}$$

Note that (8.14) is meaningful only when $2\lambda \tau < 1$. This is exactly what one would intuitively expect; a statistical equilibrium distribution for this single-server system (of two queues) will exist if and only if the total load offered to the server is less than unity. Numerical evaluation of equation (8.14) requires calculation of only one state probability, $P(0)$, which can be computed to any desired degree of accuracy from equations (8.11), (8.6), and (5.59). Observe that although numerical values of the Laplace–Stieltjes transform $\beta(s)$ are required for this calculation, inversion of the transform is not. [Note also that, in general, $P(0) \neq 1 - 2\lambda\tau$. Why?]

Because of the symmetry in the special case we have considered here, the mean wait $E(W)$ for service to commence for a customer arriving at a given queue is given by equation (5.7) with $\rho = 2\lambda\tau$. In the general case, however, the required formula is more complicated. It is worth mentioning that this general formula does not require any iteration for its numerical evaluation. The interested reader should see Cooper [1970].

Exercises

1. P. J. Burke [1968, unpublished]. Consider a birth-and-death process with birth rate λ_j and death rate μ_j when the system is in state E_j $(j = 0, 1, \ldots ; \mu_0 = 0)$. Let $\{\Pi_j\}$ be the state distribution just prior to arrival epochs (births).

a. Prove that

$$\lambda_{j+1}\Pi_j = \mu_{j+1}\Pi_{j+1} \tag{1.1}$$

and compare with equation (3.15) of Chapter 2. [*Hint:* Show that

$$\Pi_j^* = \Pi_j P\{E_{j+1} \to E_j\} + \Pi_{j+1}^* P\{E_{j+1} \to E_j\},$$

where $\{\Pi_j^*\}$ is the state distribution just subsequent to departure epochs (deaths) and $P\{E_{j+1} \to E_j\}$ is the conditional probability that the next transition will take the system into state E_j, given that it is currently in state E_{j+1}.]

b. Use the result (1.1) of this exercise to prove that in any system whose state process constitutes a (one-dimensional) birth-and-death process, the arriving customer's distribution is the same as the outside observer's distribution for a similar system with one less source. [This proves, in particular, the result (8.7) of Chapter 3 for birth-and-death systems with quasirandom input.]

2. *Burke's theorem.* For the $M/M/s$ queue in equilibrium, the distribution of the number of service completions in an arbitrary time interval is Poisson; that is, the output process is the same as the input process.

   Proof: Let $F_j(t)$ be the joint probability that the number of customers in the system at a time t after the last previous departure is j and that the time separating this last departure and the next successive service completion epoch exceeds t.

   a. Obtain a set of differential-difference equations for $F_j(t)$ and show that the unique solution satisfying the initial condition $F_j(0) = \Pi_j^*$ is

   $$F_j(t) = \Pi_j^* e^{-\lambda t}. \tag{2.1}$$

   b. Show that equation (2.1) implies that the time separating two successive departures is exponentially distributed with the same mean as the interarrival times.

   c. To complete the proof of the theorem, show that the interdeparture intervals are mutually independent. [*Hint:* Because of the Markov property of the $M/M/s$ queue, it is sufficient to show that the length of an interdeparture interval and the number of customers in the system at the start of the next interval are independent. To do this use the fact that the joint probability that the interdeparture interval length is in $(t, t + dt)$ and the number of customers in the system at the start of the next interdeparture interval is j is given by $F_{j+1}(t)\mu(j + 1) \, dt$, where $\mu(j + 1) = (j + 1)\mu$ if $j + 1 \leq s$ and $\mu(j + 1) = s\mu$ if $j + 1 > s$, and μ^{-1} is the average service time.]

   For references and another proof, see Exercise 8 of Chapter 4.

3. Carry out the calculations leading from equation (4.7) to equation (4.8). [*Hint:* Use the fact that

   $$\int_0^\infty x[1 - G(x)] \, dx = \int_0^\infty x \int_x^\infty dG(t) \, dx,$$

   and interchange the order of integration.]

4. Derive equation (4.6) by using equation (4.9).

5. Prove equation (4.11).

6. Using equation (4.9), solve Exercise 14 of Chapter 2.

7. Verify equations (5.20) and (5.21) by
   a. Direct calculation.
   b. Application of equation (6.6) of Chapter 2.

8. a. Use the fact that $g(1) = 1$ in equation (5.34) to prove that

$$\Pi_0^* = 1 - \rho.$$

b. Derive the result (5.22) by differentiation of equation (5.37).

9. For the $M/M/1$ queue,

  a. Use equation (5.37) to find the equilibrium state distribution.

  b. Invert the Pollaczek–Khintchine formula.

10. Derive equation (5.7) directly from equation (5.41).

11. Consider the order-of-arrival $M/G/1$ queue with the following variation. The server serves the queue continuously as long as there is at least one customer in the system. When the server finishes serving a customer and finds the system empty, it goes away for a length of time called a *vacation*. At the end of the vacation the server returns to the queue, and begins to serve those customers, if any, who have arrived during the vacation. If the server finds the system empty at the end of a vacation, it immediately takes another vacation, and continues in this manner until it finds at least one waiting customer upon return from a vacation. Let λ be the arrival rate, $\eta(s)$ be the Laplace–Stieltjes transform of the service time distribution function, and

$$f(z) = \sum_{j=0}^{\infty} P(j)z^j$$

be the probability generating function of the number of customers waiting for service at the end of a vacation.

  a. Show that the probability generating function

$$\hat{g}(z) = \sum_{j=0}^{\infty} \hat{\Pi}_j^* z^j$$

  of the number of customers left behind by a departing customer is given by

$$\hat{g}(z) = \frac{[f(z) - 1]\eta(\lambda - \lambda z)}{z - \eta(\lambda - \lambda z)} \frac{(1 - \rho)}{f'(1)}. \tag{11.1}$$

  b. Show that equation (11.1) reduces to equation (5.37) if the vacation always ends the instant the first customer arrives at an otherwise empty system.

  c. Show that if the vacation lengths are independent of the arrival process, then the Laplace–Stieltjes transform $\hat{\omega}(s)$ of the waiting time distribution function for an arbitrary customer is given by

$$\hat{\omega}(s) = \frac{1 - f(1 - s/\lambda)}{s - \lambda[1 - \eta(s)]} \frac{(1 - \rho)\lambda}{f'(1)}. \qquad (11.2)$$

d. Find the probability generating function of the number of customers in the system found by an arriving customer.

e. Find the probability that an arriving customer must wait for service.

f. If $\hat{W}$ is the length of time a customer waits for service to commence, show that

$$E(\hat{W}) = E(W) + \frac{f''(1)}{2\lambda f'(1)}, \qquad (11.3)$$

where $E(W)$ is given by equation (5.7).

g. Suppose that $f(z) = z^j$. Show that equation (11.2) reduces to the Pollaczek–Khintchine formula when $j = 1$. Is equation (11.2) correct when $j \geq 2$? Why? What about (11.1)?

12. In the equilibrium $M/G/1$ queue, let

$$h_j = \int_0^\infty x^j \, dH(x) \qquad (j = 1, 2, \ldots)$$

and

$$b_j = \int_0^\infty x^j \, dB(x) \qquad (j = 1, 2, \ldots),$$

where $H(x)$ and $B(x)$ are the distribution functions of the service time and the busy period, respectively. Show that

$$b_1 = \frac{h_1}{1 - \rho} = -\beta'(0) = \frac{-\eta'(0)}{1 - \rho}$$

$$b_2 = \frac{h_2}{(1 - \rho)^3} = \beta''(0) = \frac{\eta''(0)}{(1 - \rho)^3}$$

where $\eta(s)$ and $\beta(s)$ are the Laplace–Stieltjes transforms of $H(x)$ and $B(x)$, respectively, and ρ is the utilization factor.

13. Show that for the $M/M/1$ queue, equation (5.51) reduces to

$$\beta(s) = \frac{(\lambda + \mu + s) - \sqrt{(\lambda + \mu + s)^2 - 4\lambda\mu}}{2\lambda}. \qquad (13.1)$$

14. Show that for the $M/M/1$ queue, the busy period distribution function $B(t)$ satisfies

$$B(t) = \int_0^t e^{-(\lambda+\mu)x}\mu \, dx + \int_0^t e^{-(\lambda+\mu)x}B_2(t - x)\lambda \, dx. \qquad (14.1)$$

Use equation (14.1) to obtain the result (13.1).

15. Let N_k be the number of customers served during a k-busy period in the $M/G/1$ queue. Give an argument, similar to that following equation (5.45), to prove that

$$N_{i+j} = N_i + N_j, \qquad (15.1)$$

where N_i and N_j are independent.

16. Verify that (5.55) is the solution of equations (5.54).

17. Show that the truth of equation (15.1) for the $M/D/1$ queue implies the identity

$$\sum_{k=j}^{n-i} \frac{k^{k-j-1}}{(k - j)!} \frac{(n - k)^{n-k-i-1}}{(n - k - i)!} = \frac{(i + j)}{ij} \frac{n^{n-i-j-1}}{(n - i - j)!}$$

$$(i \geq 1, j \geq 1, n \geq i + j). \qquad (17.1)$$

In particular, when $i = j = 1$ in equation (17.1), we have the interesting identity

$$\sum_{k=1}^{n-1} \binom{n}{k} k^{k-1}(n - k)^{n-k-1} = 2(n - 1)n^{n-2} \qquad (n \geq 2). \qquad (17.2)$$

Note: A well-known theorem of graph theory, proved almost a century ago by Cayley, states that the number T_n of spanning trees of the complete graph with n labeled vertices is $T_n = n^{n-2}$. An easy inductive argument of Rényi (see pp. 137–138 of Busacker and Saaty [1965]) shows that

$$T_n = \frac{1}{2(n - 1)} \sum_{k=1}^{n-1} \binom{n}{k} k^{k-1}(n - k)^{n-k-1},$$

from which Cayley's result easily follows with application of the identity (17.2). Equation (17.2) also follows from the Abel identity

$A_n(x, y; p, q)$ with $x = y = 0$ and $p = q = -1$ (see pp. 18–23 of Riordan [1968]).

18. It is required to calculate the arriving customer's equilibrium state distribution $\{\Pi_j\}$ for the $M/G/1$ queue with n waiting positions.

   a. Show that $\{\Pi_j\}$ can be calculated from the following algorithm:

   (1) Assume an arbitrary value for Π_0^*, say $\Pi_0^* = 1$, and calculate $\Pi_1^*, \ldots, \Pi_n^*$ from equation (6.1).

   (2) Set $c = \Pi_0^* + \Pi_1^* + \cdots + \Pi_n^*$ and calculate

   $$\Pi_j = \frac{\Pi_j^*}{\Pi_0^* + ac} \qquad (j = 0, 1, \ldots, n)$$

   $$\Pi_{n+1} = \frac{\Pi_0^* + (a - 1)c}{\Pi_0^* + ac}.$$

   b. Suppose that the state distribution, say $\{\hat{\Pi}_j\}$, for the corresponding infinite-waiting room queue has been previously calculated. Show that

   $$\Pi_j = \frac{\hat{\Pi}_j}{\hat{\Pi}_0 + a \sum\limits_{v=0}^{n} \hat{\Pi}_v} \qquad (j = 0, 1, \ldots, n)$$

   $$\Pi_{n+1} = \frac{\hat{\Pi}_0 + (a - 1) \sum\limits_{v=0}^{n} \hat{\Pi}_v}{\hat{\Pi}_0 + a \sum\limits_{v=0}^{n} \hat{\Pi}_v}.$$

   c. Using the results of part **b**, calculate the distribution $\{\Pi_j\}$ for the particular case of exponential service times. Compare with equation (22.1) of Exercise 22 of Chapter 3.

19. A particle counting device consists of three one-particle buffers and a recorder that visits the buffers and counts the particles. Particles arrive at each of the buffers in three independent Poisson streams, each with rate λ. Any particle that finds its particular buffer occupied is cleared from the system, that is, not counted. A buffer is held by a particle both while waiting for the counter and while being counted. The time required for the recorder to count a particle (and empty a buffer) is a constant of length unity. Show that the proportion p of particles not counted by this device is

$$p = 1 - \frac{e^{3\lambda} + e^{\lambda} - e^{2\lambda}}{1 + 3\lambda(e^{3\lambda} + e^{\lambda} - e^{2\lambda})}.$$

20. *The $M/G/1$ queue from the viewpoint of arrivals.* Let N be the number of customers in the system just prior to an arbitrary arrival epoch T_c and let R be the time needed to complete the service of the customer (if there is one) in service at T_c. Define

$$P\{N = j\} = \Pi_j \qquad\qquad (j = 0, 1, \ldots) \qquad (20.1)$$

$$P\{R \le x, N = j\} = \Pi_j(x) \qquad\qquad (x \ge 0; j = 1, 2, \ldots) \qquad (20.2)$$

and

$$\psi_j(s) = \int_0^\infty e^{-sx}\, d\Pi_j(x) \qquad (j = 1, 2, \ldots). \qquad (20.3)$$

Wishart [1961] (see also Takács [1963]) has shown that for $\lambda\tau = \rho < 1$ the generating function $u(s, z)$ of the Laplace–Stieltjes transform (20.3),

$$u(s, z) = \sum_{j=1}^\infty \psi_j(s)z^j, \qquad (20.4)$$

is given by

$$u(s, z) = \frac{\Pi_0\lambda z(1 - z)}{z - \eta(\lambda - \lambda z)} \frac{\eta(s) - \eta(\lambda - \lambda z)}{s - \lambda(1 - z)} \qquad (20.5)$$

with

$$\Pi_0 = 1 - \rho, \qquad (20.6)$$

where $\eta(s)$ is the Laplace–Stieltjes transform of the service time distribution function $H(x)$, τ is the mean service time, and λ is the customer arrival rate. Finally, inversion of (20.5) gives

$$\sum_{j=1}^\infty \Pi_j(x)z^j = \frac{(1 - \rho)\lambda z(1 - z)}{z - \eta(\lambda - \lambda z)} \int_0^\infty e^{-\lambda(1 - z)\xi}[H(\xi + x) - H(\xi)]\, d\xi. \qquad (20.7)$$

a. Using the normalizing equation

$$\Pi_0 + \sum_{j=1}^\infty \psi_j(0) = 1$$

and (20.5), prove equation (20.6).

b. Starting with equation (20.7), show that

$$\sum_{j=1}^\infty \Pi_j(x) = \lambda \int_0^x [1 - H(\xi)]\, d\xi$$

and that this in turn implies

$$P\{R \leq x \mid N \geq 1\} = \frac{1}{\tau} \int_0^x [1 - H(\xi)]\, d\xi. \qquad (20.8)$$

Compare equations (20.8) and (4.6) and discuss. [*Hint:*

$$\int_0^\infty [H(\xi + x) - H(\xi)]\, d\xi = \int_0^\infty [1 - H(\xi)]\, d\xi$$

$$- \int_0^\infty [1 - H(\xi + x)]\, d\xi.]$$

c. Show that

$$\sum_{j=0}^\infty \Pi_j z^j = \frac{(z - 1)\eta(\lambda - \lambda z)}{z - \eta(\lambda - \lambda z)}\, (1 - \rho). \qquad (20.9)$$

Compare equations (20.9) and (5.37) and discuss.

d. Let $W(x)$ be the waiting time distribution function for an arbitrary customer when service is in order of arrival. Show that (Takács [1963])

$$W(x) = \Pi_0 + \sum_{j=1}^\infty \int_0^x \Pi_j(t - \xi)\, dH^{*(j-1)}(\xi) \qquad (20.10)$$

and that therefore $W(x)$ has Laplace–Stieltjes transform $\omega(s)$:

$$\omega(s) = \frac{s(1 - \rho)}{s - \lambda[1 - \eta(s)]}. \qquad (20.11)$$

Compare equations (20.11) and (5.41).

21. Show that the transition probabilities $\{p_{ij}\}$ that appear in the state equations (7.3) for the $GI/M/s$ queue are given by

$$p_{ij} = \int_0^\infty \binom{i + 1}{j} e^{-j\mu x}(1 - e^{-\mu x})^{i+1-j}\, dG(x)$$

$$(i < s,\, i + 1 \geq j)$$

$$p_{ij} = \int_0^\infty \binom{s}{j} e^{-j\mu x} \left\{ \int_0^x \frac{(s\mu y)^{i-s}}{(i - s)!} (e^{-\mu y} - e^{-\mu x})^{s-j} s\mu\, dy \right\} dG(x)$$

$$(i \geq s,\, j < s).$$

[The transition probabilities $\{p_{ij}\}$ are given by equation (7.5) for $j > i + 1$ and by equation (7.6) for $i \geq s, j \geq s, i + 1 \geq j.$]

22. Show that for Poisson input equation (7.16) reduces to the Erlang delay formula.

23. Prove that in a $GI/M/s$ system with order-of-arrival service, the conditional probability that a blocked customer will still be waiting in the queue when the next arrival occurs is equal to the generalized occupancy ω. (See Exercise 10 of Chapter 3.)

24. *The $M/G/1$ queue with gating.* An arriving customer who finds the server idle causes a gate to close. When this customer's service is complete the gate opens and admits into a waiting room all those customers who arrived during this service time, and then closes. When all the customers in the waiting room have been served, the gate opens and admits into the waiting room all those customers who arrived during the collective service times of the preceding group of customers, after which it closes. The process continues in this manner. When the gate opens and finds no waiting customers, it remains open until it again closes behind the next arrival. Show that the average $\bar{n}$ of the number of customers who enter the waiting room when the gate opens is given by

$$\bar{n} = \frac{\rho}{1 - \rho} \left\{ 1 + \sum_{j=1}^{\infty} (1 - x_j) \right\}^{-1}$$

with

$$x_{j+1} = \eta(\lambda - \lambda x_j) \qquad (j = 1, 2, \ldots; x_1 = 0),$$

where ρ is the utilization factor, λ is the arrival rate, and $\eta(s)$ is the Laplace–Stieltjes transform of the service time distribution function. [*Hint:* How is this problem related to that of queues served in cyclic order?]

Waiting Times 6

6-1. Introduction

In this chapter we shall study the stationary waiting time distribution functions corresponding to three different queue disciplines—service in order of arrival, service in random order, and service in reverse order of arrival—for each of the standard queueing models, $M/M/s$, $GI/M/s$, and $M/G/1$, that have been discussed in previous chapters. In addition, we shall discuss order-of-arrival waiting times in the $GI/G/1$ queue.

The queue disciplines to be discussed here are what we have termed *nonscheduled*; that is, every time a customer is chosen to begin service, the customer's service time is drawn from the same distribution as that of an arbitrary customer. This excludes the case, for example, where the customers are selected in the reverse order of their service times, termed shortest processing time first. In this case, the fact that a customer is served *j*th in order allows inference to be drawn about his service time. Although we continue to refer only to nonscheduled queue disciplines, it is important to observe that other types of disciplines exist.

Our emphasis throughout this chapter will be on observing the similarities and the differences in the analyses of the different models studied. Sometimes, several derivations of the same result will be given in the text, and sometimes additional derivations of results given in the text will be outlined in the exercises.

The material of this chapter is largely theoretical rather than practical in the sense of leading to methods of numerical calculations. In many cases, it will prove easier to obtain numerical results through simulation than to invert the transforms or implement the algorithms that theory provides. The reader interested in making calculations should consult the references before writing a word of FORTRAN. As will become evident, there is fertile ground for research in the subject of waiting times.

In addition it will soon become clear that the mathematics underlying waiting times analysis is more advanced and more difficult than that of past chapters. As usual, we shall avoid strictly mathematical questions and concentrate on the queueing formulations, although the limitations of this approach will be more apparent. This chapter is intended to provide insight into an important area where work is yet to be done.

We begin with a review of some important results derived in previous chapters. Recall that in Chapter 5 we gave a heuristic derivation of the equation (in the usual notation of the literature of queueing theory) $L = \lambda W$. This very general formula relates the average queue length L to the average waiting time W, where λ is the customer arrival rate. This result is valid for any queueing system in equilibrium. We shall have occasion to use this result in the analyses of this chapter, and for completeness it should be mentioned in any discussion of waiting times. This equation shows, at least insofar as averages are concerned, that it is sufficient to calculate either the average of the queue size or the average of the waiting times. In any particular case, direct calculation of one of these quantities may be much easier than direct calculation of the other. As we shall see, calculation of the complete waiting time distribution function may, in any particular case, be more easily accomplished through consideration of the (discrete) state probabilities rather than directly in terms of the (continuous) waiting times or vice versa.

Since the state probabilities are (clearly) independent of the order of service of waiting customers, it follows from the equation $L = \lambda W$ that the mean waiting time is also independent of the order of service. Therefore the main practical information to be gained from any waiting time analysis concerns the higher moments and the tails of the waiting time distribution function.

Sometimes it is convenient to consider the system directly from the viewpoint of an arriving customer, and sometimes it is more convenient to infer the arriving customer's viewpoint by considering the system from the vantage point of an outside observer or a departing customer. As in previous chapters, we shall denote the arriving customer's distribution by $\{\Pi_j\}$, the departing customer's distribution by $\{\Pi_j^*\}$, and the outside observer's distribution by $\{P_j\}$. In all cases we shall be concerned with the calculation of the customer's waiting time distribution function

$$W(t) = 1 - P\{W > t\}, \tag{1.1}$$

where we define the random variable W as the time spent by an arbitrary customer waiting for service to commence. When the equations are written from the viewpoint of a hypothetical customer, that customer will be referred to as the *test customer*.

Frequently it is convenient to write the equations in terms of the complementary conditional waiting time distribution function $P\{W > t \mid W > 0\}$. The unconditional waiting time distribution function is then obtained from the relation

$$P\{W > t\} = P\{W > t \mid W > 0\}P\{W > 0\} \tag{1.2}$$

and equation (1.1). Note that the probability $P\{W > 0\}$ that an arbitrary customer will not begin service immediately, given by

$$P\{W > 0\} = \sum_{j=0}^{\infty} \Pi_{s+j}, \tag{1.3}$$

where s is the number of servers, is independent of the order of service of waiting customers. It follows that the order of service is reflected in the conditional probability $P\{W > t \mid W > 0\}$.

From the law of total probability we may write

$$P\{W > t\} = \sum_{j=0}^{\infty} P\{W > t \mid N = s + j\}\Pi_{s+j}, \tag{1.4}$$

where N is the number of customers in the system when the test customer arrives. If we define

$$W_j(t) = P\{W > t \mid N = s + j\} \qquad (j = 0, 1, \ldots), \tag{1.5}$$

then from equations (1.2), (1.3), and (1.4) we have the formula

$$P\{W > t \mid W > 0\} = \frac{\sum\limits_{j=0}^{\infty} \Pi_{s+j}W_j(t)}{\sum\limits_{j=0}^{\infty} \Pi_{s+j}}. \tag{1.6}$$

These equations are valid for any queueing system whatever. In some cases they indicate the most convenient method of analysis of waiting times, and in some cases they are of little or no value in waiting time studies.

6–2. The *GI/G/*1 Queue: Service in Order of Arrival

When service is in order of arrival, an analysis of the waiting times is relatively simple, even for the general model *GI/G/*1. The following analysis is that of Lindley [1952].

Let the random variables W_k and S_k be the waiting time and the service time, respectively, of the kth arriving (and departing) customer, and let X_k be the elapsed time between the arrival of the kth and the arrival of the $(k + 1)$th customer. Then we have, for $k = 1, 2, \ldots,$

$$W_{k+1} = \begin{cases} W_k + S_k - X_k & \text{if } W_k + S_k - X_k > 0 \\ 0 & \text{if } W_k + S_k - X_k \leq 0. \end{cases} \tag{2.1}$$

By assumption, the service times S_k are nonnegative, mutually independent, and identically distributed random variables. Let

$$H(x) = P\{S_k \leq x\} \qquad (k = 1, 2, \ldots) \tag{2.2}$$

be the service time distribution function. Also by assumption, the interarrival intervals X_k are independent of each other and of the service times. Let

$$G(x) = P\{X_k \leq x\} \qquad (k = 1, 2, \ldots) \tag{2.3}$$

be the interarrival time distribution function.

Let us denote by $F(x)$ the distribution function of the random variable $S_k - X_k$ (which can take negative values with a positive probability). Then

$$F(x) = \int_0^\infty H(x + \xi) \, dG(\xi). \tag{2.4}$$

Finally, let $W_{(k)}(t)$ be the waiting time distribution function for the kth customer,

$$W_{(k)}(t) = P\{W_k \leq t\} \qquad (k = 1, 2, \ldots). \tag{2.5}$$

Then it follows from the independence of the random variables in equation (2.1) that

$$W_{(k+1)}(t) = \begin{cases} \displaystyle\int_{-\infty}^{t} W_{(k)}(t - x) \, dF(x) & \text{when } t \geq 0 \\ 0 & \text{when } t < 0. \end{cases} \tag{2.6}$$

Since $F(x)$ is assumed known [see equation (2.4)], this equation permits calculation by recurrence of all $W_{(k)}(t)$.

If a stationary limit

$$\lim_{k \to \infty} W_{(k)}(t) = W(t) \qquad (2.7)$$

exists, then, from (2.6), it must satisfy the equation

$$W(t) = \begin{cases} \displaystyle\int_{-\infty}^{t} W(t - x) \, dF(x) & \text{when } t \geq 0 \\ 0 & \text{when } t < 0. \end{cases} \qquad (2.8)$$

Note that the waiting time distribution function $W(t)$ depends only on the distribution function $F(x)$ of the difference between the service time S_k and the interarrival time X_k, rather than on their individual distribution functions.

Equation (2.8) is a member of a class of equations called *Wiener–Hopf* equations. In general, solution of Wiener–Hopf equations is difficult, and requires advanced mathematical techniques. We shall solve equation (2.8) for some special cases, but shall avoid discussions of general methods. The reader is referred to Smith [1953] for a discussion of the general solution of (2.8). (See also Prabhu [1965], Riordan [1962], and Syski [1960].)

Lindley [1952] has shown that, as one might anticipate, the limit (2.7) exists if and only if the utilization factor $\rho = \lambda \tau$ is less than unity, where λ is the customer arrival rate and τ is the mean service time.

Our task is now to solve equation (2.8) for the waiting time distribution function $W(t)$. To this end, note that although the integral on the right-hand side of (2.8) has no physical significance when $t < 0$, it does have a numerical value for any $t < 0$. Therefore, let us define $W^-(t)$ as the value of the integral on the right-hand side of (2.8) for negative t:

$$W^-(t) = \begin{cases} \displaystyle\int_{-\infty}^{t} W(t - x) \, dF(x) & \text{when } t < 0 \\ 0 & \text{when } t \geq 0. \end{cases} \qquad (2.9)$$

Then, combining equations (2.8) and (2.9), we can write

$$W^-(t) + W(t) = \int_{-\infty}^{t} W(t - x) \, dF(x) \qquad (-\infty < t < \infty), \qquad (2.10)$$

which holds for all real values of t. Let us now define the transforms

$$\omega_0^-(s) = \int_{-\infty}^{\infty} e^{-s\xi} W^-(\xi)\, d\xi = \int_{-\infty}^{0} e^{-s\xi} W^-(\xi)\, d\xi \qquad (2.11)$$

$$\omega_0(s) = \int_{-\infty}^{\infty} e^{-s\xi} W(\xi)\, d\xi = \int_{0}^{\infty} e^{-s\xi} W(\xi)\, d\xi \qquad (2.12)$$

and

$$\omega(s) = \int_{0}^{\infty} e^{-s\xi}\, dW(\xi). \qquad (2.13)$$

Note that $\omega_0(s)$ and $\omega(s)$ are, respectively, the Laplace and Laplace–Stieltjes transforms of the waiting time distribution function $W(t)$. Hence [see equation (6.3) of Chapter 2]

$$\omega(s) = s\omega_0(s). \qquad (2.14)$$

We also define the Laplace–Stieltjes transforms

$$\gamma(s) = \int_{0}^{\infty} e^{-s\xi}\, dG(\xi) \qquad (2.15)$$

and

$$\eta(s) = \int_{0}^{\infty} e^{-s\xi}\, dH(\xi). \qquad (2.16)$$

Since we may write (see Exercise 2)

$$\int_{-\infty}^{\infty} e^{-s\xi}\, dF(\xi) = \gamma(-s)\eta(s), \qquad (2.17)$$

it then follows from equation (2.10) that (see Exercise 3)

$$\omega_0^-(s) + \omega_0(s) = \omega_0(s)\gamma(-s)\eta(s). \qquad (2.18)$$

Taking into account equation (2.14), equation (2.18) yields

$$\omega(s) = \frac{s}{\gamma(-s)\eta(s) - 1}\, \omega_0^-(s). \qquad (2.19)$$

Equation (2.19) expresses the Laplace–Stieltjes transform $\omega(s)$ of the waiting time distribution function in terms of the given Laplace–Stieltjes transforms $\gamma(-s)$ and $\eta(s)$ and the unknown function $\omega_0^-(s)$. The determination of the function $\omega_0^-(s)$ is the principal difficulty in the application of Lindley's method; needed to make this calculation are results from the theory of functions of a complex variable that are beyond the scope of this text.

As an example of Lindley's method, we consider the simplest application, the $M/M/1$ queue. In this case, we have $G(\xi) = 1 - e^{-\lambda\xi}$ and $H(\xi) = 1 - e^{-\mu\xi}$, where $\mu^{-1} = \tau$, so that

$$\gamma(s) = \frac{\lambda}{\lambda + s} \tag{2.20}$$

and

$$\eta(s) = \frac{\mu}{\mu + s}. \tag{2.21}$$

Then equation (2.19) becomes

$$\omega(s) = \frac{(\lambda - s)(\mu + s)}{(\mu - \lambda + s)} \omega_0^-(s). \tag{2.22}$$

Since $W(\xi)$ is a distribution function, it follows from equation (2.13) that

$$\omega(s) > 0 \qquad \text{when } s \geq 0 \tag{2.23}$$

and

$$\omega(0) = 1. \tag{2.24}$$

The denominator in (2.22) has no zeros for $s \geq 0$ since $\rho = (\lambda/\mu) < 1$. However, the numerator has a zero at $s = \lambda$. Therefore, $\omega_0^-(s)$ may be of the form

$$\omega_0^-(s) = \frac{c}{\lambda - s}. \tag{2.25}$$

[It can be shown that, indeed, $\omega_0^-(s)$ *must* be of the form (2.25).] The constant c is easily evaluated using the normalization equation (2.24). The result is $c = 1 - \rho$, so that the solution is

$$\omega(s) = \frac{(s + \mu)}{(s - \lambda + \mu)} (1 - \rho). \tag{2.26}$$

Equation (2.26) is the Pollaczek–Khintchine formula for the special case of exponential service times. Inversion of (2.26) gives the well-known result for the $M/M/1$ queue with service in order of arrival,

$$W(t) = 1 - \rho e^{-(1-\rho)\mu t}. \tag{2.27}$$

[See equation (17.10) of Exercise 17 of Chapter 2.]

It is interesting to note that the function $\omega_0^-(s)$ was determined in part by the condition $\omega(\lambda) \neq 0$. From the definition of the Laplace–Stieltjes transform (2.13), we see that

$$\omega(\lambda) = \int_0^\infty e^{-\lambda\xi} \, dW(\xi). \tag{2.28}$$

For the $M/M/1$ queue, we can interpret the right-hand side of equation (2.28) as the probability that no customers arrive during the waiting time of an arbitrary customer. Equivalently, this is the probability that an arriving customer finds no other customers waiting for service; that is, $\omega(\lambda)$ is the probability that an arrival finds the system empty or with one customer in service. But from our previous analysis of the $M/M/1$ queue (see Section 3–4) we know this probability to equal $\sum_{j=0}^1 (1 - \rho)\rho^j$, which simplifies to

$$\sum_{j=0}^1 (1 - \rho)\rho^j = (1 + \rho)(1 - \rho). \tag{2.29}$$

We conclude that we must have

$$\omega(\lambda) = (1 + \rho)(1 - \rho). \tag{2.30}$$

Evaluation of equation (2.26) at $s = \lambda$ does indeed give the result (2.30).

It is important to observe that the waiting time process for the $GI/G/1$ queue is an imbedded Markov chain. Previously we have studied processes that either are Markov processes, such as the birth-and-death process, or have imbedded Markov chains, such as the $M/G/1$ queue and the $GI/M/s$ queue. In the $M/G/1$ queue the renewal points are the service completion epochs; in the $GI/M/s$ queue they are the customer arrival epochs; and in the birth-and-death process, every point is a renewal point.

Furthermore, in each of these cases, the process we considered directly was discrete-valued; that is, the process was an integer-valued random variable $N(t)$, where the parameter t was either continuous as in the case of a Markov process, or discrete as in the case of the imbedded Markov chain. Although the waiting time process is inherently continuous-valued, we were always able previously to obtain it in terms of the discrete-valued process $N(t)$.

We will now show that the waiting time process for the $GI/G/1$ queue is in fact a continuous-valued imbedded Markov chain. This follows from equation (2.6), which shows that $W_{(k+1)}$ depends only on the preceding random variable $W_{(k)}$, so that the eopchs of commencement of service constitute a set of renewal points. In fact, we can write, symbolically,

$$P\{W_{(k+1)} \leq t\} = \sum_x P\{W_{(k)} = x\} P\{W_{(k+1)} \leq t \mid W_{(k)} = x\},$$

where the Markov chain transition probabilities are

$$P\{W_{(k+1)} \leq t \mid W_{(k)} = x\} = P\{S_k - X_k \leq t - x\} = F(t - x)$$

$$(2.31)$$

and where the second equality in equation (2.31) follows from the definition (2.4). Thus we may write

$$W_{(k+1)}(t) = \int_{0-}^{\infty} F(t - x) \, dW_{(k)}(x). \qquad (2.32)$$

Formally taking limits as $k \to \infty$ in (2.32) we obtain

$$W(t) = \int_{0-}^{\infty} F(t - x) \, dW(x). \qquad (2.33)$$

Equation (2.33) can easily be shown to be equivalent to the basic equation (2.8). (See Exercise 4.)

In this section we have studied the order-of-arrival waiting time process in the $GI/G/1$ queue. In particular, we have derived the well-known integral equation (2.8) of Lindley, and have illustrated its use in the simplest case, the $M/M/1$ queue. It should be clear to the reader that the mathematics of this section is much more advanced than that used previously. For a good discussion of the interrelationship between the mathematics of the $GI/G/1$ queue, Wiener–Hopf equations, and the theory of random walks, see Feller [1971].

6-3. The $M/M/s$ Queue

In this section we shall study the waiting times in the $M/M/s$ queue for three queue disciplines—service in order of arrival, service in random order, and service in reverse order of arrival. In addition, we shall obtain a bound on all waiting time distribution functions by examining the case of the "polite" customer, who refuses to enter service until no one else is waiting in the queue. We shall use methods that reflect recognition of the fact that the $M/M/s$ queue can be viewed as a birth-and-death process. All the results to be obtained for the $M/M/s$ queue can be obtained by specialization of corresponding results for more general models that will be obtained in subsequent sections. However, it is often instructive to compare the different approaches necessary to solve corresponding problems under different assumptions concerning the component distribution functions.

Let the customer arrival rate be λ and the mean service time be μ^{-1}. The arriving customer's distribution $\{\Pi_j\}$ and the outside observer's distribution $\{P_j\}$ are equal because the input is Poisson. These probabilities are given by equations (4.3), (4.4), and (4.5) of Chapter 3. In particular, we have

$$\Pi_{s+j} = \frac{a^s}{s!} \left(\frac{a}{s}\right)^j P_0 \qquad (j = 0, 1, \ldots), \qquad (3.1)$$

where $a = \lambda/\mu$. It follows from equation (1.6) that

$$P\{W > t \mid W > 0\} = (1 - \rho) \sum_{j=0}^{\infty} \rho^j W_j(t), \qquad (3.2)$$

where $\rho = a/s < 1$ is the server occupancy or utilization factor. Since equation (3.2) holds for all orders of service, it follows that it is sufficient to determine the conditional probabilities $W_j(t) = P\{W > t \mid N = s + j\}$ $(j = 0, 1, \ldots)$ for each order of service. Then the conditional waiting time distribution function can be obtained from (3.2), and the unconditional waiting time distribution function (1.1) can be obtained from equations (1.2) and (3.2), where, for the $M/M/s$ queue,

$$P\{W > 0\} = C(s, a) = \frac{a^s/[(s - 1)! \, (s - a)]}{\sum_{k=0}^{s-1} (a^k/k!) + a^s/[(s - 1)! \, (s - a)]} . \qquad (3.3)$$

Consider a test customer who finds all s servers busy on arrival, at time T_c, say. Let X_1 be the elapsed time from the arrival epoch T_c until the first subsequent service completion epoch T_1; $X_1 = T_1 - T_c$. Since the service times are, by assumption, exponentially distributed with mean

μ^{-1}, it follows that X_1 is exponentially distributed with mean $(s\mu)^{-1}$. If the test customer is not chosen for service at T_1, then he will wait in the queue for at least a time interval $X_2 = T_2 - T_1$, where T_2 is the second service completion epoch subsequent to T_c. Again, X_2 is exponentially distributed with mean $(s\mu)^{-1}$, independently of X_1. Clearly, the waiting time of a blocked test customer is a sum

$$S_M = X_1 + \cdots + X_M \qquad (3.4)$$

of M mutually independent, identical exponential variables, where

$$P\{X_i > t\} = e^{-s\mu t} \qquad (3.5)$$

and where the number M of terms in the sum is itself a random variable. The form of the distribution of M depends, of course, only on the order of service.

The above argument shows that, in any queue with exponential service times (regardless of the input process or the order of service), the conditional waiting time distribution function can be expressed in terms of the argument $x = s\mu t$. Hence the conditional waiting time distribution function depends only on the product $s\mu t$ and not on these factors individually.

Service in Order of Arrival

We have already considered this question in several ways. In Section 3–5 we showed that the random variable M in the sum (3.4) is simply one plus the number of customers that the (blocked) test customer finds on arrival. That is, with service in order of arrival, the waiting time for a blocked customer is the sum of the times that each of the customers waiting in the queue at epoch T_c subsequently spends at the head of the queue, plus the time that the test customer himself spends waiting at the head of the queue.

Therefore

$$W_j(t) = P\{S_M > t \mid M = j + 1\} = P\{X_1 + \cdots + X_{j+1} > t\}, \qquad (3.6)$$

where X_i $(i = 1, \ldots, j + 1)$ is distributed according to equation (3.5). As we have argued previously, S_{j+1} will exceed t if and only if the number of service completions in the interval $(0, t)$ does not exceed j. Since the random variables $\{X_i\}$ are mutually independent with common exponential distribution (3.5), it follows that

$$W_j(t) = \sum_{k=0}^{j} \frac{(s\mu t)^k}{k!} e^{-s\mu t}. \tag{3.7}$$

Equation (3.7) is identical to equation (5.6) of Chapter 3. Substitution of equation (3.7) into equation (3.2) and interchange of the order of summation gives the well-known result

$$P\{W > t \mid W > 0\} = e^{-(1-\rho)s\mu t}, \tag{3.8}$$

which is the same as equation (5.7) of Chapter 3.

It follows from equation (3.8) that the conditional mean wait for service, given that a customer is blocked, is given by

$$E(W \mid W > 0) = \frac{1}{(1-\rho)s\mu}. \tag{3.9}$$

Although equation (3.9) was obtained above under the assumption of service in order of arrival, it is true for every $M/M/s$ queue regardless of the order of service.

This analysis is essentially the same as that of Section 3–5. The purpose of the above presentation is to facilitate an understanding of the order-of-arrival $M/M/s$ queue in the context of more general waiting time analyses.

In Section 6–2 we showed, as an example of the use of Lindley's equation for the $GI/G/1$ queue with service in order of arrival, that the waiting time distribution function for the $M/M/1$ queue is [see equation (2.27)]

$$W(t) = 1 - \rho e^{-(1-\rho)\mu t}. \tag{3.10}$$

It is easy to see that (3.10) is the special case of (3.8) with $s = 1$. Indeed, we could infer (3.8) from (3.10), if we also know the probability $P\{W > 0\}$. This follows from the remark just preceding this subsection. We simply calculate from (3.10) the conditional probability

$$P\{W > t \mid W > 0\} = \frac{1 - W(t)}{1 - W(0)} = \frac{1 - (1 - \rho e^{-(1-\rho)\mu t})}{\rho} = e^{-(1-\rho)\mu t}.$$

Now replace μ by $s\mu$ on the right-hand side of this equation; the result is (3.8). This provides another independent derivation of the important result (3.8).

Following Riordan [1962], we now derive equation (3.8) using the method of differential-difference equations that we previously used in the analysis of birth-and-death processes. We consider changes occurring in $(T_c, T_c + h)$ as $h \to 0$, where T_c is the arrival epoch of the test customer. Since service is in order of arrival, the test customer's wait is unaffected by any arrivals that might occur after T_c. Since the probability of a service completion in $(T_c, T_c + h)$ is $s\mu h + o(h)$ as $h \to 0$, and the probability of more than one service completion is $o(h)$ as $h \to 0$, we have the following recurrence:

$$W_j(h + t) = s\mu h W_{j-1}(t) + (1 - s\mu h)W_j(t) + o(h)$$
$$[h \to 0; j = 0, 1, \ldots; W_{-1}(t) = 0]. \qquad (3.11)$$

Note that the assumptions underlying equation (3.11) are service in order of arrival and exponential service times; the assumption of Poisson input has not yet been used.

Transposing equation (3.11) and passing to the limit as $h \to 0$, we obtain the differential-difference equations

$$\frac{d}{dt} W_j(t) = s\mu W_{j-1}(t) - s\mu W_j(t) \qquad [j = 0, 1, \ldots; W_{-1}(t) = 0].$$
$$(3.12)$$

Equation (3.12) is easily solved by recurrence; if the initial conditions are

$$W_j(0) = 1 \qquad (j = 0, 1, \ldots), \qquad (3.13)$$

then equation (3.12) has solution given by equation (3.7). [Note that (3.12) is of the same form as equation (2.5) of Chapter 2 for the Poisson process. The reason that the solutions are different, of course, is that the initial conditions are different.]

Although our problem is solved, since equation (3.8) follows after straightforward calculation from (3.7) and (3.2), it is interesting to derive (3.8) directly from equations (3.12) and (3.2). To this end, define the generating function

$$W(x, t) = \sum_{j=0}^{\infty} W_j(t)x^j. \qquad (3.14)$$

Then it follows from equations (3.12) and (3.14) that $W(x, t)$ satisfies the partial differential equation

$$\frac{\partial}{\partial t} W(x, t) = s\mu(x - 1)W(x, t), \tag{3.15}$$

whose solution is

$$W(x, t) = W(x, 0)e^{-(1-x)s\mu t}. \tag{3.16}$$

It follows from equations (3.13) and (3.14) that

$$W(x, 0) = \sum_{j=0}^{\infty} x^j \tag{3.17}$$

so that, after summing the geometric series in (3.17), equation (3.16) becomes

$$W(x, t) = \frac{1}{1 - x} e^{-(1-x)s\mu t}. \tag{3.18}$$

Now note that, by virtue of equation (3.14), equation (3.2) can be written

$$P\{W > t \mid W > 0\} = (1 - \rho)W(\rho, t). \tag{3.19}$$

Equation (3.8) now follows from equations (3.18) and (3.19). (See Exercise 12 of Chapter 3.)

Service in Random Order

We shall calculate, for the $M/M/s$ queue with service in random order, the conditional probability

$$W_j(t) = P\{W > t \mid N = s + j\} \qquad (j = 0, 1, \ldots),$$

from which the conditional probability $P\{W > t \mid W > 0\}$ can be calculated according to equation (3.2).

In contrast to the case of service in order of arrival, when service is in random order, the waiting time of a (blocked) test customer depends on customers who arrive after the test customer's arrival epoch T_c as well as on customers who arrive prior to T_c. Also, when service is at random, the future waiting time of each customer in the queue has the same distribution function. By considering, in the usual manner, all possible transitions during a time interval of length h, we have

$$W_j(h + t) = \lambda h W_{j+1}(t) + \frac{j}{j + 1} s\mu h W_{j-1}(t)$$

$$+ [1 - (\lambda + s\mu)h]W_j(t) + o(h)$$

$$[h \to 0; j = 0, 1, \ldots; W_{-1}(t) = 0]. \qquad (3.20)$$

In equation (3.20), the term $[j/(j + 1)]s\mu h W_{j-1}(t)$, for example, reflects the fact that if at T_c there are $j + 1$ customers (including the test customer) in the queue, and a customer completes service in $(T_c, T_c + h)$ [with probability $s\mu h + o(h)$], then if the test customer is not the next one chosen to enter service [with probability $j/(j + 1)$], he will wait in excess of an additional time t for service to commence with probability $W_{j-1}(t)$, as if he had just arrived and found $j - 1$ other waiting customers.

Transposing and taking limits as $h \to 0$ in equation (3.20), we obtain the basic set of differential-difference equations

$$\frac{d}{dt} W_j(t) = \lambda W_{j+1}(t) + \frac{j}{j + 1} s\mu W_{j-1}(t)$$

$$- (\lambda + s\mu)W_j(t) \qquad [j = 0, 1, \ldots; W_{-1}(t) = 0]. \qquad (3.21)$$

Equations (3.21) are complemented by

$$W_j(0) = 1 \qquad (j = 0, 1, \ldots). \qquad (3.22)$$

Equation (3.21) was derived independently by Vaulot [1946] and Palm [1957]. (According to Syski [1960], Palm's work was done in 1938 but was not published until 1946. An English version was published in 1957.) Pollaczek [1946] obtained a closed-form solution for the conditional waiting time probability $P\{W > t \mid W > 0\}$. Pollaczek's result is

$$P\{W > t \mid W > 0\} = 2(1 - \rho) \int_0^\pi \exp{(-At)} \frac{B \sin x \, dx}{1 + \exp{(\pi \cot x)}},$$

where $\qquad\qquad\qquad\qquad\qquad\qquad\qquad\qquad\qquad\qquad\qquad\qquad$ (3.23)

$$A = 1 + \rho - 2\sqrt{\rho} \cos x$$

$$B = A^{-2} \exp{(x + 2\theta)} \cot x$$

$$\theta = \frac{\arctan \sqrt{\rho} \sin x}{1 - \sqrt{\rho} \cos x} \qquad (0 < \theta < \pi/2).$$

Pollaczek also gives some asymptotic results.

Summaries of these and other studies on the $M/M/s$ random service queue are given in Riordan [1962] and Syski [1960].

Riordan [1953] obtained the Maclaurin series representation of the conditional probability $P\{W > t \mid W > 0\}$ as follows: Let

$$W_j^{(v)} = \frac{d^v}{dt^v} W_j(t)\Big|_{t=0} \qquad (j = 0, 1, \ldots; v = 0, 1, \ldots; W_j^{(0)} = 1) \tag{3.24}$$

and assume that $W_j(t)$ has the Maclaurin series representation

$$W_j(t) = \sum_{v=0}^{\infty} \frac{t^v}{v!} W_j^{(v)} \qquad (j = 0, 1, \ldots). \tag{3.25}$$

Then equation (3.2) can be written

$$P\{W > t \mid W > 0\} = 1 + (1 - \rho) \sum_{v=1}^{\infty} \frac{t^v}{v!} \sum_{j=0}^{\infty} \rho^j W_j^{(v)}. \tag{3.26}$$

The derivatives $\{W_j^{(v)}\}$ appearing on the right-hand side of equation (3.26) can be determined from the basic recurrence (3.21). Riordan evaluates the coefficients of t, t^2, and t^3 explicitly, giving (see Exercise 7)

$P\{W > t \mid W > 0\}$

$$= 1 - s\mu t \frac{1 - \rho}{\rho} \ln \frac{1}{1 - \rho}$$

$$+ \frac{(s\mu t)^2}{2!} (1 - \rho) \left[2 - \frac{1 - \rho}{\rho} \ln \frac{1}{1 - \rho} \right]$$

$$- \frac{(s\mu t)^3}{3!} (1 - \rho) \left[1 + 3\rho - (1 - \rho) \ln \frac{1}{1 - \rho} \right.$$

$$\left. - \sum_{j=1}^{\infty} \frac{\rho^j}{j^2} \right] + - \cdots. \tag{3.27}$$

[Note that (3.27) is a power series in $s\mu t$.] However, Riordan mentions this result only for the sake of "completeness"; his main result is an approximation of $1 - W(t)$ as a weighted sum of exponential terms. As we shall discuss later in this chapter, recent results of P. J. Burke show that the series (3.27) converges for all $s\mu t \geqq 0$, although its value for numerical calculations is not thereby assured.

Service in Reverse Order of Arrival

We shall now consider the $M/M/s$ queue with service in reverse order of arrival and, in addition, a variation of this discipline that leads to some interesting results. Following Vaulot [1954], let us define $V_j(t)$ as the conditional probability that a waiting test customer who is $(j + 1)$th in order for service will wait in excess of an additional time t for service to commence, given that he waits at all. Thus the probability that the (blocked) test customer will wait in excess of t from his arrival epoch until he begins service is $V_0(t) = P\{W > t \mid W > 0\}$. From the usual arguments concerning possible changes in an interval of length h, as $h \to 0$, we have

$$V_j(h + t) = s\mu h V_{j-1}(t) + \lambda h V_{j+1}(t)$$

$$+ [1 - (\lambda + s\mu)h]V_j(t) + o(h)$$

$$[h \to 0; j = 0, 1, \ldots; V_{-1}(t) = 0], \qquad (3.28)$$

where the term $\lambda h V_{j+1}(t)$, for example, reflects the fact that if the test customer is $(j + 1)$th in line for service (j customers have already arrived during the test customer's waiting time) and another customer arrives in an interval of length h, then the test customer becomes $(j + 2)$th in line for service, and with probability $V_{j+1}(t)$ will wait in excess of an additional time t for service to begin. Transposing and taking limits as $h \to 0$ in equation (3.28), we have

$$\frac{d}{dt} V_j(t) = s\mu V_{j-1}(t) + \lambda V_{j+1}(t) - (\lambda + s\mu)V_j(t)$$

$$[j = 0, 1, \ldots; V_{-1}(t) = 0]. \qquad (3.29)$$

As usual, define the generating function

$$V(x, t) = \sum_{j=0}^{\infty} V_j(t)x^j. \qquad (3.30)$$

Then it follows from equations (3.29) and (3.30) that $V(x, t)$ satisfies the partial differential equation

$$(s\mu)^{-1}x \frac{\partial}{\partial t} V(x, t) - (x - 1)(x - \rho)V(x, t) + \rho V_0(t) = 0. \qquad (3.31)$$

By taking Laplace transforms in equation (3.31) and inverting, it can be shown (see, for example, Riordan [1962], pp. 106–107) that

$$1 - V_0(t) = \rho^{-1/2} \int_0^{s\mu t} e^{-(1+\rho)x} I_1(2x\sqrt{\rho}) \frac{dx}{x}, \qquad (3.32)$$

where I_1 is the Bessel function of the first kind and imaginary argument. Since $V_0(t) = P\{W > t \mid W > 0\}$, equation (3.32) is the desired solution.

With a little extra effort, we can obtain from the preceding analysis an interesting bound. Since $V_j(t)$ is the probability of additional delay beyond t for a waiting test customer who is $(j + 1)$th in order for service, and who does not enter service if any customer who arrived after the test customer is waiting, it follows that, for every $t \geq 0$,

$$V_j(t) \geqq W_j(t) \qquad (j = 0, 1, \ldots), \qquad (3.33)$$

where $W_j(t)$ now refers to any order of service.

Let us call a customer *polite* if he declines to enter service as long as anyone else is waiting in the queue, and let V be the waiting time of a polite customer. (Clearly, no queue is big enough for more than one polite customer at a time.) Then, in analogy with equation (3.2), we have

$$P\{V > t \mid V > 0\} = (1 - \rho) \sum_{j=0}^{\infty} \rho^j V_j(t). \qquad (3.34)$$

From equations (3.2), (3.33), and (3.34) we see that, as one might expect, the conditional probability of delay for the polite customer will not be less than the corresponding conditional probability of delay for an arbitrary customer in a system with any order of service whatever:

$$P\{W > t \mid W > 0\} \leqq P\{V > t \mid V > 0\}. \qquad (3.35)$$

To evaluate $P\{V > t \mid V > 0\}$, note that equations (3.30) and (3.34) imply

$$P\{V > t \mid V > 0\} = (1 - \rho) V(\rho, t). \qquad (3.36)$$

It follows from equation (3.31) that

$$\frac{\partial}{\partial t} V(\rho, t) = -s\mu V_0(t) \qquad (3.37)$$

and, since $V_0(\infty) = 0$, equation (3.37) can be written

$$V(\rho, t) = s\mu \int_t^\infty V_0(x) \, dx. \tag{3.38}$$

We conclude that, for the polite customer in the $M/M/s$ queue,

$$P\{V > t \mid V > 0\} = (1 - \rho)s\mu \int_t^\infty V_0(x) \, dx \tag{3.39}$$

and, for an arbitrary customer in the $M/M/s$ queue with any order of service whatever,

$$P\{W > t \mid W > 0\} \leq (1 - \rho)s\mu \int_t^\infty V_0(x) \, dx, \tag{3.40}$$

where $V_0(x)$ is given by equation (3.32).

We have already shown [see equation (3.9)] that, for the $M/M/s$ queue with any order of service, the average (over all delayed customers) wait for service to commence is

$$E(W \mid W > 0) = \frac{1}{(1 - \rho)s\mu}. \tag{3.41}$$

We shall show presently that, for the polite customer,

$$E(V \mid V > 0) = \frac{1}{(1 - \rho)^2 s\mu}. \tag{3.42}$$

We have previously discussed the busy period for the single-server queue. The following generalization of the definition of busy period, to apply to the s-server queue with exponential service times, is useful. An s-server queue is said to be busy if all s servers are busy, and it is not busy if at least one server is idle. A busy period is the length of time from the instant a queue becomes busy until it next becomes not busy. Thus the busy period is the length of time during which all s servers are continuously busy. The concept of the j-busy period generalizes similarly.

It should now be clear that any result for the busy period of the $M/M/s$ queue can be formally obtained from the corresponding result for the $M/M/1$ queue, simply by replacing μ for the $M/M/1$ queue by $s\mu$.

It should now also be clear that the conditional waiting time distribution function $P\{W \leq t \mid W > 0\}$ for the $M/M/s$ queue with service in reverse order of arrival is the same as the corresponding busy period distribution function $B(t)$ (which is independent of the order of service). Therefore, $1 - V_{j-1}(t)$ is the same as the distribution function $B_j(t)$ of the j-busy period. From equation (5.45) of Chapter 5, we see that

$$1 - V_j(t) = \{1 - V_0(t)\}^{*(j+1)}. \tag{3.43}$$

Thus, equation (3.32) with $s = 1$ gives the inverse of the transform (13.1) of Exercise 13 of Chapter 5.

In Section 3–5 we noticed the following "coincidence" for the $M/M/1$ queue: the conditional mean waiting time in the order-of-arrival $M/M/1$ queue is the same as the corresponding mean busy period. We can now generalize this statement by replacing $M/M/1$ with $M/M/s$. And, of course, the truth of this statement is no longer surprising, since we have shown that the mean waiting time is independent of the order of service and that the waiting time for blocked customers in the $M/M/s$ queue with service in reverse order of arrival has the same distribution function as the corresponding busy period. This explains the "coincidence."

We can now derive the result (3.42) for the conditional mean waiting time for the polite customer. From the definition of conditional expectation, we have

$$E(V \mid V > 0) = \sum_{j=0}^{\infty} E(V \mid N = s + j)P\{N = s + j \mid N \geq s\}, \tag{3.44}$$

where N is the number of customers in the system when the polite customer arrives. Clearly, the convolution property (3.43) implies

$$E(V \mid N = s + j) = (j + 1)E(V \mid N = s). \tag{3.45}$$

Now, the waiting time of the polite customer who is the only waiting customer is the same as the length of a 1-busy period, which is the same as the conditional mean waiting time given by (3.41). Therefore

$$E(V \mid N = s) = \frac{1}{(1 - \rho)s\mu}. \tag{3.46}$$

Finally, since it follows from (3.1) that

$$P\{N = s + j \mid N \geq s\} = (1 - \rho)\rho^j \quad (j = 0, 1, \ldots), \tag{3.47}$$

equation (3.44) becomes

$$E(V \mid V > 0) = \frac{1}{(1 - \rho)s\mu} \sum_{j=0}^{\infty} (j + 1)(1 - \rho)\rho^j. \qquad (3.48)$$

Since the sum on the right-hand side of equation (3.48) is one plus the mean $\rho/(1 - \rho)$ of a geometric distribution, equation (3.42) follows.

6–4. The *GI/M/s* Queue

In this section we shall study the waiting times in the $GI/M/s$ queue for three queue disciplines—service in order of arrival, service in random order, and service in reverse order of arrival.

Let the customer interarrival time distribution function be $G(t)$ with Laplace–Stieltjes transform

$$\gamma(z) = \int_0^\infty e^{-zt} \, dG(t). \qquad (4.1)$$

As usual we denote the mean service time by μ^{-1}, and the number of servers by s. (Note that in this section we are using the symbol z as the dummy variable of the Laplace–Stieltjes transform instead of the more conventional s, which we have consistently used to denote the number of servers.)

In Section 5–7 we showed that the arriving customer's distribution $\{\Pi_j\}$ is given, for $\rho = \lambda/s\mu < 1$ and $j \geq s$, by

$$\Pi_j = A\omega^{j-s} \qquad (j \geq s), \qquad (4.2)$$

where ω is the unique root in $(0, 1)$ of the equation

$$\omega = \gamma[(1 - \omega)s\mu] \qquad (4.3)$$

and the constant A is given by formulas (7.13)–(7.15) of Chapter 5.

As before, let $W_j(t) = P\{W > t \mid N = s + j\}$. Then it follows from equation (1.6) that

$$P\{W > t \mid W > 0\} = (1 - \omega) \sum_{j=0}^{\infty} \omega^j W_j(t). \qquad (4.4)$$

Equation (4.4) is of the same form as equation (3.2), with the root ω replacing the occupancy $\rho = \lambda/s\mu$.

As we have done in the studies of the $M/M/s$ queue, we shall turn our attention to the calculation of the conditional probabilities $W_j(t)$ $(j = 0, 1, \ldots)$ for each different order of service.

Service in Order of Arrival

We need only recognize that, with exponential service times and service in order of arrival, the conditional delay probability $W_j(t)$ is independent of the arrival process. Thus the various derivations of $W_j(t)$ already given in the context of the $M/M/s$ queue remain valid. Specifically, equation (3.7) for $W_j(t)$ remains valid, and substitution of (3.7) into equation (4.4) gives the well-known result

$$P\{W > t \mid W > 0\} = e^{-(1-\omega)s\mu t}, \qquad (4.5)$$

which is analogous to equation (3.8), and the same as the previously derived result (7.22) of Chapter 5. It follows that the conditional mean wait for service is given by

$$E(W \mid W > 0) = \frac{1}{(1 - \omega)s\mu} . \qquad (4.6)$$

Equation (4.6) is valid for any order of service.

Similarly, the development leading from equation (3.11) to equation (3.18) remains correct. The analogue of (3.19), with ρ replaced by ω,

$$P\{W > t \mid W > 0\} = (1 - \omega)W(\omega, t), \qquad (4.7)$$

follows by analogous reasoning, again yielding the conclusion (4.5).

It is also possible to derive equation (4.5) by applying Lindley's $GI/G/1$ analysis to the $GI/M/1$ queue with service rate $s\mu$, as we did in Section 6–3 for the case of Poisson input. In the non-Poisson case, however, the mathematical difficulties inherent in the implementation of Lindley's analysis preclude its presentation here. The interested reader is referred to Riordan [1962] or Syski [1960].

Service in Random Order

The $GI/M/s$ random service queue has been studied by LeGall [1962], Takács [1962b], Burke [1967, unpublished], and Carter and Cooper [1972]. LeGall gives an expression for the characteristic function of the waiting time distribution function, while Takács gives a similarly complicated expression for the corresponding Laplace–Stieltjes transform. Their results are quite formidable, and reduction to practice (through explicit or numerical inversion) does not appear simple.

Takács also shows that the waiting time distribution function has second moment $w_2 = \int_0^\infty x^2 \, dW(x)$ given by

$$w_2 = \frac{2A}{(s\mu)^2(1-\omega)^3} \left[\frac{2}{2 + s\mu\gamma'[s\mu(1-\omega)]} \right]. \tag{4.8}$$

We shall first give a heuristic derivation of the Maclaurin series expansion of the conditional probability $P\{W > t \mid W > 0\}$, and show that our results include equation (3.27) (for the $M/M/s$ random service queue) as a special case. This method, which we call the Maclaurin series method, results in an algorithm that may be computationally useful in some cases. Burke's method, which we call the additional conditioning variable method, is an extension of the Maclaurin series method.

We begin with the *Maclaurin series method* (Carter and Cooper [1972]). Consider a test customer who, upon arrival at time T_c, say, finds all s servers busy and $j \geq 0$ other customers waiting for service. We wish to calculate the probability $W_j(t)$ that the test customer waits in excess of t for his service to begin. The conditional probability $P\{W > t \mid W > 0\}$ can then be calculated from equation (4.4).

Consider the following two events: (a) the next customer arrives after time $T_c + t$, or (b) the next customer arrives prior to time $T_c + t$.

In case (a), the test customer will wait more than t for service to begin if and only if he is one of the i ($1 \leq i \leq j + 1$) customers still waiting for service at time $T_c + t$. (If $i = 0$, the test customer will necessarily have begun service.) Since service times are assumed to be independently exponentially distributed with common mean μ^{-1}, the probability $p_i(x)$ that exactly i customers complete service in an interval of length x, given that all s servers are continuously busy throughout this interval, is the Poisson probability

$$p_i(x) = \frac{(s\mu x)^i}{i!} e^{-s\mu x} \qquad (i = 0, 1, \ldots). \tag{4.9}$$

Let $T_{c'}$ be the next arrival epoch after T_c. If $T_{c'} - T_c > t$, then the (conditional) probability that the test customer waits in excess of t for service to commence is

$$P\{W > t \mid N = s + j, T_{c'} - T_c > t\} = \sum_{i=1}^{j+1} \frac{i}{j+1} p_{j+1-i}(t), \tag{4.10}$$

where the factor $i/(j + 1)$ is the probability that the test customer is not among the $j + 1 - i$ customers selected (according to the random selection procedure) to begin service during the interval $(T_c, T_c + t)$. Since the interarrival time distribution function is $G(x)$, and since T_c is an arrival epoch, event (a) occurs with probability $1 - G(t)$.

Now consider event (b); that is, suppose that the next customer arrives at time $T_{c'} = T_c + \xi$, where $\xi \leq t$. The probability that the test customer will be among the remaining i waiting customers is

$$\frac{i}{j + 1} p_{j+1-i}(\xi).$$

The test customer will now experience a total wait in excess of t for service to begin if and only if he suffers an additional delay exceeding length $t - \xi$. But since waiting customers are selected for service in random order, the probability that the test customer's additional waiting time will exceed $t - \xi$ (if he has not yet begun service) is the same as the probability that a new arrival waits in excess of $t - \xi$ for service to begin. The latter probability is $W_i(t - \xi)$. Thus, if the next customer arrives at time $T_{c'} = T_c + \xi$, where $\xi \leq t$, then the test customer's waiting time will exceed t with probability

$$P\{W > t \mid N = s + j, T_{c'} - T_c = \xi \leq t\}$$

$$= \sum_{i=1}^{j+1} \frac{i}{j + 1} p_{j+1-i}(\xi) W_i(t - \xi). \tag{4.11}$$

Finally, the probability that the next arrival epoch $T_{c'}$ will occur in an infinitesimal interval about the point $T_c + \xi$ is $dG(\xi)$.

Therefore, combining events (a) and (b), we have the following recurrence for the conditional probability $W_j(t)$ that the test customer waits in excess of t for service to begin, given that on arrival he finds all s servers busy and $j \geq 0$ other customers waiting for service:

$$W_j(t) = [1 - G(t)] \sum_{i=1}^{j+1} \frac{i}{j + 1} p_{j+1-i}(t)$$

$$+ \sum_{i=1}^{j+1} \frac{i}{j + 1} \int_0^t p_{j+1-i}(\xi) W_i(t - \xi) \, dG(\xi) \qquad (j = 0, 1, \ldots),$$

$$\tag{4.12}$$

where $G(x)$ is the interarrival time distribution function and $p_i(x)$ is given by equation (4.9).

We now assume that $W_j(t)$ for the $GI/M/s$ queue has the Maclaurin series representation

$$W_j(t) = \sum_{v=0}^{\infty} \frac{t^v}{v!} W_j^{(v)} \qquad (j = 0, 1, \ldots; \; W_j^{(0)} = 1). \qquad (4.13)$$

Equation (4.13) is the same as equation (3.25), except that (4.13) refers to the $GI/M/s$ queue, while (3.25) refers to the $M/M/s$ queue. In analogy with equation (3.26) for the $M/M/s$ queue, we have the corresponding equation for the $GI/M/s$ queue:

$$P\{W > t \mid W > 0\} = 1 + (1 - \omega) \sum_{v=1}^{\infty} \frac{t^v}{v!} \sum_{j=0}^{\infty} \omega^j W_j^{(v)}. \qquad (4.14)$$

It remains to determine the derivatives $\{W_j^{(v)}\}$ appearing on the right-hand side of equation (4.14) from the basic recurrence (4.12).

Differentiating v times on both sides of equation (4.12) we have

$$\frac{d^v}{dt^v} W_j(t) = \frac{d^v}{dt^v} \left[[1 - G(t)] \sum_{i=1}^{j+1} \frac{i}{j+1} P_{j+1-i}(t) \right]$$

$$+ \sum_{i=1}^{j+1} \frac{i}{j+1} \int_0^t P_{j+1-i}(\xi) g(\xi) \frac{\partial^v}{\partial t^v} W_i(t - \xi) \, d\xi$$

$$+ \sum_{i=1}^{j+1} \frac{i}{j+1} \sum_{k=0}^{v-1} \frac{d^k}{dt^k} [P_{j+1-i}(t) g(t)] W_i^{(v-1-k)}$$

$$(j = 0, 1, \ldots; \; v = 1, 2, \ldots), \qquad (4.15)$$

where $g(\xi)$ is the interarrival time density function,

$$g(\xi) = \frac{d}{d\xi} G(\xi). \qquad (4.16)$$

For convenience we set

$$a_{j+1}(t) = [1 - G(t)] \sum_{i=1}^{j+1} \frac{i}{j+1} P_{j+1-i}(t) \qquad (4.17)$$

and

$$b_{j+1-i}(t) = g(t) p_{j+1-i}(t). \qquad (4.18)$$

Now set $t = 0$ in equation (4.15). The integral on the right-hand side vanishes and we have

$$W_j^{(v)} = a_{j+1}^{(v)} + \sum_{i=1}^{j+1} \frac{i}{j+1} \sum_{k=0}^{v-1} b_{j+1-i}^{(k)} W_i^{(v-1-k)}$$

$$(j = 0, 1, \ldots; \; v = 1, 2, \ldots). \qquad (4.19)$$

The recurrence (4.19) permits evaluation of the sum on the right-hand side of equation (4.14). The problem is solved if the series converges and if the assumed derivatives exist. If, in addition, the terms of the series are easy to calculate, the solution is also useful.

It is easy to verify (see Exercise 8) that for Poisson input, $G(x) = 1 - e^{-\lambda x}$, this algorithm yields the result (3.27), obtained previously for the $M/M/s$ random service queue.

One might note the steps taken in the above development that are mathematically questionable. In particular, we assumed the existence of the Maclaurin series expansion (4.13) while ignoring possible effects on convergence of the values of t and ρ, the differentiability of $W_j(t)$, and the vanishing of the integral on the right-hand side of (4.15) at $t = 0$. It is because of these (not unreasonable) assumptions that we term this derivation heuristic. The fact that the method gives agreement with an independently obtained result for the special case of Poisson input is encouraging, but proves little. Clearly, work remains to be done.

Questions of rigor aside, the Maclaurin series method certainly requires that the interarrival time distribution function $G(x)$ possess a density, and this constraint precludes analysis of the important case of constant interarrival times. P. J. Burke [1967, unpublished] has given yet another analysis, based on the introduction of an additional "conditioning variable." According to Burke, this method yields results that appear to be well suited for computation on a digital computer. For the particular case of Poisson input, Burke's method yields a power series representation for $P\{W > t \mid W > 0\}$ that is easily shown to be convergent for all $s\mu t \geqq 0$. It follows from the uniqueness property of power series representations that the Maclaurin series (3.27) exists and converges for all $s\mu t \geqq 0$. It appears that further investigation of the $GI/M/s$ random service queue by Burke's additional conditioning variable method might similarly throw light on the existence and convergence properties of the Maclaurin series representation of $P\{W > t \mid W > 0\}$ for other choices of the input process. Then the choice of method to be used for computation could be based solely on other (computational) considerations.

We now briefly describe Burke's *additional conditioning variable method*, which we shall later extend to the analysis of the $M/G/1$ random service queue.

The Maclaurin series method was based on obtaining an expression for $W_j(t) = P\{W > t \mid N = s + j\}$ for $j = 0, 1, \ldots$, where W is the waiting time of the test customer, and N is the number of customers present in the system just prior to the test customer's arrival epoch T_c. Burke considers the additional random variable $X(t)$, defined as the number of customers who arrive in $(T_c, T_c + t]$, with $t > 0$, and $X(0) = 0$ with probability 1. Instead of calculating $W_j(t)$, Burke's basic calculation is that of $W_{j,k}(t)$, where we define

$$W_{j,k}(t) = P\{W > t \mid N = s + j, X(t) = k\}$$

$$(j = 0, 1, \ldots; k = 0, 1, \ldots). \qquad (4.20)$$

We have that

$$P\{X(t) = k\} = G^{*k}(t) - G^{*(k+1)}(t)$$

$$[k = 0, 1, \ldots; G^{*0}(t) = 1; t \geq 0], \qquad (4.21)$$

where $G^{*k}(t)$ is the k-fold convolution of the interarrival time distribution function $G(t)$ with itself. [See equation (1.2) of Chapter 5.] Also, from the law of total probability,

$$P\{W > t \mid N = s + j\}$$

$$= \sum_{k=0}^{\infty} P\{X(t) = k\}P\{W > t \mid N = s + j, X(t) = k\}. \qquad (4.22)$$

Since the conditional waiting time distribution function is determined by equation (4.4), it follows from equation (4.22) that it is now sufficient to determine the conditional probabilities $W_{j,k}(t)$.

First note that $X(t) = 0$ if and only if $T_{c'} - T_c > t$. It follows from equation (4.10) and the definition (4.20) of $W_{j,k}(t)$ that

$$W_{j,0}(t) = \sum_{i=1}^{j+1} \frac{i}{j+1} p_{j+1-i}(t) \qquad (j = 0, 1, \ldots), \qquad (4.23)$$

where $p_i(x)$ is given by equation (4.9).

For $k > 0$, we define

$$G(\xi \mid k, t) = P\{T_{c'} - T_c \leq \xi \mid X(t) = k\}, \qquad (4.24)$$

which is the conditional distribution function of the elapsed time $T_{c'} - T_c$ between the arrival epoch T_c of the test customer and the next arrival epoch $T_{c'}$, given that k arrivals occur in $(T_c, T_c + t]$. It follows from the definition of a conditional probability density function that

$$d_\xi G(\xi \mid k, t) = \frac{P\{X(t - \xi) = k - 1\} \, dG(\xi)}{P\{X(t) = k\}} \qquad (k = 1, 2, \ldots).$$

$$(4.25)$$

Then, reasoning in a manner similar to that leading to equation (4.12), we have the following general recurrence for $k \geq 1$:

$$W_{j,k}(t) = \sum_{i=1}^{j+1} \frac{i}{j+1} \int_0^t P_{j+1-i}(\xi) W_{i,k-1}(t - \xi) \, d_\xi G(\xi \mid k, t)$$

$$(j = 0, 1, \ldots; k = 1, 2, \ldots). \qquad (4.26)$$

Thus by use of equations (4.23) and (4.26) one can compute $P\{W > t \mid W > 0\}$ to any desired degree of accuracy. Burke illustrates his method for the case of constant interarrival times, for which the Maclaurin series method is inapplicable, and the case of exponential interarrival times, for which he obtains an infinite series whose convergence is assured, and from which we can infer the convergence of the Maclaurin series (3.27) for all values of the argument.

Service in Reverse Order of Arrival

As is true for the $M/M/s$ queue, the conditional waiting time distribution function $P\{W \leq t \mid W > 0\}$ for the $GI/M/s$ queue with service in reverse order of arrival is the same as the corresponding busy period distribution function $B(t)$:

$$P\{W \leq t \mid W > 0\} = B(t). \qquad (4.27)$$

Pollaczek [1957] has shown (see also Takács [1960]) that, for the $GI/M/s$ queue, the busy period distribution function $B(t)$ has Laplace–Stieltjes transform $\beta(z)$,

$$\beta(z) = \int_0^\infty e^{-zt} \, dB(t), \qquad (4.28)$$

given by

$$\beta(z) = \frac{s\mu[1 - x(z)]}{z + s\mu[1 - x(z)]}, \qquad (4.29)$$

where $x(z)$ is the only root of the equation

$$x(z) = \gamma\{z + s\mu[1 - x(z)]\} \qquad (4.30)$$

in the unit circle. Takács [1962b] has shown that the Laplace–Stieltjes transform defined by equations (4.29) and (4.30) has inverse

$$B(t) = s\mu \sum_{j=1}^{\infty} e^{-s\mu t} \frac{(s\mu t)^{j-1}}{j!} \int_0^t [1 - G^{*j}(x)] \, dx, \qquad (4.31)$$

where $G^{*j}(x)$ is the j-fold convolution with itself of the interarrival time distribution function $G(x)$.

Hence, the waiting time distribution function $W(t)$ for the $GI/M/s$ queue with service in reverse order of arrival is given by

$$W(t) = 1 - \frac{A}{1 - \omega} + \frac{A}{1 - \omega} B(t), \qquad (4.32)$$

where $B(t)$ is given by (4.31), ω is defined by equation (4.3) or, equivalently, $\omega = x(0)$ in equation (4.30), and A is given by formulas (7.13)–(7.15) of Chapter 5.

Takács [1962b] gives for the second moment $w_2 = \int_0^\infty x^2 \, dW(x)$ of the waiting time distribution function

$$w_2 = \frac{2A}{(s\mu)^2 (1 - \omega)^3} \left[\frac{1}{1 + s\mu\gamma'[s\mu(1 - \omega)]} \right]. \qquad (4.33)$$

6–5. The *M/G/1* Queue

In this section we shall study waiting times in the $M/G/1$ queue for three queue disciplines—service in order of arrival, service in random order, and service in reverse order of arrival. In addition, we shall consider the case of the "polite" customer, who refuses to begin service as long as there is anyone else waiting in the queue.

In Section 5–5 we obtained the probability generating function of the number of customers in the system just after a service completion epoch in the stationary $M/G/1$ queue. This result, given by equation (5.37) of Chapter 5, enabled us to calculate the Laplace–Stieltjes transform of the order-of-arrival waiting time distribution function, the so-called Pollaczek–Khintchine formula (5.41) of Chapter 5.

The calculations of Chapter 5 leading to the Pollaczek–Khintchine formula were made from the viewpoint of the departing customer. Although this approach easily yields the required results when service is in order of arrival, it is often easier to carry out waiting time analyses for other orders of service from the viewpoint of the arriving customer, as we have done thus far throughout this chapter.

We now summarize an analysis of the $M/G/1$ queue from the viewpoint of the arriving customer. This analysis is by Wishart [1961], is discussed in Takács [1963], and is also outlined in Exercise 20 of Chapter 5.

As usual, let λ be the arrival rate, τ the mean service time, and $\rho = \lambda\tau < 1$ the utilization factor. Let N be the number of customers in the system just prior to an arbitrary arrival epoch T_c, and let R be the time needed to complete the service of the customer (if there is one) in service at T_c. Define the arriving customer's distribution

$$\Pi_j = P\{N = j\} \qquad (j = 0, 1, \ldots) \tag{5.1}$$

and the Laplace–Stieltjes transform $\eta(s)$ of the service time distribution function,

$$\eta(s) = \int_0^\infty e^{-s\xi} \, dH(\xi). \tag{5.2}$$

Define also

$$\Pi_j(x) = P\{R \le x, N = j\} \qquad (x \ge 0; j = 1, 2, \ldots) \tag{5.3}$$

and

$$\psi_j(s) = \int_0^\infty e^{-sx} \, d\Pi_j(x) \qquad (j = 1, 2, \ldots). \tag{5.4}$$

Wishart has shown that for $\rho < 1$ the generating function $u(s, z)$ of the Laplace–Stieltjes transform (5.4),

$$u(s, z) = \sum_{j=1}^\infty \psi_j(s) z^j, \tag{5.5}$$

is given by

$$u(s, z) = \frac{(1 - \rho)\lambda z(1 - z)}{z - \eta(\lambda - \lambda z)} \frac{\eta(s) - \eta(\lambda - \lambda z)}{s - \lambda(1 - z)}. \tag{5.6}$$

Inversion of equation (5.6) gives the generating function

$$\sum_{j=1}^\infty \Pi_j(x) z^j = \frac{(1 - \rho)\lambda z(1 - z)}{z - \eta(\lambda - \lambda z)} \int_0^\infty e^{-\lambda(1 - z)\xi}[H(\xi + x) - H(\xi)] \, d\xi. \tag{5.7}$$

The development leading to equation (5.6) is rather involved, and the interested reader is referred to Wishart [1961] or Takács [1963].

An important result is obtained when $z = 1$ in equation (5.7). We have, upon setting $z = 1$ in (5.7) (see Exercise 20**b** of Chapter 5)

$$\sum_{j=1}^{\infty} \Pi_j(x) = \lambda \int_0^x [1 - H(\xi)] \, d\xi. \tag{5.8}$$

From the definition (5.3) we have

$$\sum_{j=1}^{\infty} \Pi_j(x) = P\{R \leq x, N \geq 1\}. \tag{5.9}$$

Since, from the definition of conditional probability,

$$P\{R \leq x \mid N \geq 1\} = \frac{P\{R \leq x, N \geq 1\}}{P\{N \geq 1\}} \tag{5.10}$$

and since $P\{N \geq 1\} = \rho = \lambda\tau$, we conclude from (5.8) that

$$P\{R \leq x \mid N \geq 1\} = \frac{1}{\tau} \int_0^x [1 - H(\xi)] \, d\xi. \tag{5.11}$$

Comparison with equation (4.6) of Chapter 5 shows that the result (5.11) could have been anticipated on intuitive grounds; equation (5.11) is precisely the result from renewal theory that was derived in Section 5–4.

That is, given that the test customer arrives during a service time, that service time tends to be longer than service times in general. If $H(x)$ is the service time distribution function for an arbitrary service time, with mean length τ, then, according to equation (4.9) of Chapter 5, the distribution function $\hat{H}(x)$ of the length of the particular service time during which the test customer arrives is given by

$$d\hat{H}(x) = \frac{1}{\tau} x \, dH(x). \tag{5.12}$$

Since the arrival process is Poisson, the test customer's arrival epoch is uniformly distributed throughout this interval. It follows from the latter statement and equation (5.12) that the distribution function $\tilde{H}(x)$ of the time remaining from the arrival epoch of the test customer until the first postarrival service completion epoch is given by

$$\tilde{H}(x) = P\{R \leq x \mid N \geq 1\} = \frac{1}{\tau} \int_0^x [1 - H(\xi)] \, d\xi. \tag{5.13}$$

(See Exercise 4 of Chapter 5.)

Returning to equation (5.5), we see that

$$\Pi_0 + u(0, z) = \sum_{j=0}^{\infty} \Pi_j z^j. \tag{5.14}$$

The right-hand side of (5.14) is the generating function of the arriving customer's distribution. If we set $s = 0$ in equation (5.6) and use the fact that $\Pi_0 = 1 - \rho$, we see that the left-hand side of (5.14) is, as expected, the generating function (5.37) of Chapter 5; the arriving customer's distribution $\{\Pi_j\}$ and the departing customer's distribution $\{\Pi_j^*\}$ have the same generating function and thus are equal (as we know).

Service in Order of Arrival

We have already shown, in Section 5–5, that the (unconditional) waiting time distribution function $W(t) = P\{W \le t\}$ has Laplace–Stieltjes transform

$$\omega(s) = \int_0^{\infty} e^{-st} \, dW(t) \tag{5.15}$$

given by the Pollaczek-Khintchine formula

$$\omega(s) = \frac{s(1 - \rho)}{s - \lambda[1 - \eta(s)]}. \tag{5.16}$$

As we have just discussed, that derivation of (5.16) was based on the viewpoint of the departing customer. Also in Section 5–5, we noted that the Laplace–Stieltjes transform (5.16) can be inverted explicitly to give Beneš's formula

$$W(t) = (1 - \rho) \sum_{j=0}^{\infty} \rho^j \tilde{H}^{*j}(t), \tag{5.17}$$

where $\tilde{H}^{*j}(t)$ is the j-fold convolution with itself of the distribution function $\tilde{H}(t)$ defined by equation (5.13), and $\tilde{H}^{*0}(t) = 1$. Equation (5.17) seems to invite an intuitive interpretation, but no such interpretation has been forthcoming except in the special case of exponential service times.

Continuing Wishart's analysis, we now derive the Pollaczek–Khintchine formula (5.16) directly from the viewpoint of the arriving customer. Consider a test customer who arrives at time T_c and finds $j \ge 1$ other customers in the system. The test customer's waiting time is then the sum of the time R needed to complete the service of the customer being served at T_c, and the total service time of the other $j - 1$ waiting customers. Hence

$$W(t) = \Pi_0 + \sum_{j=1}^{\infty} \int_0^t \Pi_j(t - \xi) \, dH^{*(j-1)}(\xi), \qquad (5.18)$$

where $\Pi_j(x)$ is defined by equation (5.3). Taking Laplace–Stieltjes transforms on both sides of equation (5.18) we have

$$\omega(s) = \Pi_0 + \sum_{j=1}^{\infty} \psi_j(s)[\eta(s)]^{j-1}. \qquad (5.19)$$

In light of equation (5.5), and since $\Pi_0 = 1 - \rho$, equation (5.19) can be written

$$\omega(s) = 1 - \rho + \frac{u[s, \eta(s)]}{\eta(s)}. \qquad (5.20)$$

The Pollaczek–Khintchine formula (5.16) now follows from equations (5.20) and (5.6).

All of the moments of the waiting time distribution function can be found by differentiation of equation (5.16):

$$w_n = \int_0^{\infty} t^n \, dW(t) = (-1)^n \frac{d^n}{ds^n} \, \omega(s) \bigg|_{s=0} \qquad (n = 1, 2, \ldots), \qquad (5.21)$$

where $w_1 = E(W)$ is the mean waiting time. If we define τ_n as the nth moment of the service time distribution function

$$\tau_n = \int_0^{\infty} t^n \, dH(t) = (-1)^n \frac{d^n}{ds^n} \, \eta(s) \bigg|_{s=0} \qquad (n = 1, 2, \ldots) \qquad (5.22)$$

with $\tau_1 = \tau$ the mean service time, we have (for any order of service)

$$w_1 = \frac{\lambda \tau_2}{2(1 - \lambda \tau_1)} \qquad (5.23)$$

in agreement with equation (5.7) of Chapter 5, and (for service in order of arrival)

$$w_2 = \frac{\lambda \tau_3}{3(1 - \lambda \tau_1)} + \frac{\lambda^2 \tau_2^2}{2(1 - \lambda \tau_1)^2}. \qquad (5.24)$$

Calculation of higher moments is discussed in Takács [1963].

Service in Random Order

The $M/G/1$ random service queue has been studied by LeGall [1962], Kingman [1962] (see also Takács [1963]), and Carter and Cooper [1972]. LeGall and Kingman used transform methods, and numerical implementation of their results does not appear simple.

Takács [1963] has shown that the second moment w_2 of the waiting time distribution function is given by

$$w_2 = \frac{2\lambda\tau_3}{3(1 - \lambda\tau_1)(2 - \lambda\tau_1)} + \frac{\lambda^2\tau_2^2}{(1 - \lambda\tau_1)^2(2 - \lambda\tau_1)}. \qquad (5.25)$$

The special case $M/D/1$ has also been studied by Burke [1959], who, by utilizing certain simplifying properties of the constant service time distribution that do not hold in the general case, obtained an expression suitable for the calculation of the conditional waiting time distribution function. Burke's paper includes a useful set of curves. Comments on the numerical properties of the $M/D/1$ random service waiting time distribution function are also contained in Lee [1966].

In this section we will extend, for application to the $M/G/1$ random service queue, the additional conditioning variable method used in the analysis of the $GI/M/s$ random service queue presented in Section 6-4. (See Carter and Cooper [1972].) As before, the method does not use transform techniques, but, nevertheless, numerical calculations seem to be impractical except in special cases.

Suppose that the test customer arrives at time T_c and finds $j \geq 1$ other customers in the system (either in service or waiting for service). Then the length of time that the test customer waits for service to begin is the sum of

1. The elapsed time between the test customer's arrival epoch T_c and the first subsequent service completion epoch T_1.
2. The elapsed time between T_1 and the instant at which the test customer commences service.

The analysis of the total waiting time is complicated by two facts. First, the time intervals (1) and (2) are not, in general, statistically independent. Second, as we have pointed out, any customer in service at epoch T_c when the test customer arrives does not, in general, have the same service time distribution function as does an arbitrary customer. Specifically, the relationship of the distribution function $\hat{H}(x)$ of the length of the service interval containing the arrival epoch T_c to the distribution function $H(x)$ of the length of an arbitrary service interval is given by equation (5.12); likewise, the distribution function $\tilde{H}(x)$ of the length of the remainder of this service interval, from T_c to T_1, is given by equation (5.13).

Note that in the special case of constant service times, these difficulties disappear. When the service times are constant, the delay suffered by a blocked customer between the instant of his arrival and the first post-arrival departure epoch is independent of the delay subsequent to this epoch; and the distribution of the service interval containing T_c is the same as that of an arbitrary service interval (that is, constant).

As before, we let W be the duration of the test customer's wait for service to begin, and we calculate the conditional probability $P\{W > t \mid W > 0\}$. We denote by T_c the test customer's arrival epoch, and by T_1 the first departure epoch subsequent to T_c. We also define $N(T)$ as the number of customers in the system (including service) at any time T, and $W(T)$ as the remaining waiting time for service to commence for a customer who is waiting at time T. Then we may write

$$P\{W > t \mid W > 0\}$$

$$= P\{T_1 - T_c > t \mid W > 0\}$$

$$+ \sum_{j=2}^{\infty} \frac{j-1}{j} \int_0^t P\{W(T_1 + 0) > t - \xi \mid W > 0, N(T_1 + 0) = j\}$$

$$\times d_\xi P\{N(T_1 + 0) = j, T_1 - T_c \leq \xi \mid W > 0\}. \tag{5.26}$$

Let us define

$$Q_j(\xi) = P\{N(T_1 + 0) = j, T_1 - T_c \leq \xi \mid W > 0\}$$

$$(j = 0, 1, \ldots). \tag{5.27}$$

Now consider the service interval containing the test customer's arrival epoch T_c. The probability that this interval has length between x and $x + dx$ is $d\hat{H}(x)$, given by equation (5.12). The probability $p_i(x)$ that exactly i customers arrive during such an interval of length x is, by assumption, the Poisson probability

$$p_i(x) = \frac{(\lambda x)^i}{i!} e^{-\lambda x} \qquad (i = 0, 1, \ldots). \tag{5.28}$$

Since the arrival process is Poisson, then for fixed x the length of the interval (T_c, T_1) is uniformly distributed over $(0, x)$. It follows that $Q_j(\xi)$ has density

$$\frac{d}{d\xi} Q_j(\xi) = Q_j'(\xi)$$

given by

$$Q_j'(\xi) = \int_\xi^\infty \left(\Pi_0^* p_{j-1}(x) + \sum_{i=1}^j \Pi_i^* p_{j-i}(x) \right) \frac{d\hat{H}(x)}{x} \qquad (j = 1, 2, \ldots),$$

$$(5.29)$$

which, in view of equation (5.12), can be written

$$Q_j'(\xi) = \frac{1}{\tau} \int_\xi^\infty \left(\Pi_0^* p_{j-1}(x) + \sum_{i=1}^j \Pi_i^* p_{j-i}(x) \right) dH(x)$$

$$(j = 1, 2, \ldots). \qquad (5.30)$$

Now let us define

$$\check{W}_j(x) = P\{W(T_1 + 0) > x \mid W > 0, N(T_1 + 0) = j\}$$

$$(j = 2, 3, \ldots). \qquad (5.31)$$

Then equation (5.26) can be written

$$P\{W > t \mid W > 0\} = 1 - \tilde{H}(t) + \sum_{j=2}^\infty \frac{j-1}{j} \int_0^t \check{W}_j(t - \xi) Q_j'(\xi) \, d\xi,$$

$$(5.32)$$

where $\tilde{H}(x)$ is given by equation (5.13), $Q_j'(\xi)$ is given by equation (5.30), and $\check{W}_j(x)$ satisfies the following set of integral equations:

$$\check{W}_j(x) = 1 - H(x) + \sum_{i=0}^\infty \frac{j+i-2}{j+i-1} \int_0^x p_i(\xi) \check{W}_{j+i-1}(x - \xi) \, dH(\xi)$$

$$(j = 2, 3, \ldots). \qquad (5.33)$$

Equation (5.33) for the $M/G/1$ random service queue corresponds to equation (4.12) for the $GI/M/s$ random service queue. [Note that $p_i(\xi)$ in equation (4.12) is defined by (4.9), whereas $p_i(\xi)$ in equation (5.33) is defined by (5.28).]

At this point, we may follow the Maclaurin series method, or we may follow the additional conditioning variable method. In the former case, we assume that $\check{W}_j(x)$ has a Maclaurin series representation, and we then obtain a recurrence relation similar to equation (4.19). This method is outlined in Exercise 10. Continuing with the additional conditioning variable method, let S_k be the sum of the first k service times commencing at epoch T_1, and let the additional conditioning variable $\check{X}(x)$ be the value of the largest integer k ($k = 0, 1, \ldots$) such that $S_k < x$. We define $\check{W}_{j,k}(x)$ as follows:

$$\check{W}_{j,k}(x) = P\{W(T_1 + 0) > x \mid W > 0, N(T_1 + 0) = j, \check{X}(x) = k\}$$
$$(j = 2, 3, \ldots ; k = 0, 1, \ldots), \quad (5.34)$$

where, as before, T_1 is the first service completion epoch after the arrival of the test customer, $N(T_1 + 0)$ is the number of customers in the system (including service) just after epoch T_1, and $W(T_1 + 0)$ is the remaining waiting time for service to commence for a customer who is waiting just after time T_1.

We have that [see equation (4.21)]

$$P\{\check{X}(x) = k\} = H^{*k}(x) - H^{*(k+1)}(x)$$
$$(k = 0, 1, \ldots ; H^{*0}(x) = 1; x \geq 0), \quad (5.35)$$

where $H^{*k}(x)$ is the k-fold convolution with itself of the service time distribution function. From the law of total probability it follows that

$$\check{W}_j(x) = \sum_{k=0}^{\infty} \check{W}_{j,k}(x) P\{\check{X}(x) = k\} \quad (5.36)$$

and hence our problem will be solved if we can determine the conditional probabilities $\check{W}_{j,k}(x)$ ($j = 2, 3, \ldots ; k = 0, 1, \ldots$).

Clearly

$$\check{W}_{j,0}(x) = 1 \quad (j = 2, 3, \ldots). \quad (5.37)$$

Let us define for $k > 0$

$$H(\xi \mid k, x) = P\{S_1 \leq \xi \mid \check{X}(x) = k\}. \quad (5.38)$$

It follows from the definition of conditional probability that

$$d_\xi H(\xi \mid k, x) = \frac{P\{\check{X}(x - \xi) = k - 1\} \, dH(\xi)}{P\{\check{X}(x) = k\}} \quad (k = 1, 2, \ldots).$$
$$(5.39)$$

We now have the following recurrence for $k \geq 1$:

$$\check{W}_{j,k}(x) = \sum_{i=0}^{\infty} \frac{j + i - 2}{j + i - 1} \int_0^x p_i(\xi) \check{W}_{j+i-1, k-1}(x - \xi) \, d_\xi H(\xi \mid k, x)$$
$$(j = 2, 3, \ldots ; k = 1, 2, \ldots). \quad (5.40)$$

The required function $P\{W > t \mid W > 0\}$ can now be determined in principle from equation (5.32), complemented by equations (5.30), (5.36), and (5.37) and (5.40). (For an outline of an analysis of the $M/D/1$ random service queue by this method, see Exercise 12.)

Clearly, the theory of waiting times for the $M/G/1$ random service queue is complicated, and reduction to practice of any of the algorithms we have discussed will require much effort, except in certain special cases. From a practical point of view, in many cases simulation on a digital computer may well be more productive than attempted reduction to practice of existing theories. Work remains to be done, and it is hoped the preceding discussion will help somewhat in understanding the difficulties of the problem.

Service in Reverse Order of Arrival

This model has been studied by Riordan [1961], Wishart [1960], and Takács [1963].

The waiting time of a test customer who arrives when the server is busy is the sum of the duration of time from his arrival epoch T_c to the first subsequent service completion epoch T_1, and the length of the j-busy period generated by the $j \geq 0$ other customers who arrive in (T_c, T_1).

Let $\tilde{P}_j(x)$ be the joint probability that j customers arrive in (T_c, T_1) and that $T_1 - T_c \leq x$. Then

$$\tilde{P}_j(x) = \int_0^x \frac{(\lambda \xi)^j}{j!} e^{-\lambda \xi} \, d\tilde{H}(\xi), \tag{5.41}$$

where $\tilde{H}(\xi)$ is given by equation (5.13).

Since $\Pi_0 = 1 - \rho$, it follows that the test customer's waiting time distribution function $W(t)$ is given by

$$W(t) = (1 - \rho) + \rho \sum_{j=0}^{\infty} \int_0^t \tilde{P}_j(t - x) \, dB_j(x), \tag{5.42}$$

where $B_j(x)$ is the distribution function of the j-busy period. Although the right-hand side of equation (5.42) contains no unknown terms, let us proceed and form Laplace–Stieltjes transforms on both sides of the equation. We have (see Exercise 13)

$$\omega(s) = (1 - \rho) + \lambda \frac{1 - \eta[s + \lambda - \lambda \beta(s)]}{s + \lambda[1 - \beta(s)]}, \tag{5.43}$$

where $\eta(s)$ and $\beta(s)$ are the Laplace–Stieltjes transforms of the service time and busy period distribution functions, respectively.

Now, according to equation (5.51) of Chapter 5, equation (5.43) can be written

$$\omega(s) = (1 - \rho) + \frac{\lambda[1 - \beta(s)]}{s + \lambda[1 - \beta(s)]}. \qquad (5.44)$$

Takács [1963] shows that the second moment w_2 of the waiting time distribution function is given by

$$w_2 = \frac{\lambda\tau_3}{3(1 - \lambda\tau_1)^2} + \frac{\lambda^2\tau_2^2}{2(1 - \lambda\tau_1)^3}, \qquad (5.45)$$

where τ_n is the nth moment of the service time distribution function.

For reasons that will become obvious in a moment, let us use the dummy variable z in place of s in (5.44). Then we have

$$\omega(z) = (1 - \rho) + \frac{\lambda[1 - \beta(z)]}{z + \lambda[1 - \beta(z)]}. \qquad (5.46)$$

Observe that the second term on the right-hand side of equation (5.46) is of the same form as the right-hand side of equation (4.29), with the correspondences $s\mu \leftrightarrow \lambda$ and $x(z) \leftrightarrow \beta(z)$. [The $\beta(z)$ on the left-hand side of (4.29) refers to the busy period in the $GI/M/s$ queue, whereas the $\beta(z)$ on the right-hand side of (5.46) refers to the busy period in the $M/G/1$ queue.] Therefore, by analogy with equation (4.31), we see that (5.46) has inverse

$$W(t) = (1 - \rho) + \lambda \sum_{j=1}^{\infty} e^{-\lambda t} \frac{(\lambda t)^{j-1}}{j!} \int_0^t [1 - H^{*j}(x)] \, dx. \qquad (5.47)$$

The similarity in form between the Laplace–Stieltjes transform (5.46) of the waiting time distribution function for the $M/G/1$ queue with service in reverse order of arrival and the Laplace–Stieltjes transform (4.29) of the busy period distribution function for the $GI/M/s$ queue is striking. The argument leading to (5.46) is straightforward (although the calculations are not elementary), whereas that leading to (4.29) is more difficult and has been omitted. No heuristic "explanation" of this similarity has been forthcoming.

Finally, we shall derive the waiting time distribution function $V(t) = P\{V \leq t\}$ for the polite customer, who will not enter service if any other customer is waiting. The waiting time of the polite customer is the time duration from his arrival epoch until the server first becomes idle and there is no one waiting except the polite customer himself. Therefore, if the polite customer does not find the server idle on arrival, he arrives during a busy period, and waits until that busy period is over except for his own service and any additional busy time that his own service time may generate.

By analogy with equation (5.13), we might anticipate that the waiting time distribution function of a polite customer who arrives during a busy period is given by

$$\tilde{B}(x) = \frac{1}{b} \int_0^x [1 - B(\xi)] \, d\xi, \tag{5.48}$$

where $B(\xi)$ is the distribution function of a busy period, with mean b. We have from equation (5.53) of Chapter 5

$$b = \frac{\tau}{1 - \rho}, \tag{5.49}$$

where τ is the mean service time. We conclude that the polite customer's (unconditional) waiting time distribution function is given by

$$V(t) = (1 - \rho) + \frac{\rho(1 - \rho)}{\tau} \int_0^t [1 - B(\xi)] \, d\xi. \tag{5.50}$$

A rigorous derivation of equation (5.50) is given in Takács [1963].

It is easy to show (see Exercise 14) that the conditional mean waiting time $E(V \mid V > 0)$ for the polite customer in the $M/G/1$ queue is given by

$$E(V \mid V > 0) = \frac{\tau^2 + \sigma^2}{2\tau(1 - \rho)^2}, \tag{5.51}$$

where τ is the mean and σ^2 is the variance of the service time distribution function.

Exercises

1. Consider the $M/G/1$ queue with shortest processing time first. That is, each customer is assigned, upon arrival, a service time drawn

independently from the same arbitrary distribution. Whenever a customer completes service and other customers are waiting for service, the next customer chosen to enter service is the one with shortest service time of those waiting. (Note that this is not a non-scheduled queue discipline.)

a. Is the equation $L = \lambda W$ valid for this queue?

b. Is the mean waiting time in this queue equal to or less than the mean waiting time in the corresponding $M/G/1$ queue with a nonscheduled queue discipline?

c. What is $P\{W > 0\}$?

2. Prove equation (2.17).

3. Carry out the calculations indicated in the statement, "it then follows from equation (2.10) that," leading to equation (2.18).

4. Show that equations (2.8) and (2.33) are equivalent.

5. Starting from equation (2.6) show that, if the server is initially idle, then, for $t \geqq 0$,

$$W_{(k+1)}(t) = P\{Y_1 \leqq t, \ Y_1 + Y_2 \leqq t, \ldots, \ Y_1 + \cdots + Y_k \leqq t\},$$

where $Y_j = S_j - X_j$. (In terms of random-walk theory, this result, sometimes called the *Pollaczek–Spitzer identity*, says that the waiting time of the $(k + 1)$th customer will not exceed t if and only if the first passage of the random walk $\{Y_j\}$ through the boundary t occurs after the kth step. For a discussion of the relationship between random walks and Wiener–Hopf equations, see Feller [1971].)

6. Show that the arriving customer's distribution for the $M/D/k$ queue with arrival rate λ equals that of the $E_k/D/1$ queue with arrival rate λ/k. [*Hint:* Consider the $M/D/k$ queue in which the servers are selected in cyclic order.] (This result broadens the applicability of Lindley's waiting time analysis. For a more complete discussion and a list of references, see Riordan [1962] and Syski [1960]. Numerical results for this important model are given in Dietrich et al. [1967].)

7. Fill in the details of the derivation of equation (3.27) from equation (3.21).

8. Derive equation (3.27) by specialization of the Maclaurin series method of Section 6–4.

9. Using Lindley's method, derive the Pollaczek–Khintchine formula (5.16).

10. *The Maclaurin series method for the $M/G/1$ random service queue* (Carter and Cooper [1972]). Assume that $\check{W}_j(x)$, defined by equation

(5.33), has the Maclaurin series expansion

$$\check{W}_j(x) = \sum_{\nu=0}^{\infty} \frac{x^\nu}{\nu!} \check{W}_j^{(\nu)} \qquad (j = 2, 3, \ldots; \check{W}_j^{(0)} = 1). \tag{10.1}$$

Set

$$h(x) = \frac{d}{dx} H(x) \tag{10.2}$$

and

$$\check{b}_i(x) = h(x)p_i(x). \tag{10.3}$$

Also, for any function $f(x)$, define

$$f^{(k)} = \frac{d^k}{dx^k} f(x) \bigg|_{x=0}.$$

a. Show that

$$\check{W}_j^{(\nu)} = -H^{(\nu)} + \sum_{i=0}^{\nu-1} \frac{j + i - 2}{j + i - 1} \sum_{k=0}^{\nu-1} \check{b}_i^{(k)} \check{W}_{j+i-1}^{(\nu-i-k)}$$

$$(j = 2, 3, \ldots; \nu = 1, 2, \ldots). \tag{10.4}$$

[Equation (10.4) permits, in principle, evaluation of the sum on the right-hand side of (10.1).]

b. Let $F(t) = P\{W > t \mid W > 0\}$ and assume the representation

$$F(t) = \sum_{\nu=0}^{\infty} \frac{t^\nu}{\nu!} F^{(\nu)} \qquad (F^{(0)} = 1). \tag{10.5}$$

Show that equation (5.32) yields the following recurrence for the coefficients $\{F^{(\nu)}\}$ in the expansion (10.5):

$$F^{(\nu)} = -\tilde{H}^{(\nu)} + \sum_{j=2}^{\infty} \frac{j - 1}{j} \sum_{k=0}^{\nu-1} Q_j^{(k+1)} \check{W}_j^{(\nu-1-k)}$$

$$(\nu = 1, 2, \ldots). \tag{10.6}$$

c. Show that equation (5.30) yields

$$Q_j^{(1)} = Q_j'(0) = \frac{1}{\tau} \Pi_{j-1}^* \qquad (j = 1, 2, \ldots) \tag{10.7}$$

and

$$Q_j^{(k+1)} = -\frac{1}{\tau} \sum_{m=0}^{k-1} \binom{k-1}{m} H^{(k-m)} \left(\Pi_0^* p_{j-1}^{(m)} + \sum_{i=1}^{j} \Pi_i^* p_{j-i}^{(m)} \right)$$

$$(k = 1, 2, \ldots; j = 1, 2, \ldots). \tag{10.8}$$

Thus equations (10.4), (10.6), (10.7), and (10.8) permit calculation of the Maclaurin series representation (10.5) of the conditional waiting time probability $P\{W > t \mid W > 0\}$. Sample calculations according to this algorithm for the $M/E_k/1$ random service queue are given in Carter and Cooper [1972].

11. Carter and Cooper [1972]. Suppose that

$$H(x) = 1 - e^{-x/\tau}. \tag{11.1}$$

a. Show that for $v = 1$, equation (10.6) becomes

$$F^{(1)} = -\frac{1}{\tau} + \sum_{j=2}^{\infty} \frac{j-1}{j} Q_j^{(1)}. \tag{11.2}$$

b. Show that equation (11.2) reduces to

$$F^{(1)} = -\frac{1}{\tau} \frac{1-\rho}{\rho} \ln \frac{1}{1-\rho}. \tag{11.3}$$

c. Show that for $v = 2$, equation (10.6) becomes

$$F^{(2)} = -\frac{1}{\tau^2} + \sum_{j=2}^{\infty} \frac{j-1}{j} (Q_j^{(1)} \breve{W}_j^{(1)} + Q_j^{(2)}). \tag{11.4}$$

d. Show that

$$Q_j^{(2)} = -\frac{1}{\tau} H^{(1)} \left(\Pi_0^* p_{j-1}(0) + \sum_{i=1}^{j} \Pi_i^* p_{j-i}(0) \right) \tag{11.5}$$

and that this reduces to

$$Q_j^{(2)} = -\frac{1}{\tau^2} (1 - \rho)\rho^j \quad (j = 1, 2, \ldots). \tag{11.6}$$

e. Show that equation (10.4) yields

$$\breve{W}_j^{(1)} = -\frac{1}{\tau} + \left(\frac{j-2}{j-1} \right) \frac{1}{\tau}. \tag{11.7}$$

f. Show that equation (11.4) reduces to

$$F^{(2)} = \frac{1}{\tau^2} (1 - \rho) \left[2 - \frac{1-\rho}{\rho} \ln \frac{1}{1-\rho} \right]. \tag{11.8}$$

g. Compare the results (11.3) and (11.8) with the expansion (3.27).

12. *The additional conditioning variable method for the M/D/1 random service queue.* (Carter and Cooper [1972].)   Suppose that

$$H(x) = \begin{cases} 0 & \text{when } x < \tau \\ 1 & \text{when } x \geq \tau. \end{cases} \tag{12.1}$$

a. Show that equation (5.30) reduces to

$$Q_j'(\xi) = \begin{cases} \dfrac{1}{\tau}\, \Pi_{j-1}^* & \text{when } \xi \leq \tau \\ 0 & \text{when } \xi > \tau. \end{cases} \tag{12.2}$$

b. Show that equation (5.32) reduces to, for $t < \tau$,

$$P\{W > t \mid W > 0\}$$
$$= 1 - \frac{t}{\tau} + \frac{1}{\tau} \sum_{j=2}^{\infty} \frac{j-1}{j}\, \Pi_{j-1}^* \int_0^t \check{W}_j(t - \xi)\, d\xi$$
$$(0 \leq t < \tau) \tag{12.3}$$

and, for $t \geq \tau$,

$$P\{W > t \mid W > 0\} = \frac{1}{\tau} \sum_{j=2}^{\infty} \frac{j-1}{j}\, \Pi_{j-1}^* \int_0^\tau \check{W}_j(t - \xi)\, d\xi$$
$$(\tau \leq t < \infty). \tag{12.4}$$

c. Show that, since $\check{W}_j(x)$ is a step function, the integrals on the right-hand side of equations (12.3) and (12.4) can be evaluated, giving

$$P\{W > t \mid W > 0\} = 1 - \frac{t}{\tau} + \frac{t}{\tau} \sum_{j=2}^{\infty} \frac{j-1}{j}\, \Pi_{j-1}^*$$
$$(0 \leq t < \tau) \tag{12.5}$$

and

$$P\{W > t \mid W > 0\}$$
$$= \frac{1}{\tau} \sum_{j=2}^{\infty} \frac{j-1}{j}\, \Pi_{j-1}^* \left\{ \left(t - \left[\frac{t}{\tau}\right]\tau\right) \check{W}_j(t) \right.$$
$$\left. + \left(\tau - t + \left[\frac{t}{\tau}\right]\tau\right) \check{W}_j(t - \tau) \right\}$$
$$(\tau \leq t < \infty), \tag{12.6}$$

where $[x]$ is defined as the largest integer not exceeding x.

d. Show that

$$H(\xi \mid k, x) = H(\xi).\qquad(12.7)$$

e. Show that equation (5.40) reduces to

$$\breve{W}_{j,k}(x) = \sum_{i=0}^{\infty} \frac{j + i - 2}{j + i - 1}\, p_i(\tau)\breve{W}_{j+i-1,k-1}(x - \tau)$$

$$(j = 2, 3, \ldots; k = 1, 2, \ldots).\qquad(12.8)$$

f. Show that equation (5.35) reduces to

$$P\{\breve{X}(x) = k\} = \begin{cases} 1 & \text{when } k = \left[\dfrac{t}{\tau}\right] \\ 0 & \text{otherwise.} \end{cases}\qquad(12.9)$$

g. Show that equations (12.9) and (5.36) imply

$$\breve{W}_j(x) = \breve{W}_{j,[x/\tau]}(x) \qquad (j = 2, 3, \ldots).\qquad(12.10)$$

h. Show that, if we set $k = [x/\tau]$ in equation (12.8), we obtain

$$\breve{W}_j(x) = \sum_{i=0}^{\infty} \frac{j + i - 2}{j + i - 1}\, p_i(\tau)\breve{W}_{j+i-1}(x - \tau)$$

$$(j = 2, 3, \ldots; x \geqq \tau).\qquad(12.11)$$

i. Show that equation (12.11) is complemented by

$$\breve{W}_j(x) = 1 \qquad (j = 2, 3, \ldots; x < \tau).\qquad(12.12)$$

j. Show that the recurrence (12.11) follows immediately from equation (5.33).

Equations (12.11) and (12.12) permit calculation of equation (12.6) It can be shown in a straightforward manner that these results are equivalent to those of Burke [1959], who gives several useful sets of curves for the $M/D/1$ random service queue.

13. Fill in the steps leading from equation (5.42) to equation (5.43).

14. a. Show that the conditional mean waiting time $E(V \mid V > 0)$ for the polite customer in the $M/G/1$ queue is given by

$$E(V \mid V > 0) = \frac{\tau/(1 - \rho)}{2} + \frac{\sigma_B^2}{2\tau/(1 - \rho)},$$

where σ_B^2 is the variance of the busy period.

b. Show that

$$\sigma_B^2 = \frac{\sigma^2 + \tau^2}{(1 - \rho)^3} - \frac{\tau^2}{(1 - \rho)^2},$$

where σ^2 is the variance of the service time.

c. Conclude that equation (5.51) is correct.

Overview

7

In this chapter we shall summarize briefly the areas of queueing theory that we have covered, and indicate some important areas of the theory that we have not discussed. We shall also give some brief comments on other books on queueing theory with the hope that this chapter will be helpful to the reader who wishes to pursue more advanced work.

In Chapter 1 we discussed the nature of queueing theory, and we gave some historical background. We emphasized that queueing theory has attracted the attention of researchers throughout the world since the early 1900s largely because of its important applications. We also stressed the interplay between the often enlightening intuitive methods and interpretations and the abstract mathematical base underlying the theory. With regard to the applications, we observed that queueing theory has been very profitably applied in the telecommunications industry, and that teletraffic researchers have made many contributions to the theory.

Two journals devoted mainly to communications research and technology that often carry important papers on queueing theory are *The Bell System Technical Journal* and *Ericsson Technics*. Important work is fostered by the triennial International Teletraffic Congress, whose sixth gathering was held in September 1970, in Munich. Finally, two important books on queueing, those by Riordan [1962] and Syski [1960], are written in the context of teletraffic theory.

In Chapter 2 we discussed some topics from applied mathematics and probability theory that are particularly important in queueing theory. The discussion was intended as a review, in the context of queueing theory, of topics with which the reader was assumed already familiar. Although these topics are covered in many different texts, Feller's two volumes [1968, 1971] are particularly noteworthy. The first volume is an excellent treatment of applied probability, with valuable material on discrete probability distributions, generating functions, and stochastic processes. The second volume, which is considerably more advanced than the first, includes chapters on the negative exponential and uniform distributions, renewal theory, and Laplace–Stieltjes transforms. Feller also has a short section on "The Queuing Process" that clarifies the relationship between queueing theory and other parts of probability theory.

Chapter 3, on birth-and-death queueing models, uses the concepts of the first two chapters to construct models of simple queueing processes. Among the results of this chapter are the Erlang loss, Erlang delay, and Poisson blocking formulas. These results are most important in terms of practical applications of the theory.

In Chapter 4 we extended the models of Chapter 3 to include queueing processes whose "states" require more than one variable for representation. Despite their initial complexity, these models often yield easily to solution. Some of the results of this chapter are not widely known and should prove useful in practical applications.

In Chapter 5 we studied queueing models, such as the $M/G/1$ and $GI/M/s$ queues, that can be formulated in terms of an imbedded Markov chain. These models, along with the birth-and-death models, comprise the core of what is usually considered standard queueing theory.

In Chapter 6 we discussed waiting time distribution functions for the $M/M/s$, $GI/M/s$, and $M/G/1$ queues with various orders of service, and the $GI/G/1$ queue with service in order of arrival. Some of this material reflects current research and illustrates some theoretical and practical problems that remain to be solved.

Since this is a textbook, we have concentrated mainly on "standard" and elementary material rather than on topics that are relatively specialized or difficult. Important topics that we have mentioned only briefly or not at all include

1. Transient phenomena—systems that are not in statistical equilibrium.
2. Networks of queues—interacting queueing systems such as queues in tandem and communications networks.
3. Priority queues—queues in which the customers are segregated into classes, and the order of service, for example, depends on the class of the customer. (A recent book, Jaiswal [1968], is devoted completely to this subject.)

4. Traffic measurement—statistical questions concerned with inference of parameter values.

5. Reduction to practice—numerical application of difficult theoretical results, such as calculations of waiting time distribution functions from Laplace–Stieltjes transforms or complicated algorithms.

The literature of queueing theory is voluminous. (See, for example, Saaty [1966].) Besides the previously mentioned journals, papers on queueing theory appear in journals devoted to such areas as management science, electrical engineering, industrial engineering, probability, statistics, and mathematics. In particular, each issue of *Operations Research* usually contains at least one paper on queueing.

Also, it is worth reiterating that the mathematical theory of queues is quite similar to mathematical theories of seemingly unrelated subjects, such as inventories, dams, and insurance. (See, for example, Moran [1959], Prabhu [1965], Seal [1969], and Takács [1967].)

Among the most important books on queueing theory are Beneš [1963], Brockmeyer et al. [1948], Cohen [1969], Cox and Smith [1961], Gnedenko and Kovalenko [1968], Jaiswal [1968], Khintchine [1969], LeGall [1962], Morse [1958], Pollaczek [1957], Prabhu [1965], Riordan [1962], Saaty [1961], Syski [1960], and Takács [1962a and 1967].

Finally, there is the present text, which we hope will prove interesting and useful to students of queueing theory.

Engineering Curves for Systems with Poisson Input

In the following figures, the number of servers is denoted by s, and the magnitude in erlangs of the offered load is denoted by a ($a = \lambda/\mu$, where λ is the customer arrival rate, and μ^{-1} is the average service time).

Figure A–1. Erlang loss formula $B(s, a)$ plotted against offered load a in erlangs for different values of the number s of servers.

For systems with Poisson input in which blocked customers are cleared, $B(s, a)$ is the proportion of customers who find all servers busy and are consequently cleared from the system without receiving service. The service time distribution need not be exponential.

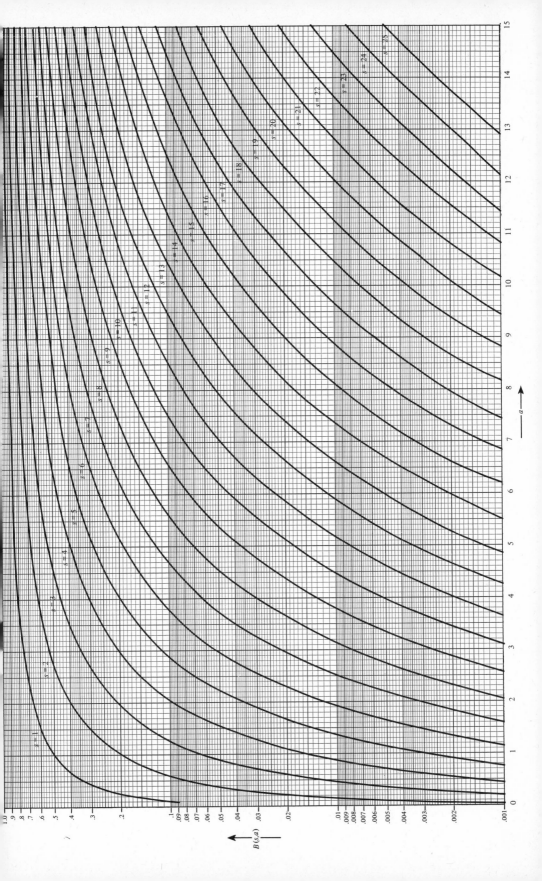

Figure A–2. Erlang loss formula $B(s, a)$ plotted against offered load a in erlangs for different values of the number s of servers.

For systems with Poisson input in which blocked customers are cleared, $B(s, a)$ is the proportion of customers who find all servers busy and are consequently cleared from the system without receiving service. The service time distribution need not be exponential.

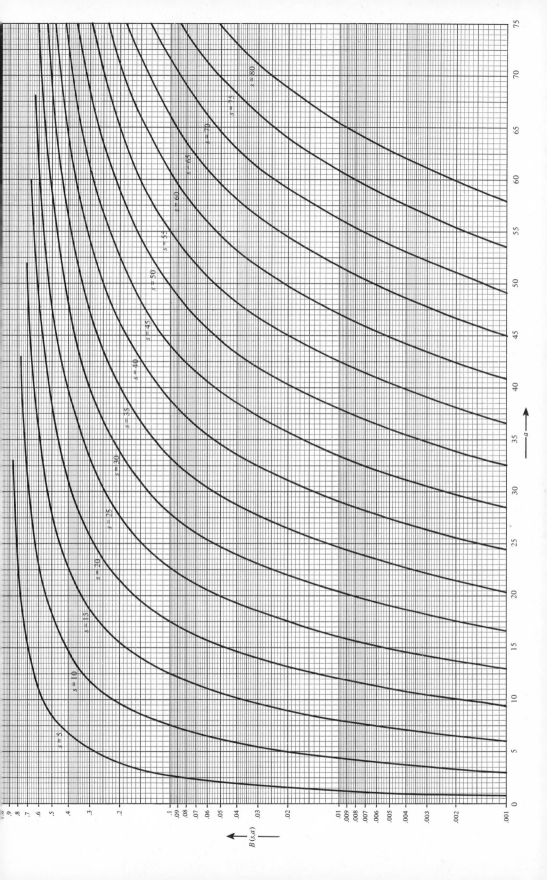

Figure A–3. Erlang delay formula $C(s, a)$ plotted against offered load a in erlangs for different values of the number s of servers.

For systems with Poisson input and exponential service times in which blocked customers are delayed (blocked customers wait until served), $C(s, a)$ is the proportion of customers who find all servers busy and consequently wait until served. The order of service of waiting customers is irrelevant.

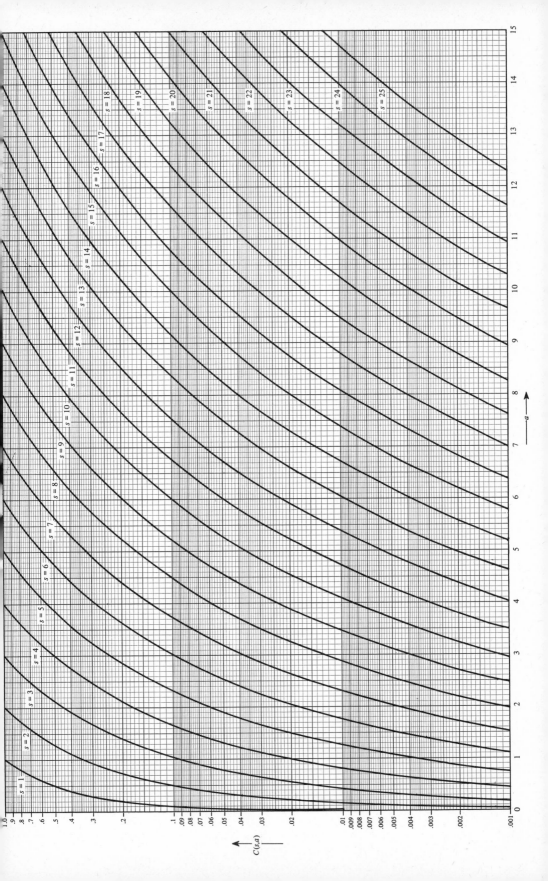

Figure A-4. Erlang delay formula $C(s, a)$ plotted against offered load a in erlangs for different values of the number s of servers.

For systems with Poisson input and exponential service times in which blocked customers are delayed (blocked customers wait until served), $C(s, a)$ is the proportion of customers who find all servers busy and consequently wait until served. The order of service of waiting customers is irrelevant.

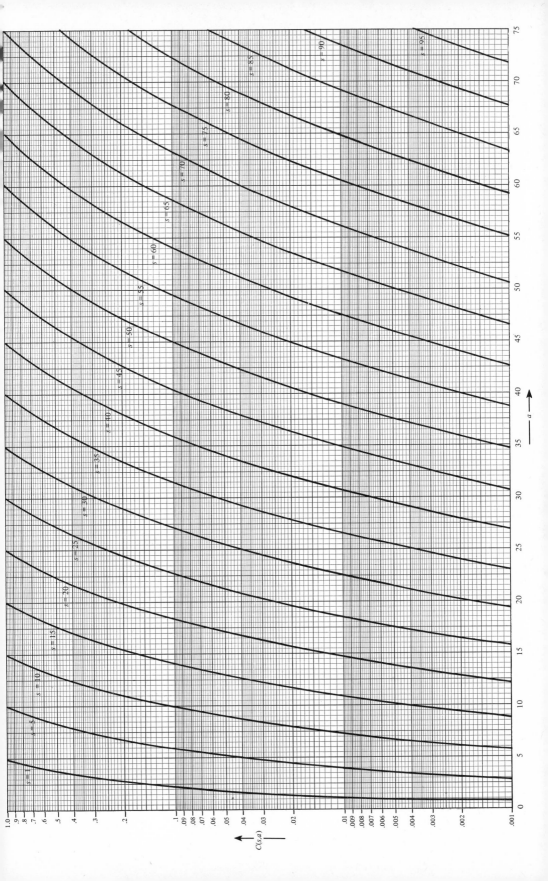

Figure A–5. Poisson formula $P(s, a)$ plotted against offered load a in erlangs for different values of the number s of servers.

For systems with Poisson input in which blocked customers are held (the length of time a customer is willing to spend in the system is not influenced by whether or not he gets served), $P(s, a)$ is the proportion of customers who find all servers busy and consequently wait (although they may leave the system before receiving service). The service time distribution need not be exponential. The order of service of waiting customers is irrelevant.

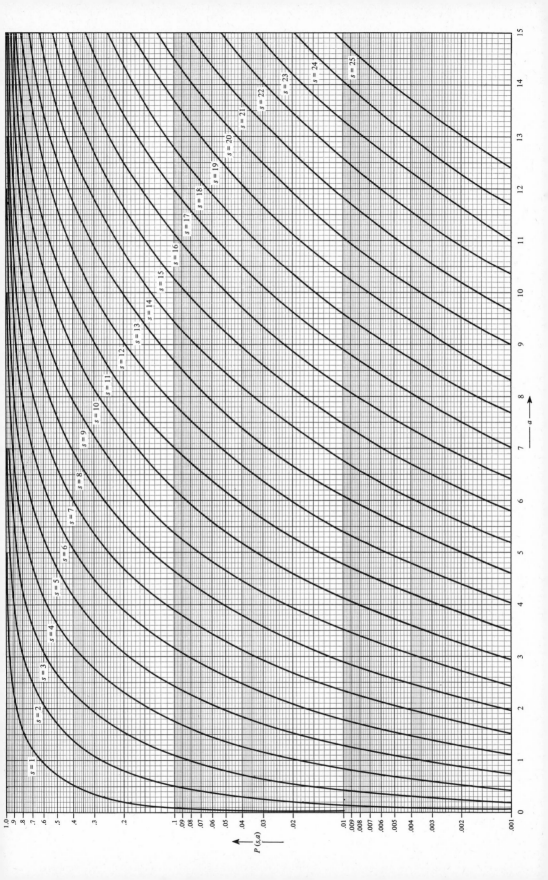

Figure A–6. Poisson formula $P(s, a)$ plotted against offered load a in erlangs for different values of the number s of servers.

For systems with Poisson input in which blocked customers are held (the length of time a customer is willing to spend in the system is not influenced by whether or not he gets served), $P(s, a)$ is the proportion of customers who find all servers busy and consequently wait (although they may leave the system before receiving service). The service time distribution need not be exponential. The order of service of waiting customers is irrelevant.

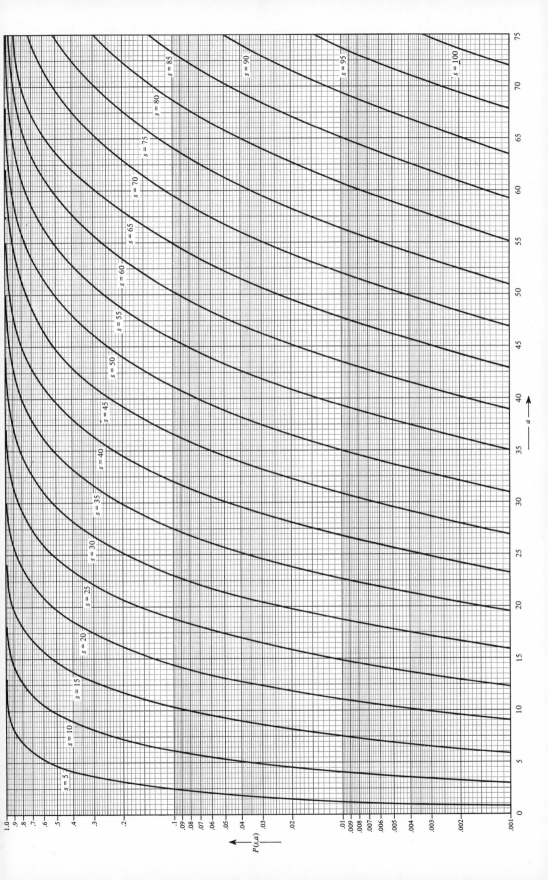

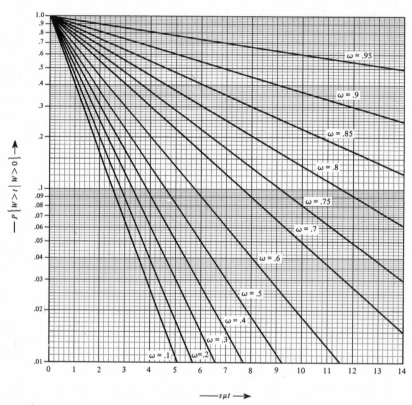

Figure A-7. Conditional probability $P\{W > t \mid W > 0\} = e^{-(1-\omega)s\mu t}$ that a blocked customer waits beyond t for service to commence in a delay system (blocked customers wait until served) with exponential service times and service in order of arrival, plotted against $s\mu t$, for different values of the generalized occupancy.

For Erlang delay systems (Poisson input, exponential service times), $\omega = p = a/s$. To calculate the unconditional probability $P\{W > t\}$ that a customer waits beyond t for service to commence in an Erlang delay system with service in order of arrival, use the formula $P\{W > t\} = P\{W > t \mid W > 0\}C(s, a)$, where $C(s, a)$ is determined from Figure A–3 or A–4.

References

B

Appendix

ABRAMOWITZ, M., and I. A. STEGUN, Eds. *Handbook of Mathematical Functions*. Washington D.C.: National Bureau of Standards, 1964.

BAILEY, N. T. J. *The Elements of Stochastic Processes*. New York: John Wiley & Sons, Inc., 1964.

BENEŠ, V. E. "On Queues with Poisson Arrivals." *The Annals of Mathematical Statistics*, **28** (1957), 670–77.

———. *General Stochastic Processes in the Theory of Queues*. Reading, Mass.: Addison-Wesley Publishing Company, Inc., 1963.

BRETSCHNEIDER, G. "Die Berechnung von Leitungsgruppen für überfliessenden Verkeher in Fernsprechwahlanlagen." *Nachrichtentechnische Zeitschrift*, **9** (1956), 533–40.

BROCKMEYER, E. "The Simple Overflow Problem in the Theory of Telephone Traffic." *Teleteknik*, **5** (Dec. 1954), 361–74.

———, H. A. HALSTRØM, and A. JENSEN. *The Life and Works of A. K. Erlang*. Trans. 2. Copenhagen: Danish Academy of Technical Sciences, 1948, 1–277.

BUCHNER, M. M., JR., and S. R. NEAL. "Inherent Load-Balancing in Step-by-Step Switching Systems." *The Bell System Technical Journal*, **50**, No. 1 (Jan. 1971), 135–65.

BURKE, P. J. "The Output of a Queuing System." *Operations Research*, **4**, No. 6 (Dec. 1956), 699–704.

———. "Equilibrium Delay Distribution for One Channel with Constant Holding Time, Poisson Input and Random Service." *The Bell System Technical Journal*, **38** (July 1959), 1021–31.

BURKE, P. J. "The Output Process of a Stationary $M/M/s$ Queueing System." *The Annals of Mathematical Statistics,* **39**, No. 4 (1968), 1144–52.

———. "The Overflow Distribution for Constant Holding Time." *Proceedings of the Sixth International Teletraffic Congress,* Munich, Sept. 9–15, 1970. *The Bell System Technical Journal,* **50**, No. 10 (Dec. 1971), 3195–210.

BUSACKER, R. G., and T. L. SAATY, *Finite Graphs and Networks.* New York: McGraw-Hill Book Company, Inc., 1965.

CARTER, G. M., and R. B. COOPER. "Queues with Service in Random Order." To be published in *Operations Research,* 1972.

COHEN, J. W. "The Generalized Engset Formulae." *Philips Telecommunication Review,* **18**, No. 4 (Nov. 1957), 158–70.

———. *The Single Server Queue.* New York: Wiley-Interscience, 1969.

COOPER, R. B. "Queues Served in Cyclic Order: Waiting Times." *The Bell System Technical Journal,* **49**, No. 3 (March 1970), 399–413.

———, and G. MURRAY. "Queues Served in Cyclic Order." *The Bell System Technical Journal,* **48**, No. 3 (March 1969), 675–89.

COX, D. R. *Renewal Theory.* London: Methuen & Co., Ltd., 1962.

———, and H. D. MILLER. *The Theory of Stochastic Processes.* London: Methuen & Co., Ltd., 1965.

———, and W. L. SMITH. *Queues.* London: Methuen & Co., Ltd., 1961.

DESCLOUX, A. *Delay Tables for Finite- and Infinite-Source Systems.* New York: McGraw-Hill Book Company, Inc., 1962.

———. "On the Validity of the Particular Subscriber's Point of View." Abstract in *Proceedings of the Fifth International Teletraffic Congress,* New York, June 14–20, 1967.

———. "On Overflow Processes of Trunk Groups with Poisson Inputs and Exponential Service Times." *The Bell System Technical Journal,* **42**, No. 2 (March 1963), 383–98.

———. "On Markovian Servers with Recurrent Input." *Proceedings of the Sixth International Teletraffic Congress,* Munich, Sept. 9–15, 1970.

DIETRICH, G., W. KRUSE, R. MICHEL, F. ONDRA, E. PETER, and H. WAGNER. *Teletraffic Engineering Manual.* Stuttgart: Standard Elektrik Lorenz AG, 1966.

EISENBERG, M. "Cyclic Queue with Changeover Time." *Proceedings of the Sixth International Teletraffic Congress,* Munich, Sept. 9–15, 1970.

FELLER, W. *An Introduction to Probability Theory and Its Applications,* Vol. I, 3rd ed. New York: John Wiley & Sons, Inc., 1968.

———. *An Introduction to Probability Theory and Its Applications,* Vol. II, 2nd ed. New York: John Wiley & Sons, Inc., 1971.

FISZ, M. *Probability Theory and Mathematical Statistics*, 3rd ed. New York: John Wiley & Sons, Inc., 1963.

FORTET, R., and C. GRANDJEAN. "Study of the Congestion in a Loss System." Paper presented at the Fourth International Teletraffic Congress, London, July 15–21, 1964. Laboratoire Central de Télécommunications, 46 Avenue de Breteuil, Paris (VII^c), as internal memorandum, Feb. 12, 1963.

FRY, T. C. *Probability and Its Engineering Uses*, 2nd ed., New York: Van Nostrand, 1965.

GALLIHER, H. P. *Notes on Operations Research*. Cambridge, Mass.: M.I.T. Technology Press, Operations Research Center, 1959, Chap. 4.

GARABEDIAN, P. R. *Partial Differential Equations*. New York: John Wiley & Sons, Inc., 1964, Chap. 2, Sec. 1.

GNEDENKO, B. V., and I. N. KOVALENKO. *Introduction to Queuing Theory*. Jerusalem: Israel Program for Scientific Translations, 1968.

JACKSON, R. R. P. "Queueing Systems with Phase Type Service." *Operational Research Quarterly*, **5** (Dec. 1954). 109–120.

———. "Queueing Processes with Phase-type Service." *Journal of the Royal Statistical Society*, **B18**, No. 1 (1956), 129–32.

JAISWAL, N. K. *Priority Queues*. New York: Academic Press, Inc., 1968.

JEWELL, W. S. "A Simple Proof of: $L = \lambda W$." *Operations Research*, **15**, No. 6 (1967), 1109–16.

KARLIN, S. *A First Course in Stochastic Processes*. New York: Academic Press, Inc., 1966.

KENDALL, D. G. "Some Problems in the Theory of Queues." *Journal of the Royal Statistical Society*, **B13**, (1951), 151–85.

———. "Stochastic Processes Occurring in the Theory of Queues and Their Analysis by Means of the Imbedded Markov Chain." *The Annals of Mathematical Statistics*, **24** (1953), 338–54.

KHINTCHINE, A. Y. *Mathematical Methods in the Theory of Queueing*, 2nd ed. New York: Hafner Publishing Company, 1969.

KINGMAN, J. F. C. "On Queues in Which Customers Are Served in Random Order." *Proceedings of the Cambridge Philosophical Society*, **58** (1962), 79–91.

KOSTEN, L. "Über Sperrungswahrscheinlichkeiten bei Staffelschaltungen," *Elektro Nachrichten.–Technik*, **14** (1937), 5–12.

LEE, A. M. *Applied Queueing Theory*. New York: St. Martin's Press.

LEGALL, P. *Les Systèmes avec ou sans attente et les processes stochastiques*, Tome 1. Paris: Dunod, 1962.

LINDLEY, D. V. "The Theory of Queues with a Single Server." *Proceedings of the Cambridge Philosophical Society*, **48** (1952), 277–89.

LITTLE, J. D. C. "A Proof for the Queuing Formula: $L = \lambda W$." *Operations Research*, **9**, No. 3 (1961), 383–87.

LOTZE, A. "A Traffic Variance Method for Gradings of Arbitrary Type." *Proceedings of the Fourth International Teletraffic Congress*, Vol. III, London, July 15–21, 1964.

MORAN, P. A. P. *The Theory of Storage*. London: Methuen & Co., Ltd., 1959.

MORSE, P. *Queues, Inventories and Maintenance*. New York: John Wiley & Sons, Inc., 1958.

NEAL, S., "Combining Correlated Streams of Nonrandom Traffic." *The Bell System Technical Journal*, 50, No. 6 (July–August 1971), 2015–37.

PALM, C. "Intensitatsschwankungen im Fernsprechverkehr." *Ericsson Technics*, **44** (1943), 1–189.

———. "Research on Telephone Traffic Carried by Full Availability Groups." *Tele*, No. 1 (English ed.) (1957), 1–107.

PECK, L. G., and R. N. HAZELWOOD. *Finite Queuing Tables*. New York: John Wiley & Sons, Inc., 1958.

POLLACZEK, F. "La Loi d'attente des appels téléphoniques." *Comptes Rendus Académie des Sciences*, Paris, **222** (1946), 353–355.

———. "Problèmes stochastiques posés par le phénomène de formation d'une queue d'attente à un guichet et par des phénomènes apparentés." *Memorial de Sciences Mathematiques* No. 136. Paris: Fauthier–Villars, 1957.

PRABHU, N. U. *Queues and Inventories*. New York: John Wiley & Sons, Inc., 1965.

RAPP, Y. "Planning of Junction Network in a Multiexchange Area." *Ericsson Technics*, **20**, No. 1 (1964), 77–130.

REICH, E. "Waiting Time When Queues Are in Tandem." *The Annals of Mathematical Statistics*, **28** (1957), 768–73.

———. *Congestion Theory* (W. L. Smith and W. E. Wilkinson, eds.). Chapel Hill: University of North Carolina Press, 1965, Chap. 14.

RIORDAN, J. "Delay Curves for Calls Served at Random." *The Bell System Technical Journal*, **32** (1953), 100–19.

———. "Derivation of Moments of Overflow Traffic." Appendix I of R. I. Wilkinson. "Theories for Toll Traffic Engineering in the U.S.A." *The Bell System Technical Journal*, **35**, No. 2 (March 1956), 421–514.

———. "Delays for Last-Come First-Served Service and the Busy Period." *The Bell System Technical Journal*, **40**, No. 3 (May 1961), 785–93.

————. *Stochastic Service Systems.* New York: John Wiley & Sons, Inc., 1962.

————. *Combinatorial Identities.* New York: John Wiley & Sons, Inc., 1968.

RUNNENBURG, J. TH. *Congestion Theory* (W. L. Smith and W. E. Wilkinson, eds.). Chapel Hill: University of North Carolina Press, 1965, Chap. 13.

SAATY, T. L. *Elements of Queueing Theory.* New York: McGraw-Hill Book Company, Inc., 1961.

————. "Seven More Years of Queues, a Lament and a Bibliography." *Naval Research Logistics Quarterly,* **13**, No. 4 (Dec. 1966), 447–76.

SEAL, H. L. *Stochastic Theory of a Risk Business.* New York: John Wiley & Sons, Inc., 1969.

SMITH, W. L., "On the Distribution of Queueing Times," *Proceedings of the Cambridge Philosophical Society,* **49** (1953), 449–61.

STIDHAM, S., JR. "Optimal Control of a Signalized Intersection, Part III: Descriptive Stochastic Models." *DT-FHA Report 13, Technical Report 96.* Ithaca, N.Y.: Cornell University, Department of Operations Research, 1969.

SYKES, J. S. "Simplified Analysis of an Alternating-Priority Queuing Model with Setup Times." *Operations Research,* **18**, No. 6 (Nov.–Dec. 1970), 1182–92.

SYSKI, R. *Introduction to Congestion Theory in Telephone Systems.* London: Oliver & Boyd, Ltd., 1960.

TAKÁCS, L. "Transient Behavior of Single-Server Queuing Processes with Recurrent Input and Exponentially Distributed Service Times." *Operations Research,* **8** (1960), 231–45.

————. *Introduction to the Theory of Queues.* New York: Oxford University Press, 1962a.

————. "Delay Distributions for Simple Trunk Groups with Recurrent Input and Exponential Service Times." *The Bell System Technical Journal,* **41**, No. 1 (Jan. 1962b), 311–20.

————. "Delay Distributions for One Line with Poisson Input, General Holding Times, and Various Orders of Service." *The Bell System Technical Journal,* **42**, No. 2 (March 1963), 487–503.

————. *Combinatorial Methods in the Theory of Stochastic Processes.* New York: John Wiley & Sons, Inc., 1967.

————. "On Erlang's Formula." *The Annals of Mathematical Statistics,* **40** (1969), 71–78.

VARGA, R. S. *Matrix Iterative Analysis.* Englewood Cliffs, N.J.: Prentice-Hall, Inc., 1962.

VAULOT, E. "Delais d'attente des appels téléphoniques traités au hasard." *Comptes rendus Académie des Sciences,* Paris, **222** (1946), 268–69.

———. "Delais d'attente de appels téléphonique dans l'ordre inverse de leur arrivée." *Comptes rendus Académie des Sciences,* Paris, **238** (1954) 1188–89.

WALLSTRÖM, B. "Congestion Studies in Telephone Systems with Overflow Facilities." *Ericsson Technics,* No. 3 (1966), 190–351.

WILKINSON, R. I. "Theories for Toll Traffic Engineering in the U.S.A." *The Bell System Technical Journal,* **35**, No. 2 (March 1956), 421–514.

———. *Nonrandom Traffic Curves and Tables for Engineering and Administrative Purposes.* Holmdel, N.J.: Bell Telephone Laboratories, Traffic Studies Center, 1970.

WISHART, D. M. G. "Queuing Systems in Which the Discipline Is 'Last-Come, First-Served'." *Operations Research,* **8** (1960), 591–99.

———. "An Application of Ergodic Theorems in the Theory of Queues." *Proceedings of the Fourth Berkeley Symposium on Mathematical Statistics and Probability,* Vol. 2. Berkeley and Los Angeles: University of California Press, 1961, 581–92.

Index